L A M A R C K

L A M A R C K

ALPHEUS S. PACKARD

ARNO PRESS

A New York Times Company
New York • 1980

Editorial Supervision: Steve Bedney

Reprint Edition 1980 by Arno Press Inc.

Reprinted from a copy in the Pennsylvania State Library

THREE CENTURIES OF SCIENCE IN AMERICA
ISBN for complete set: 0-405-12525-9
See last pages of this volume for titles.

Manufactured in the United States of America

Library of Congress Cataloging in Publication Data

Packard, Alpheus Spring, 1839-1905.
  Lamarck, the founder of evolution.

  (Three centuries of science in America)
  Reprint of the ed. published by Longmans, Green,
New York.
  Bibliography: p.
  Includes index.
  1. Lamarck, Jean Baptiste Pierre Antoine de Monet
de, 1744-1829. 2. Evolution. 3. Naturalists--
France--Biography. I. Title. II. 'Series.
QH31.L2P12 1980   575'.0092'4 [B]   79-7980
ISBN 0-405-12562-3

LAMARCK

Attempt at a reconstruction of the Profile of Lamarck
from an unpublished etching by Dr Gachet.

L A M A R C K

THE FOUNDER OF EVOLUTION

HIS LIFE AND WORK

WITH TRANSLATIONS OF HIS
WRITINGS ON ORGANIC EVOLUTION

By

ALPHEUS S. PACKARD, M.D., LL.D.

Professor of Zoology and Geology in Brown University ; author of " Guide to the
Study of Insects," " Text-book of Entomology," etc., etc.

" La postérité vous honorera ! "
—*Mlle. Cornelie de Lamarck*

LONGMANS, GREEN, AND CO.

91 AND 93 FIFTH AVENUE, NEW YORK
LONDON AND BOMBAY
1901

Press of J. J. Little & Co.
Astor Place, New York

PREFACE

ALTHOUGH it is now a century since Lamarck published the germs of his theory, it is perhaps only within the past fifty years that the scientific world and the general public have become familiar with the name of Lamarck and of Lamarckism.

The rise and rehabilitation of the Lamarckian theory of organic evolution, so that it has become a rival of Darwinism; the prevalence of these views in the United States, Germany, England, and especially in France, where its author is justly regarded as the real founder of organic evolution, has invested his name with a new interest, and led to a desire to learn some of the details of his life and work, and of his theory as he unfolded it in 1800 and subsequent years, and finally expounded it in 1809. The time seems ripe, therefore, for a more extended sketch of Lamarck and his theory, as well as of his work as a philosophical biologist, than has yet appeared.

But the seeker after the details of his life is baffled by the general ignorance about the man—his antecedents, his parentage, the date of his birth, his early training and education, his work as a professor in the Jardin des Plantes, the house he lived in, the place of his burial, and his relations to his scientific contemporaries.

Except the *éloges* of Geoffroy St. Hilaire and Cuvier,

and the brief notices of Martins, Duval, Bourguignat, and Bourguin, there is no special biography, however brief, except a *brochure* of thirty-one pages, reprinted from a few scattered articles by the distinguished anthropologist, M. Gabriel de Mortillet, in the fourth and last volume of a little-known journal, *l'Homme*, entitled *Lamarck. Par un Groupe de Transformistes, ses Disciples*, Paris, 1887. This exceedingly rare pamphlet was written by the late M. Gabriel de Mortillet, with the assistance of Philippe Salmon and Dr. A. Mondière, who with others, under the leadership of Paul Nicole, met in 1884 and formed a *Réunion Lamarck* and a *Dîner Lamarck*, to maintain and perpetuate the memory of the great French transformist. Owing to their efforts, the exact date of Lamarck's birth, the house in which he lived during his lifetime at Paris, and all that we shall ever know of his place of burial have been established. It is a lasting shame that his remains were not laid in a grave, but were allowed to be put into a trench, with no headstone to mark the site, on one side of a row of graves of others better cared for, from which trench his bones, with those of others unknown and neglected, were exhumed and thrown into the catacombs of Paris. Lamarck left behind him no letters or manuscripts; nothing could be ascertained regarding the dates of his marriages, the names of his wives or of all his children. Of his descendants but one is known to be living, an officer in the army. But his aims in life, his undying love of science, his noble character and generous disposition are constantly revealed in his writings.

The name of Lamarck has been familiar to me from my youth up. When a boy, I used to arrange my collection of shells by the Lamarckian system, which had replaced the old Linnean classification. For over thirty years the Lamarckian factors of evolution have seemed to me to afford the foundation on which natural selection rests, to be the primary and efficient causes of organic change, and thus to account for the origin of variations, which Darwin himself assumed as the starting point or basis of his selection theory. It is not lessening the value of Darwin's labors, to recognize the originality of Lamarck's views, the vigor with which he asserted their truth, and the heroic manner in which, against adverse and contemptuous criticism, to his dying day he clung to them.

During a residence in Paris in the spring and summer of 1899, I spent my leisure hours in gathering material for this biography. I visited the place of his birth—the little hamlet of Bazentin, near Amiens—and, thanks to the kindness of the schoolmaster of that village, M. Duval, was shown the house where Lamarck was born, the records in the old parish register at the *mairie* of the birth of the father of Lamarck and of Lamarck himself. The Jesuit Seminary at Amiens was also visited, in order to obtain traces of his student life there, though the search was unsuccessful.

My thanks are due to Professor A. Giard of Paris for kind assistance in the loan of rare books, for copies of his own essays, especially his *Leçon d'Ouverture des Cours de l'Évolution des Êtres organisés*, 1888, and in facilitating the work of collecting data. Introduced by him to Professor Hamy, the learned anthropologist and archivist of the Muséum d'Histoire Naturelle, I was given by him the freest access to the archives in the Maison de Buffon, which, among other papers, contained the MS. *Archives du Muséum ;* i.e., the *Procès verbaux des Séances tenues par les Officiers du Jardin des Plantes,* from 1790 to 1830, bound in vellum, in thirty-four volumes. These were all looked through, though found to contain but little of biographical interest relating to Lamarck, beyond proving that he lived in that ancient edifice from 1793 until his death in 1829. Dr. Hamy's elaborate history of the last years of the Royal Garden and of the foundation of the Muséum d'Histoire Naturelle, in the volume commemorating the centennial of the foundation of the Museum, has been of essential service.

My warmest thanks are due to M. Adrien de Mortillet, formerly secretary of the Society of Anthropology of Paris, for most essential aid. He kindly gave me a copy of a very rare pamphlet, entitled *Lamarck. Par un Groupe de Transformistes, ses Disciples.* He also referred me to notices bearing on the genealogy of Lamarck and his family in the *Revue de Gascogne* for 1876. To him also I am indebted for the privilege of having electrotypes made of the five illustrations in the *Lamarck,* for copies of the composite portrait of Lamarck by Dr. Gachet, and also for a photograph of the *Acte de Naissance* reproduced by the late M. Salmon.

I have also to acknowledge the kindness shown me

by Dr. J. Deniker, the librarian of the Bibliothèque du Muséum d'Histoire Naturelle.

I had begun in the museum library, which contains nearly if not every one of Lamarck's publications, to prepare a bibliography of all of Lamarck's writings, when, to my surprise and pleasure, I was presented with a very full and elaborate one by the assistant-librarian, M. Godefroy Malloisel.

To Professor Edmond Perrier I am indebted for a copy of his valuable *Lamarck et le Transformisme Actuel*, reprinted from the noble volume commemorative of the centennial of the foundation of the Muséum d'Histoire Naturelle, which has proved of much use.

Other sources from which biographical details have been taken are Cuvier's *éloge*, and the notice of Lamarck, with a list of many of his writings, in the *Revue biographique de la Société malacologique de France*, 1886. This notice, which is illustrated by three portraits of Lamarck, one of which has been reproduced, I was informed by M. Paul Kleinsieck was prepared by the late J. R. Bourguignat, the eminent malacologist and anthropologist. The notices by Professor Mathias Duval and by L. A. Bourguin have been of essential service.

As regards the account of Lamarck's speculative and theoretical views, I have, so far as possible, preferred, by abstracts and translations, to let him tell his own story, rather than to comment at much length myself on points about which the ablest thinkers and students differ so much.

It is hoped that Lamarck's writings referring to

the evolution theory may, at no distant date, be reprinted in the original, as they are not bulky and could be comprised in a single volume.

This life is offered with much diffidence, though the pleasure of collecting the materials and of putting them together has been very great.

BROWN UNIVERSITY, PROVIDENCE, R. I.,
October, 1901.

CONTENTS

CHAPTER   PAGE

I. BIRTH, FAMILY, YOUTH, AND MILITARY CAREER . . 1

II. STUDENT LIFE AND BOTANICAL CAREER 15

III. LAMARCK'S SHARE IN THE REORGANIZATION OF THE JARDIN DES PLANTES AND MUSEUM OF NATURAL HISTORY 23

IV. PROFESSOR OF INVERTEBRATE ZOÖLOGY AT THE MUSEUM 32

V. LAST DAYS AND DEATH 51

VI. POSITION IN THE HISTORY OF SCIENCE; OPINIONS OF HIS CONTEMPORARIES AND SOME LATER BIOLOGISTS 64

VII. LAMARCK'S WORK IN METEOROLOGY AND PHYSICAL SCIENCE 79

VIII. LAMARCK'S WORK IN GEOLOGY 89

IX. LAMARCK THE FOUNDER OF INVERTEBRATE PALÆ-ONTOLOGY 124

X. LAMARCK'S OPINIONS ON GENERAL PHYSIOLOGY AND BIOLOGY 156

XI. LAMARCK AS A BOTANIST 173

XII. LAMARCK THE ZOÖLOGIST 180

XIII. THE EVOLUTIONARY VIEWS OF BUFFON AND OF GEOFFROY ST. HILAIRE 198

CHAPTER   PAGE

XIV. THE VIEWS OF ERASMUS DARWIN 216

XV. WHEN DID LAMARCK CHANGE HIS VIEWS REGARD-
ING THE MUTABILITY OF SPECIES? . . . 226

XVI. THE STEPS IN THE DEVELOPMENT OF LAMARCK'S
VIEWS ON EVOLUTION BEFORE THE PUBLICATION
OF HIS "PHILOSOPHIE ZOOLOGIQUE" . . . 232

XVII. THE "PHILOSOPHIE ZOOLOGIQUE" 279

XVIII. LAMARCK'S THEORY AS TO THE EVOLUTION OF
MAN . . . . . , . . . 357

XIX. LAMARCK'S THOUGHTS ON MORALS, AND ON THE
RELATION BETWEEN SCIENCE AND RÉLIGION . 372

XX. THE RELATIONS BETWEEN LAMARCKISM AND DAR-
WINISM; NEOLAMARCKISM 382

BIBLIOGRAPHY 425

LIST OF ILLUSTRATIONS

ATTEMPT AT A RECONSTRUCTION OF THE PROFILE OF LAMARCK BY DR. GACHET (Photogravure) . *Frontispiece*

FACING
PAGE

BIRTHPLACE OF LAMARCK, FRONT VIEW }
BIRTHPLACE OF LAMARCK, " " } 4

ACT OF BIRTH 6

AUTOGRAPH OF LAMARCK, JANUARY 25, 1802 . . . 10

LAMARCK AT THE AGE OF 35 YEARS 20

BIRTHPLACE OF LAMARCK. REAR VIEW FROM THE WEST }
MAISON DE BUFFON, IN WHICH LAMARCK LIVED IN PARIS, } 42
1793–1829 }

PORTRAIT OF LAMARCK, WHEN OLD AND BLIND, IN THE
COSTUME OF A MEMBER OF THE INSTITUTE, ENGRAVED
IN 1824 54

PORTRAIT OF LAMARCK 180

MAISON DE BUFFON, IN WHICH LAMARCK LIVED, 1793–1829 198

É. GEOFFROY ST. HILAIRE 212

LAMARCK, THE FOUNDER OF EVOLUTION. HIS LIFE AND WORK

CHAPTER I

BIRTH, FAMILY, YOUTH, AND MILITARY CAREER

THE life of Lamarck is the old, old story of a man of genius who lived far in advance of his age, and who died comparatively unappreciated and neglected. But his original and philosophic views, based as they were on broad conceptions of nature, and touching on the burning questions of our day, have, after the lapse of a hundred years, gained fresh interest and appreciation, and give promise of permanent acceptance.

The author of the *Flore Française* will never be forgotten by his countrymen, who called him the French Linné ; and he who wrote the *Animaux sans Vertèbres* at once took the highest rank as the leading zoölogist of his period. But Lamarck was more than a systematic biologist of the first order. Besides rare experience and judgment in the classification of plants and of animals, he had an unusually active, inquiring, and philosophical mind, with an originality and boldness in speculation, and soundness in reasoning and in dealing with such biological facts as were known in his time, which have caused his views as to the method of organic evolution to again come to the front.

As a zoölogical philosopher no one of his time approached Lamarck. The period, however, in which he lived was not ripe for the hearty and general adoption of the theory of descent. As in the organic world we behold here and there prophetic types, anticipating, in their generalized synthetic nature, the incoming, ages after, of more specialized types, so Lamarck anticipated by more than half a century the principles underlying the present evolutionary theories.

So numerous are now the adherents, in some form, of Lamarck's views, that at the present time evolutionists are divided into Darwinians and Lamarckians or Neolamarckians. The factors of organic evolution as stated by Lamarck, it is now claimed by many, really comprise the primary or foundation principles or initiative causes of the origin of life-forms. Hence not only do many of the leading biologists of his native country, but some of those of Germany, of the United States, and of England, justly regard him as the founder of the theory of organic evolution.

Besides this, Lamarck lived in a transition period. He prepared the way for the scientific renascence in France. Moreover, his simple, unselfish character was a rare one. He led a retired life. His youth was tinged with romance, and during the last decade of his life he was blind. He manfully and patiently bore adverse criticisms, ridicule, forgetfulness, and inappreciation, while, so far from renouncing his theoretical views, he tenaciously clung to them to his dying day.

The biography of such a character is replete with interest, and the memory of his unselfish and fruitful devotion to science should be forever cherished. His life was also notable for the fact that after his fiftieth year he took up and mastered a new science; and at a period when many students of literature and science cease to be productive and rest from their labors, he accomplished the best work of his life—work which has given him lasting fame as a systematist and as a philosophic biologist. Moreover, Lamarckism comprises the fundamental principles of evolution, and will always have to be taken into consideration in accounting for the origin, not only of species, but especially of the higher groups, such as orders, classes, and phyla.

This striking personage in the history of biological science, who has made such an ineffaceable impression on the philosophy of biology, certainly demands more than a brief *éloge* to keep alive his memory.

Jean-Baptiste-Pierre-Antoine de Monet, Chevalier de Lamarck, was born August 1, 1744, at Bazentin-le-Petit. This little village is situated in Picardy, or what is now the Department of the Somme, in the Arrondissement de Péronne, Canton d'Albert, a little more than four miles from Albert, between this town and Bapaume, and near Longueval, the nearest post-office to Bazentin. The village of Bazentin-le-Grand, composed of a few more houses than its sister hamlet, is seen half a mile to the southeast, shaded by the little forest such as borders nearly every town and village in this region. The two hamlets are pleasantly situated in a richly cultivated country, on the chalk uplands or downs of Picardy, amid broad acres of wheat and barley variegated with poppies and the purple cornflower, and with roadsides shaded by tall poplars.

The peasants to the number of 251 compose the diminishing population. There were 356 in 1880, or about that date. The silence of the single little street, with its one-storied, thatched or tiled cottages, is at infrequent intervals broken by an elderly dame in her *sabots*, or by a creaking, rickety village cart driven by a farmer-boy in blouse and hob-nailed shoes. The largest inhabited building is the *mairie*, a modern structure, at one end of which is the village school, where fifteen or twenty urchins enjoy the instructions of the worthy teacher. A stone church, built in 1774, and somewhat larger than the needs of the hamlet at present require, raises its tower over the quiet scene.

Our pilgrimage to Bazentin had for its object the discovery of the birthplace of Lamarck, of which we could obtain no information in Paris. Our guide from Albert took us to the *mairie*, and it was with no little satisfaction that we learned from the excellent village teacher, M. Duval, that the house in which the great naturalist was born was still standing, and but a few steps away, in the rear of the church and of the *mairie*. With much kindness he

Joutel del., from a photograph by the author.

BIRTHPLACE OF LAMARCK, FRONT VIEW

Joutel del., from a photograph by the author.

BIRTHPLACE OF LAMARCK

left his duties in the schoolroom, and accompanied us to the ancient structure.

The modest *château* stands a few rods to the westward of the little village, and was evidently the seat of the leading family of the place. It faces east and is a two-storied house of the shape seen everywhere in France, with its high, incurved roof; the walls, nearly a foot and a half thick, built of brick; the corners and windows of blocks of white limestone. It is about fifty feet long and twenty-five feet wide. Above the roof formerly rose a small tower. There is no porch over the front door. Within, a rather narrow hall passes through the centre, and opens into a large room on each side. What was evidently the drawing-room or *salon* was a spacious apartment with a low white wainscot and a heavy cornice. Over the large, roomy fireplace is a painting on the wood panel, representing a rural scene, in which a shepherdess and her lover are engaged in other occupations than the care of the flock of sheep visible in the distance. Over the doorway is a smaller but quaint painting of the same description. The house is uninhabited, and perhaps uninhabitable—indeed almost a ruin—and is used as a storeroom for wood and rubbish by the peasants in the adjoining house to the left, on the south.

The ground in front was cultivated with vegetables, not laid down to a lawn, and the land stretched back for perhaps three hundred to four hundred feet between the old garden walls.

Here, amid these rural scenes, even now so beautiful and tranquil, the subject of our sketch was

born and lived through his infancy and early boyhood.*

If his parents did not possess an ample fortune,
they were blessed with a numerous progeny, for Lamarck was the eleventh and youngest child, and
seems to have survived all the others. Biographers
have differed as to the date of the birth of Lamarck.†
Happily the exact date had been ascertained through
the researches of M. Philippe Salmon ; and M. Duval
kindly showed us in the thin volume of records, with
its tattered and torn leaves, the register of the *Acte de
Naissance*, and made a copy of it, as follows :

*Extrait du Registre aux Actes de Baptême de la Com-
mune de Bazentin, pour l'Année* 1744.

L'an mil sept cent quarante-quatre, le premier août
est né en légitime mariage et le lendemain a été
baptisé par moy curé soussigné Jean Baptiste Pierre
Antoine, fils de Messire Jacques Philippe de Monet,
chevalier de Lamarck, seigneur des Bazentin grand
et petit et de haute et puissante Dame Marie Françoise de Fontaine demeurant en leur château de Bazentin le petit, son parrain a été Messire Jean Baptiste de Fossé, prêtre-chanoine de l'église collégiale
de St. Farcy de Péronne, y demeurant, sa marraine
Dame Antoinette Françoise de Bucy, nièce de Messire
Louis Joseph Michelet, chevalier, ancien commissaire

---

* In the little chapel next the church lies buried, we were told by
M. Duval, a Protestant of the family of de Guillebon, the purchaser
(*acquéreur*) of the *château*. Whether the estate is now in the hands
of his heirs we did not ascertain.

† As stated by G. de Mortillet, the date of his birth is variously
given. Michaud's *Dictionnaire Biographique* gives the date April
1 ; other authors, April 11 ; others, the correct one, August 1, 1744.
(*Lamarck. Par un Groupe de Transformistes, ses Disciples. L'Homme*,
iv. p. 289, 1887.)

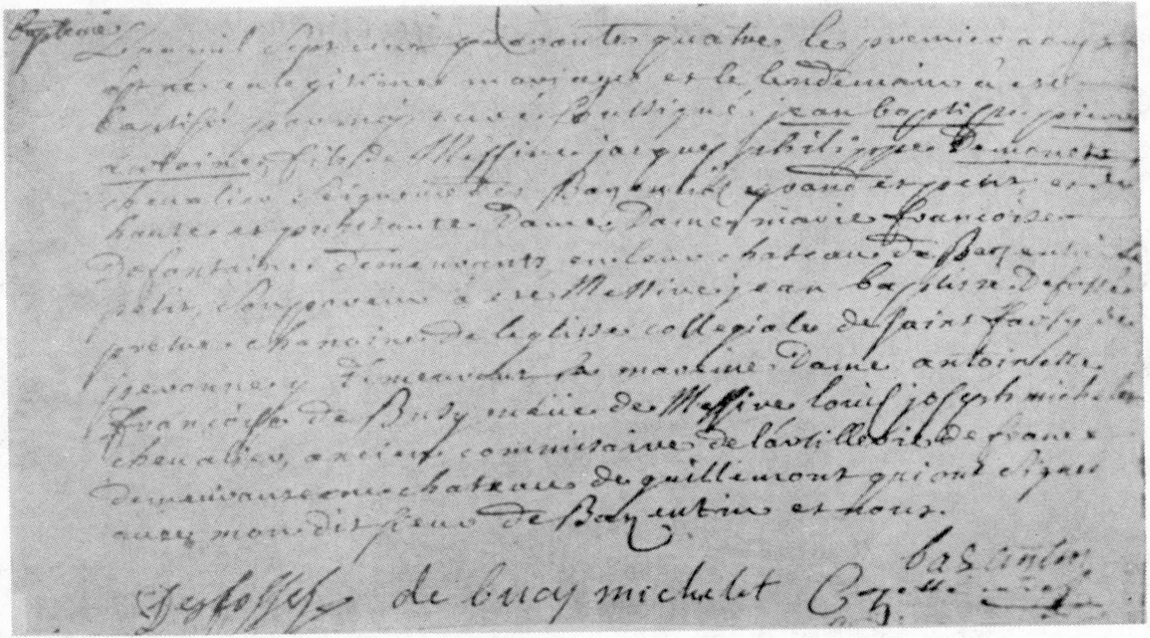

From a photograph

ACT OF BIRTH

de l'artillerie de France demeurante au château de Guillemont, qui ont signé avec mon dit sieur de Bazentin et nous.

Ont signé : De Fossé, De Bucy Michelet, Bazentin. Cozette, curé.

Of Lamarck's parentage and ancestry there are fortunately some traces. In the *Registre aux Actes de Baptême pour l'Année* 1702, still preserved in the *mairie* of Bazentin-le-Petit, the record shows that his father was born in February, 1702, at Bazentin. The infant was baptised February 16, 1702, the permission to the *curé* by Henry, Bishop of Amiens, having been signed February 3, 1702. Lamarck's grandparents were, according to this certificate of baptism, Messire Philippe de Monet de Lamarck, Ecuyer, Seigneur des Bazentin, and Dame Magdeleine de Lyonne.

The family of Lamarck, as stated by H. Masson,* notwithstanding his northern and almost Germanic name of Chevalier de Lamarck, originated in the southwest of France. Though born at Bazentin, in old Picardy, it is not less true that he descended on the paternal side from an ancient house of Béarn, whose patrimony was very modest. This house was that of Monet.

Another genealogist, Baron C. de Cauna,† tells us that there is no doubt that the family of Monet in Bigorre‡ was divided. One of its representatives

---

* "Sur la maison de Viella—les Mortiers-brévise et les Montalembert en Gascogne—et sur le naturaliste Lamarck." Par Hippolyte Masson. (*Revue de Gascogne*, xvii., pp. 141–143, 1876.)

† *Ibid.*, p. 194.

‡ A small town in southwestern France, near Lourdes and Pau ; it is about eight miles north of Tarbes, in Gascony.

formed a branch in Picardy in the reign of Louis XIV. or later.

Lamarck's grandfather, Philippe de Monet, "seigneur de Bazentin et autres lieux," was also "chevalier de l'ordre royal et militaire de Saint-Louis, commandant pour le roi en la ville et château de Dinan, pensionnaire de sa majesté."

The descendants of Philippe de Lamarck were, adds de Cauna, thus thrown into two branches, or at least two offshoots or stems (*brisures*), near Péronne. But the actual posterity of the Monet of Picardy was reduced to a single family, claiming back, with good reason, to a southern origin. One of its scions in the maternal line was a brilliant officer of the military marine and also son-in-law of a very distinguished naval officer.

The family of Monet was represented among the French nobility of 1789 by Messires de Monet de Caixon and de Monet de Saint-Martin. By marriage their grandson was connected with an honorable family of Montant, near Saint-Sever-Cap.

Another authority, the Abbé J. Dulac, has thrown additional light on the genealogy of the de Lamarck family, which, it may be seen, was for at least three centuries a military one.* The family of Monet, Seigneur de Saint-Martin et de Sombran, was maintained as a noble one by order of the Royal Council of State of June 20, 1678. He descended (I) from Bernard de Monet, esquire, captain of the château of Lourdes, who had as a son (II) Étienne de Monet,

---

* *Revue de Gascogne*, pp. 264–269, 1876.

esquire, who, by contract dated August 15, 1543,
married Marguerite de Sacaze. He was the father of
(III) Pierre de Monet, esquire, "Seigneur d'Ast, en
Béarn, guidon des gendarmes de la compagnie du roi
de Navarre." From him descended (IV) Étienne de
Monet, esquire, second of the name, "Seigneur d'Ast
et Lamarque, de Julos." He was a captain by rank,
and bought the estate of Saint-Martin in 1592. He
married, in 1612, Jeanne de Lamarque, daughter of
William de Lamarck, "Seigneur de Lamarque et de
Bretaigne." They had three children, the third of
whom was Philippe, "chevalier de Saint-Louis, commandant du château de Dinan, Seigneur de Bazentin, en Picardy," who, as we have already seen, was
the father of the naturalist Lamarck, who lived from
1744 to 1829. The abbé relates that Philippe, the
father of the naturalist, was born at Saint-Martin, in
the midst of Bigorre, "*in pleine Bigorre,*" and he
very neatly adds that "the Bigorrais have the right
to claim for their land of flowers one of the glories
of botany."*

---

* The abbé attempts to answer the question as to what place gave
origin to the name of Lamarck, and says :
"The author of the history of Béarn considered the cradle of the
race to have been the freehold of Marca, parish of Gou (Basses-
Pyrénées). A branch of the family established in le Magnoac changed
its name of Marca to that of La Marque." It was M. d'Ossat who
gave rise to this change by addressing his letters to M. de Marca (at
the time when he was preceptor of his nephew), sometimes under the
name of M. Marca, sometimes *M. la Marqua,* or of *M. de la Marca,*
but more often still under that of *M. de la Marque,* "with the object,
no doubt, of making him a Frenchman" ("*dans la vue sans doute de
le franciser*"). (*Vie du Cardinal d'Ossat,* tome i., p. 319.)
"To recall their origin, the branch of Magnoac to-day write their
name *Marque-Marca.* If the Marca of the historian belongs to
Béarn, the Lamarque of the naturalist, an orthographic name in principle, proceeds from Bigorre, actually chosen (*désignée*) by *Lamarcq,*

The name was at first variously spelled de La-marque, de la Marck, or de Lamarck. He himself signed his name, when acting as secretary of the As-sembly of Professors-administrative of the Museum of Natural History during the years of the First Re-public, as plain Lamarck.

The inquiry arises how, being the eleventh child, he acquired the title of chevalier, which would natur-ally have become extinct with the death of the oldest son. The Abbé Dulac suggests that the ten older of the children had died, or that by some family arrange-ment he was allowed to add the domanial name to the patronymic one. Certainly he never tarnished the family name, which, had it not been for him, would have remained in obscurity.

As to his father's tastes and disposition, what in-fluence his mother had in shaping his character, his home environment, as the youngest of eleven chil-dren, the nature of his education in infancy and boy-

---

Pontacq, or Lamarque près Béarn. That the *Lamarque* of the botanist of the royal cabinet distinguished himself from all the *La-marques* of Béarn or of Bigorre, which it bears (*qu'il gise*) to this day in the Hautes-Pyrénées, Canton d'Ossun, we have many proofs : Aast at some distance, Bourcat and Couet all near l'Abbaye Laïque, etc. The village so determined is called in turn *Marca, La Marque, La-marque ;* names predestined to several destinations ; judge then to the mercy of a botanist, *Lamarck, La Marck, Delamarque, De La-marck,* who shall determine their number ? As to the last, I only ex-plain it by a fantasy of the man who would de-Bigorrize himself in order to Germanize himself in the hope, apparently, that at the first utterance of the name people would believe that he was from the *outre Rhin* rather than from the borders of Gave or of Adour. Con-sequently a hundred times more learned and a hundred times more worthy of a professorship in the Museum, where Monet would seem (*entrevait*) much less than Lamarque."

It may be added that Béarn was an ancient province of southern France nearly corresponding to the present Department of Basses-Pyrénées. Its capital was Pau.

Je prie le Citoyen qui assemble dans le Magazin de l'Imprimerie du Citoyen Agasse de remettre à Mesdames chevalier Cent exemplaires de mon hydrogeologie, pour les Brocher.

Paris, ce 5 pluviose an dix

Lamarck

hood, there are no sources of information. But several of his brothers entered the army, and the domestic atmosphere was apparently a military one.

Philippe de Lamarck, with his large family, had endowed his first-born son so that he could maintain the family name and title, and had found situations for several of the others in the army. Jean Lamarck did not manifest any taste for the clerical profession. He lived in a martial atmosphere. For centuries his ancestors had borne arms. His eldest brother had been killed in the breach at the siege of Berg-op-Zoom ; two others were still in the service, and in the troublous times at the beginning of the war in 1756, a young man of high spirit and courage would naturally not like to relinquish the prospect of renown and promotion. But, yielding to the wishes of his father, he entered as a student at the college of the Jesuits at Amiens.*

His father dying in 1760, nothing could induce the incipient abbé, then seventeen years of age, to longer wear his bands. Immediately on returning home he bought himself a wretched horse, for want of means to buy a better one, and, accompanied by a poor lad

---

* We have been unable to ascertain the date when young Lamarck entered the seminary. On making inquiries in June, 1899, at the Jesuits' Seminary in Amiens, one of the faculty, after consultation with the Father Superior, kindly gave us in writing the following information as to the exact date : "The registers of the great seminary were carried away during the French Revolution, and we do not know whither they have been transported, and whether they still exist to-day. Besides, it is very doubtful whether Lamarck resided here, because only ecclesiastics preparing for receiving orders were received in the seminary. Do you not confound the seminary with the ancient college of Rue Poste de Paris, college now destroyed?"

of his village, he rode across the country to join the
French army, then campaigning in Germany.

He carried with him a letter of recommendation
from one of his neighbors on an adjoining estate in
the country, Madame de Lameth, to M. de Lastic,
colonel of the regiment of Beaujolais.*

"We can imagine [says Cuvier] the feelings of this
officer on thus finding himself hampered with a boy
whose puny appearance made him seem still younger
than he was. However, he sent him to his quarters,
and then busied himself with his duties. The period
indeed was a critical one. It was the 16th of July,
1761. The Marshal de Broglie had just united his
army with that of the Prince de Soubise, and the
next day was to attack the allied army commanded
by the Prince Ferdinand of Brunswick. At the break
of day M. de Lastic rode along the front of his corps,
and the first man that met his gaze was the new re-
cruit, who, without saying anything to him, had placed
himself in the front rank of a company of grenadiers,
and nothing could induce him to quit his post.

"It is a matter of history that this battle, which
bears the name of the little village of Fissingshausen,
between Ham and Lippstadt, in Westphalia, was lost
by the French, and that the two generals, mutually
accusing each other of this defeat, immediately separated, and abandoned the campaign.

"During the movement of the battle, de Lamarck's
company was stationed in a position exposed to the
direct fire of the enemy's artillery. In the confusion
of the retreat he was forgotten. Already all the
officers and non-commissioned officers had been

---

* We are following the *Éloge* of Cuvier almost verbatim, also reproduced in the biographical notice in the *Revue biographique de la Société Malacologique de France*, said to have been prepared by J. R.
Bourguignat.

killed; there remained only fourteen men, when the oldest grenadier, seeing that there were no more of the French troops in sight, proposed to the young volunteer, become so promptly commander, to withdraw his little troop. 'But we are assigned to this post,' said the boy, 'and we should not withdraw from it until we are relieved.' And he made them remain there until the colonel, seeing that the squad did not rally, sent him an orderly, who crept by all sorts of covered ways to reach him. This bold stand having been reported to the marshal, he promoted him on the field to the rank of an officer, although his order had prescribed that he should be very chary of these kinds of promotions."

His physical courage shown at this age was paralleled by his moral courage in later years. The staying power he showed in immovably adhering to his views on evolution through many years, and under the direct and raking fire of harsh and unrelenting criticism and ridicule from friend and foe, affords a striking contrast to the moral timidity shown by Buffon when questioned by the Sorbonne. We can see that Lamarck was the stuff martyrs are made of, and that had he been tried for heresy he would have been another Tycho Brahe.

Soon after, de Lamarck was nominated to a lieutenancy; but so glorious a beginning of his military career was most unexpectedly checked. A sudden accident forced him to leave the service and entirely change his course of life. His regiment had been, during peace, sent into garrison, first at Toulon and then at Monaco. While there a comrade in play lifted him by the head; this gave rise to an inflammation of the lymphatic glands of the neck, which, not receiving the necessary attention on the spot, obliged him to go to Paris for better treatment.

" The united efforts [says Cuvier] of several surgeons met with no better success, and danger had become very imminent, when our *confrère*, the late M. Tenon, with his usual sagacity, recognized the trouble, and put an end to it by a complicated operation, of which M. de Lamarck preserved deep scars. This treatment lasted for a year, and, during this time, the extreme scantiness of his resources confined him to a solitary life, when he had the leisure to devote himself to meditations."

CHAPTER II

THE profession of arms had not led Lamarck to forget the principles of physical science which he had received at college. During his sojourn at Monaco the singular vegetation of that rocky country had attracted his attention, and Chomel's *Traité des Plantes usuelles* accidentally falling into his hands had given him some smattering of botany.

Lodged at Paris, as he has himself said, in a room much higher up than he could have wished, the clouds, almost the only objects to be seen from his windows, interested him by their ever-changing shapes, and inspired in him his first ideas of meteorology. There were not wanting other objects to excite interest in a mind which had always been remarkably active and original. He then realized, to quote from his biographer, Cuvier, what Voltaire said of Condorcet, that solid enduring discoveries can shed a lustre quite different from that of a commander of a company of infantry. He resolved to study some profession. This last resolution was but little less courageous than the first. Reduced to a pension (*pension alimentaire*) of only 400 francs a year, he attempted to study medicine, and while waiting until he had the time to give to the necessary studies, he worked in the dreary office of a bank.

The meditations, the thoughts and aspirations of a contemplative nature like his, in his hours of work or leisure, in some degree consoled the budding philosopher during this period of uncongenial labor, and when he did have an opportunity of communicating his ideas to his friends, of discussing them, of defending them against objection, the hardships of his workaday life were for the time forgotten. In his ardor for science all the uncongenial experiences of his life as a bank clerk vanished. Like many another rising genius in art, literature, or science, his zeal for knowledge and investigation in those days of grinding poverty fed the fires of his genius, and this was the light which throughout his long poverty-stricken life shed a golden lustre on his toilsome existence. He did not then know that the great Linné, the father of the science he was to illuminate and so greatly to expand, also began life in extreme poverty, and eked out his scanty livelihood by mending over again for his own use the cast-off shoes of his fellow-students. (Cuvier.)

Bourguin * tells us that Lamarck's medical course lasted four years, and this period of severe study—for he must have made it such—evidently laid the best possible foundation that Paris could then afford for his after studies. He seems, however, to have wavered in his intentions of making medicine his life work, for he possessed a decided taste for music. His eldest brother, the Chevalier de Bazentin, strongly opposed, and induced him to abandon this project, though not without difficulty.

---

* *Les Grand Naturalists Français au Commencement du XIX Siècle.*

At about this time the two brothers lived in a quiet village * near Paris, and there for a year they studied together science and history. And now happened an event which proved to be the turning point, or rather gave a new and lasting impetus to Lamarck's career and decided his vocation in life. In one of their walks they met the philosopher and sentimentalist, Jean Jacques Rousseau. We know little about Lamarck's acquaintance with this genius, for all the details of his life, both in his early and later years, are pitifully scanty. Lamarck, however, had attended at the Jardin du Roi a botanical course, and now, having by good fortune met Rousseau, he probably improved the acquaintance, and, found by Rousseau to be a congenial spirit, he was soon invited to accompany him in his herborizations.

Still more recently Professor Giard † has unearthed from the works of Rousseau the following statement by him regarding species : " Est-ce qu'à proprement parler il n'existerait point d'espèces dans la nature,

---

* Was this quiet place in the region just out of Paris possibly near Mont Valérien ? He must have been about twenty-two years old when he met Rousseau and began to study botany seriously. His *Flore Française* appeared in 1778, when he was thirty-four years old. Rousseau, at the end of his checkered life, from 1770 to 1778, lived in Paris. He often botanized in the suburbs ; and Mr. Morley, in his *Rousseau*, says that "one of his greatest delights was to watch Mont Valérien in the sunset" (p. 436). Rousseau died in Paris in 1778. That Rousseau expressed himself vaguely in favor of evolution is stated by Isidore Geoffroy St. Hilaire, who quotes a *"Phrase, malheureusement un peu ambiguë, qui semble montrer, dans se grand écrivain, un partisan de plus de la variabilité du type."* (*Résumé des Vues sur l'espèce organique,* p. 18, Paris, 1889.) The passage is quoted in Geoffroy's *Histoire Naturelle Générale des Règnes organiques,* ii., ch. i., p. 271. I have been unable to verify this quotation.

† *Leçon d'Ouverture du Cours de l'Évolution des Êtres organisés.* Paris, 1888.

2

mais seulement des individus ? "* In his *Discours sur l'Inégalité parmi les Hommes* is the following passage, which shows, as Giard says, that Rousseau perfectly understood the influence of the *milieu* and of wants on the organism ; and this brilliant writer seems to have been the first to suggest natural selection, though only in the case of man, when he says that the weaker in Sparta were eliminated in order that the superior and stronger of the race might survive and be maintained.

" Accustomed from infancy to the severity of the weather and the rigors of the seasons, trained to undergo fatigue, and obliged to defend naked and without arms their life and their prey against ferocious beasts, or to escape them by flight, the men acquired an almost invariably robust temperament ; the infants, bringing into the world the strong constitution of their fathers, and strengthening themselves by the same kind of exercise as produced it, have thus acquired all the vigor of which the human species is capable. Nature uses them precisely as did the law of Sparta the children of her citizens. She rendered strong and robust those with a good constitution, and destroyed all the others. Our societies differ in this respect, where the state, in rendering the children burdensome to the father, indirectly kills them before birth."†

Soon Lamarck abandoned not only a military career but also music, medicine, and the bank, and devoted himself exclusively to science. He was now twenty-four years old, and, becoming a student of

---

* *Dictionnaire des Termes de la Botanique.*   Art. APHRODITE.
† *Discours sur l'Origine et les Fondements de l'Inégalité parmi les Hommes.*   1754.

botany under Bernard de Jussieu, for ten years gave unremitting attention to this science, and especially to a study of the French flora.

Cuvier states that the *Flore Française* appeared after " six months of unremitting labor." However this may be, the results of over nine preceding years of study, gathered together, written, and printed within the brief period of half a year, was no hasty *tour de force*, but a well-matured, solid work which for many years remained a standard one.

It brought him immediate fame. It appeared at a fortunate epoch. The example of Rousseau and the general enthusiasm he inspired had made the study of flowers very popular—" *une science à la mode*," as Cuvier says—even among many ladies and in the world of fashion, so that the new work of Lamarck, though published in three octavo volumes, had a rapid success.

The preface was written by Daubenton.* Buffon also took much interest in the work, opposing as it did the artificial system of Linné, for whom he had, for other reasons, no great degree of affection. He obtained the privilege of having the work published at the royal printing office at the expense of the government, and the total proceeds of the sale of the volumes were given to the author. This elaborate

---

* Since 1742, the keeper and demonstrator of the Cabinet, who shared with Thouin, the chief gardener, the care of the Royal Gardens. Daubenton was at that time the leading anatomist of France, and after Buffon's death he gathered around him all the scientific men who demanded the transformation of the superannuated and incomplete Jardin du Roi, and perhaps initiated the movement which resulted five years later in the creation of the present Museum of Natural History. (Hamy, l. c., p. 12.)

work at once placed young Lamarck in the front rank
of botanists, and now the first and greatest honor of
his life came to him. The young lieutenant, disap-
pointed in a military advancement, won his spurs in
the field of science. A place in botany had become
vacant at the Academy of Sciences, and M. de Lamarck having been presented in the second rank (*en
seconde ligne*), the ministry, a thing almost unex-
ampled, caused him to be given by the king, in 1779,
the preference over M. Descemet, whose name was
presented before his, in the first rank, and who since
then, and during a long life, never could recover
the place which he unjustly lost.* " In a word, the
poor officer, so neglected since the peace, obtained
at one stroke the good fortune, always very rare,
and especially so at that time, of being both the
recipient of the favor of the Court and of the
public."†

The interest and affection felt for him by Buffon
were of advantage to him in another way. Desiring
to have his son, whom he had planned to be his successor as Intendant of the Royal Garden, and who
had just finished his studies, enjoy the advantage of
travel in foreign lands, Buffon proposed to Lamarck to
go with him as a guide and friend ; and, not wishing
him to appear as a mere teacher, he procured for him,
in 1781, a commission as Royal Botanist, charged

---

* De Mortillet (*Lamarck. Par un Groupe de Transformistes*, p. 11)
states that Lamarck was elected to the Academy at the age of thirty;
but as he was born in 1744, and the election took place in 1779, he
must have been thirty-five years of age.

† Cuvier's *Éloge*, p. viii.; also *Revue biographique de la Société
Malacologique*, p. 67.

A. de Vaux-Bidon, del.   From an old engraving

LAMARCK AT THE AGE OF 35 YEARS

with visiting the foreign botanical gardens and museums, and of placing them in communication with those of Paris. His travels extended through portions of the years 1781 and 1782.

According to his own statement,* in pursuit of this object he collected not only rare and interesting plants which were wanting in the Royal Garden, but also minerals and other objects of natural history new to the Museum. He went to Holland, Germany, Hungary, etc., visiting universities, botanical gardens, and museums of natural history. He examined the mines of the Hartz in Hanover, of Freyburg in Saxony, of Chemnitz and of Cremnitz in Hungary, making there numerous observations which he incorporated in his work on physics, and sent collections of ores, minerals, and seeds to Paris. He also made the acquaintance of the botanists Gleditsch at Berlin, Jacquin at Vienna, and Murray at Göttingen. He obtained some idea of the magnificent establishments in these countries devoted to botany, " and which," he says, " ours do not yet approach, in spite of all that had been done for them during the last thirty years." †

On his return, as he writes, he devoted all his energies and time to research and to carrying out his great enterprises in botany ; as he stated: "Indeed, for the last ten years my works have obliged me to keep in constant activity a great number of artists, such as draughtsmen, engravers, and printers." ‡

---

* See letters to the Committee of Public Instruction.

† Cuvier's *Éloge*, p. viii ; also Bourguignat in *Revue biog. Soc. Malacologique*, p. 67.

‡ He received no remuneration for this service. As was afterwards stated in the National Archives, *État des personnes attachées au Mu-*

But the favor of Buffon, powerful as his influence was,* together with the aid of the minister, did not avail to give Lamarck a permanent salaried position. Soon after his return from his travels, however, M. d'Angiviller, the successor of Buffon as Intendant of the Royal Garden, who was related to Lamarck's family, created for him the position of keeper of the herbarium of the Royal Garden, with the paltry salary of 1,000 francs.

According to the same *État*, Lamarck had now been attached to the Royal Garden five years. In 1789 he received as salary only 1,000 livres or francs; in 1792 it was raised to the sum of 1,800 livres.

---

séum National d'Histoire Naturelle a l'epoque du messidor an II de la Republique, he "sent to this establishment seeds of rare plants, interesting minerals, and observations made during his travels in Holland, Germany, and in France. He did not receive any compensation for this service."

* "The illustrious Intendant of the Royal Garden and Cabinet had concentrated in his hands the most varied and extensive powers. Not only did he hold, like his predecessors, the *personnel* of the establishment entirely at his discretion, but he used the appropriations which were voted to him with a very great independence. Thanks to the universal renown which he had acquired both in science and in literature, Buffon maintained with the men who succeeded one another in office relations which enabled him to do almost anything he liked at the Royal Garden." His manner to public men, as Condorcet said, was conciliatory and tactful, and to his subordinates he was modest and unpretending. (Professor G. T. Hamy. *Les Derniers Jours du Jardin du Roi*, etc., p. 3.) Buffon, after nearly fifty years of service as Intendant, died April 16, 1788.

CHAPTER III

LAMARCK'S SHARE IN THE REORGANIZATION OF THE JARDIN DES PLANTES AND MUSEUM OF NATURAL HISTORY

EVEN in his humble position as keeper of the herbarium, with its pitiable compensation, Lamarck, now an eminent botanist, with a European reputation, was by no means appreciated or secure in his position. He was subjected to many worries, and, already married and with several children, suffered from a grinding poverty. His friend and supporter, La Billarderie, was a courtier, with much influence at the Tuileries, but as Intendant of the Royal Garden without the least claim to scientific fitness for the position; and in 1790 he was on the point of discharging Lamarck.* On the 20th of August the Finance Committee reduced the expenses of the Royal Garden and Cabinet, and, while raising the salary of the professor of botany, to make good the deficiency thus ensuing suppressed the position of keeper of the herbarium, filled by Lamarck. Lamarck, on learning of this, acted promptly, and though in this

---

* Another intended victim of La Billarderie, whose own salary had been at the same time reduced, was Faujas de Saint-Fond, one of the founders of geology. But his useful discoveries in economic geology having brought him distinction, the king had generously pensioned him, and he was retained in office on the printed *État* distributed by the Committee of Finance. (Hamy, l. c., p. 29.)

cavalier way stricken off from the rolls of the Royal
Garden, he at once prepared, printed, and distributed
among the members of the National Assembly an
energetic claim for restoration to his office.*   His
defence formed two brochures; in one he gave an
account of his life, travels, and works, and in the
other he showed that the place which he filled was
a pressing necessity, and could not be conveniently
or usefully added to that of the professor of botany,
who was already overworked.

This manly and able plea in his own defence also
comprised a broad, comprehensive plan for the organization and development of a great national museum,
combining both vast collections and adequate means
of public instruction.   The paper briefly stated, in
courteous language, what he wished to say to public
men, in general animated with good intentions, but
little versed in the study of the sciences and the
knowledge of their application.   It praised, in fit
terms, the work of the National Assembly, and gave,
without too much emphasis, the assurance of an entire devotion to the public business.   Then in a very
clear and comprehensive way were given all the kinds
of service which an establishment like the Royal
Garden should render to the sciences and arts, and
especially to agriculture, medicine, commerce, etc.
Museums, galleries, and botanical gardens; public lectures and demonstrations in the museum and school

---

* Hamy, l. c., p. 29.   This brochure, of which I possess a copy,
is a small quarto pamphlet of fifteen pages, signed, on the last page,
"*J. B. Lamarck, ancien Officier au Régiment de Beaujolais, de
l'Academie des Sciences de Paris, Botaniste attaché au Cabinet d'Histoire Naturelle du Jardin des Plantes.*"

of botany; an office for giving information, the distribution of seeds, etc.—all the resources already so varied, as well as the facilities for work at the Jardin, passed successively in review before the representatives of the country, and the address ended in a modest request to the Assembly that its author be allowed a few days to offer some observations regarding the future organization of this great institution.

The Assembly, adopting the wise views announced in the manifest which had been presented by the officers of the Jardin and Cabinet, sent the address to the Committee, and gave a month's time to the petitioners to prepare and present a plan and regulations which should establish the organization of their establishment.*

It was in 1790 that the decisive step was taken by the officers of the Royal Garden † and Cabinet of

---

* Hamy, l. c., p. 31; also *Pièces Justificatives*, Nos. 11 *et* 12, pp. 97–101. The Intendant of the Garden was completely ignored, and his unpopularity and inefficiency led to his resignation. But meanwhile, in his letter to Condorcet, the perpetual Secretary of the Institute of France, remonstrating against the proposed suppression by the Assembly of the place of Intendant, he partially retracted his action against Lamarck, saying that Lamarck's work, "*peut être utile, mais n'est pas absolutement nécessaire.*" The Intendant, as Hamy adds, knew well the value of the services rendered by Lamarck at the Royal Garden, and that, as a partial recompense, he had been appointed botanist to the museum. He also equally well knew that the author of the *Flore Française* was in a most precarious situation and supported on his paltry salary a family of seven persons, as he was already at this time married and had five children. "But his own place was in peril, and he did not hesitate to sacrifice the poor savant whom he had himself installed as keeper of the herbarium." (Hamy, l. c., pp. 34, 35.)

† The first idea of the foundation of the Jardin dates from 1626, but the actual carrying out of the conception was in 1635. The first act of installation took place in 1640. Gui de la Brosse, in order to please his high protectors, the first physicians of the king, named his establishment *Jardin des Plantes Medicinales*. It was renovated by Fagon, who was born in the Jardin, and whose mother was the niece

Natural History which led to the organization of the present Museum of Natural History as it is to-day. Throughout the proceedings, Lamarck, as at the outset, took a prominent part, his address having led the Assembly to invite the officers of the double establishment to draw up rules for its government.

The officers met together August 23d, and their distrust and hostility against the Intendant were shown by their nomination of Daubenton, the Nestor of the French savants, to the presidency, although La Billarderie, as representing the royal authority, was present at the meeting. At the second meeting (August 24th) he took no part in the proceedings, and absented himself from the third, held on August 27, 1790. It will be seen that even while the office of Intendant lasted, that official took no active part in the meetings or in the work of the institution, and from that day to this it has been solely under the management of a director and scientific corps of professors, all of them original investigators as well as teachers. Certainly the most practical and efficient sort of organization for such an establishment.*

---

of Gui de la Brosse. By his disinterestedness, activity, and great scientific capacity, he regenerated the garden, and under his administration flourished the great professors, Duverney, Tournefort, Geoffroy the chemist, and others (Perrier, l. c., p. 59). Fagon was succeed by Buffon, "the new legislator and second founder." His Intendancy lasted from 1739 to 1788.

* Three days after, August 30th, the report was ready, the discussion began, and the foundations of the new organization were definitely laid. "No longer any Jardin or Cabinets, but a Museum of Natural History, whose aim was clearly defined. No officers with unequal functions; all are professors and all will give instruction. They elect themselves and present to the king *a candidate for each vacant place. Finally, the general administration of the Museum will be confided to the officers of the establishment*, this implying the suppression of the Intendancy." (Hamy, l. c., p. 37.)

Lamarck, though holding a place subordinate to the other officers, was present, as the records of the proceedings of the officers of the Jardin des Plantes at this meeting show.

During the middle of 1791, the Intendant, La Billarderie, after "four years of incapacity," placed his resignation in the hands of the king. The Minister of the Interior, instead of nominating Daubenton as Intendant, reserved the place for a *protégé*, and, July 1, 1791, sent in the name of Jacques-Henri Bernardin de Saint-Pierre, the distinguished author of *Paul et Virginie* and of *Études sur la Nature*. The new Intendant was literary in his tastes, fond of nature, but not a practical naturalist. M. Hamy wittily states that "Bernardin Saint-Pierre contemplated and dreamed, and in his solitary meditations had imagined a system of the world which had nothing in common with that which was to be seen in the Faubourg Saint Victor, and one can readily imagine the welcome that the officers of the Jardin gave to the singular naturalist the Tuileries had sent them."*

Lamarck suffered an indignity from the intermeddling of this second Intendant of the Jardin. In his budget of expenses† sent to the Minister of

---

* Hamy, l. c., p. 37. The Faubourg Saint Victor was a part of the Quartier Latin, and included the Jardin des Plantes.

† *Devis de la Dépense du Jardin National des Plantes et du Cabinet d'Histoire Naturelle pour l'Année 1793*, presented to the National Convention by Citoyen Bernardin de Saint-Pierre. In it appeared a note relative to Lamarck, which, after stating that, though full of zeal and of knowledge of botany, his time was not entirely occupied ; that for two months he had written him in regard to the duties of his position ; referred to the statements of two of his seniors, who repeated the old gossip as to the claim of La Billarderie that his place was useless,

the Interior, Bernardin de Saint-Pierre took occasion
to refer to Lamarck in a disingenuous and blundering
way, which may have both amused and disgusted
him.

But the last days of the Jardin du Roi were drawing
to a close, and a new era in French natural science,
signalized by the reorganization of the Jardin and
Cabinet under the name of the *Muséum d'Histoire
Naturelle*, was dawning. On the 6th of February,
1793, the National Convention, at the request of
Lakanal,* ordered the Committees of Public Instruc-

---

and also found fault with him for not recognizing the artificial system
of Linné in the arrangement of the herbarium, added : " However,
desirous of retaining M. La Marck, father of six children, in the position which he needs, and not wishing to let his talents be useless, after
several conversations with the older officers of the Jardin, I have believed
that, M. Desfontaines being charged with the botanical lectures in the
school, and M. Jussieu in the neighborhood of Paris, it would be well
to send M. La Marck to herborize in some parts of the kingdom, in
order to complete the French flora, as this will be to his taste, and at
the same time very useful to the progress of botany ; thus everybody
will be employed and satisfied."—Perrier, *Lamarck et le Transformisme Actuel*, pp. 13, 14. (Copied from the National Archives.) " The
life of Bernardin de St. Pierre (1737-1814) was nearly as irregular as
that of his friend and master [Rousseau]. But his character was
essentially crafty and selfish, like that of many other sentimentalists
of the first order." (Morley's *Rousseau*, p. 437, footnote.)

* Joseph Lakanal was born in 1762, and died in 1845. He was a
professor of philosophy in a college of the Oratory, and doctor of the
faculty at Angers, when in 1792 he was sent as a representative
(*député*) to the National Convention, and being versed in educational
questions he was placed on the Committee of Public Instruction and
elected its president. He was the means, as Hamy states, of saving
from a lamentable destruction, by rejuvenating them, the scientific
institutions of ancient France. During the Revolution he voted for
the death of Louis XVI.

Lakanal also presented a plan of organization of a National Institute, what is now the Institut de France, and was charged with
designating the first forty-eight members, who should elect all the
others. He was by the first forty-eight thus elected. Proscribed as
a regicide at the second restoration, he sailed for the United States,
where he was warmly welcomed by Jefferson. The United States

tion and of Finances to at once make a report on the new organization of the administration of the Jardin des Plantes.

Lakanal consulted with Daubenton, and inquired into the condition and needs of the establishment; Daubenton placed in his hands the brochure of 1790, written by Lamarck. The next day Lakanal, after a short conference with his colleagues of the Committee of Public Instruction, read in the tribune a short report and a decree which the Committee adopted without discussion.

Their minds were elsewhere, for grave news had come in from all quarters. The Austrians were bombarding Valenciennes, the Prussians had invested Mayence, the Spanish were menacing Perpignan, and bands of Vendeans had seized Saumur after a bloody battle; while at Caen, at Evreux, at Bordeaux, at Marseilles, and elsewhere, muttered the thunders of the outbreaks provoked by the proscription of the Girondins. So that under these alarming conditions

---

Congress voted him five hundred acres of land. The government of Louisiana offered him the presidency of its university, which, however, he did not accept. In 1825 he went to live on the shores of Mobile Bay on land which he purchased from the proceeds of the sale of the land given him by Congress. Here he became a pioneer and planter.

In 1830 he manifested a desire to return to his native country, and offered his services to the new government, but received no answer and was completely ignored. But two years later, thanks to the initiative of Geoffroy St. Hilaire, who was the means of his reëlection to the French Academy, he decided to return, and did so in 1837. He lived in retirement in Paris, where he occupied himself until his death in 1845 in writing a book entitled *Séjour d'un Membre de l'Institut de France aux États-Unis pendant vingt-deux ans*. The manuscript mysteriously disappeared, no trace of it ever having been found. (Larousse, *Grand Dictionnaire Universel*, Art. LAKANAL.) His bust now occupies a prominent place among those of other great men in the French Academy of Sciences.

the decree of the 10th of June, in spite of its importance to science and higher learning in France, was passed without discussion.

In his *Lamarck* De Mortillet states explicitly that Lamarck, in his address of 1790, changed the name of the Jardin du Roi to Jardin des Plantes.* As the article states, " Entirely devoted to his studies, Lamarck entered into no intrigue under the falling monarchy, so he always remained in a position straitened and inferior to his merits." It was owing to this and his retired mode of life that the single-minded student of nature was not disturbed in his studies and meditations by the Revolution. And when the name of the Jardin du Roi threatened to be fatal to this establishment, it was he who presented a memoir to transform it, under the name of Jardin des Plantes, into an institution of higher instruction, with six professors. In 1793, Lakanal adopted Lamarck's plan, and, enlarging upon it, created twelve chairs for the teaching of the natural sciences.

Bourguin thus puts the matter:

" In June, 1793, Lakanal, having learned that ' the Vandals' (that is his expression) had demanded of the tribune of the Convention the suppression of the Royal Garden, as being an annex of the king's palace, recurred to the memoirs of Lamarck presented in 1790 and gave his plan of organization. He inspired himself with Lamarck's ideas, but enlarged upon them. Instead of six positions of professors-administrative, which La-

---

* This is seen to be the case by the title of the pamphlet : *Mémoire sur les Cabinets d'Histoire Naturelle, et particulièrement sur celui du Jardin des Plantes.*

marck asked for, Lakanal established twelve chairs for the teaching of different branches of natural science." *

---

* Bourguin also adds that " on one point Lamarck, with more foresight, went farther than Lakanal. He had insisted on the necessity of the appointment of four demonstrators for zoölogy. In the decree of June 10, 1793, they were even reduced to two. Afterwards they saw that this number was insufficient, and to-day (1863) the department of zoölogy is administered at the museum by four professors, in conformity with the division indicated by Lamarck."

CHAPTER IV

LAMARCK'S career as a botanist comprised about twenty-five years. We now come to the third stage of his life—Lamarck the zoölogist and evolutionist. He was in his fiftieth year when he assumed the duties of his professorship of the zoölogy of the invertebrate animals; and at a period when many men desire rest and freedom from responsibility, with the vigor of an intellectual giant Lamarck took upon his shoulders new labors in an untrodden field both in pure science and philosophic thought.

It was now the summer of 1793, and on the eve of the Reign of Terror, when Paris, from early in October until the end of the year, was in the deadliest throes of revolution. The dull thud of the guillotine, placed in front of the Tuileries, in the Place de la Revolution, which is now the Place de la Concorde, a little to the east of where the obelisk of Luxor now stands, could almost be heard by the quiet workers in the Museum, for sansculottism in its most aggressive and hideous forms raged not far from the Jardin des Plantes, then just on the border of the densest part of the Paris of the first Revolution. Lavoisier, the founder of modern chemistry, was guillotined some months later. The Abbé Haüy, the founder of

crystallography, had been, the year previous, rescued from prison by young Geoffroy St. Hilaire, his neck being barely saved from the gleaming axe. Roland, the friend of science and letters, had been so hunted down that at Rouen, in a moment of despair, on hearing of his wife's death, he thrust his sword-cane through his heart. Madame Roland had been beheaded, as also a cousin of her husband, and we can well imagine that these fateful summer and autumn days were scarcely favorable to scientific enterprises.*
Still, however, amid the loud alarums of this social tempest, the Museum underwent a new birth which proved not to be untimely. The Minister of the Interior (Garat) invited the professors of the Museum to constitute an assembly to nominate a director and a treasurer, and he begged them to present extracts of their deliberations for him to send to the executive council, "under the supervision of which the

* Most men of science of the Revolution, like Monge and others, were advanced republicans, and the Chevalier Lamarck, though of noble birth, was perhaps not without sympathy with the ideas which led to the establishment of the republic. It is possible that in his walks and intercourse with Rousseau he may have been inspired with the new notions of liberty and equality first promulgated by that philosopher.

His studies and meditations were probably not interrupted by the events of the Terror. Stevens, in his history of the French Revolution, tells us that Paris was never gayer than in the summer of 1793, and that during the Reign of Terror the restaurants, *cafés*, and theatres were always full. There were never more theatres open at the same period than then, though no single great play or opera was produced. Meanwhile the great painter David at this time built up a school of art and made that city a centre for art students. Indeed the Revolution was "a grand time for enthusiastic young men," while people in general lived their ordinary lives. There is little doubt, then, that the savants, except the few who were occupied by their duties as members of the *Convention Nationale*, worked away quietly at their specialties, each in his own study or laboratory or lecture-room.

3

National Museum is for the future placed;" though in general the assembly only reported to the Minister matters relating to the expenses, the first annual grant of the Museum being 100,000 livres.

Four days after, June 14th, the assembly met and adopted the name of the establishment in the following terms: *Muséum d'Histoire Naturelle décrété par la Convention Nationale le 10 Juin,* 1793; and at a meeting held on the 9th of July the assembly definitely organized the first bureau, with Daubenton as director, Thouin treasurer, and Desfontaines secretary. Lamarck, as the records show, was present at all these meetings, and at the first one, June 14th, Lamarck and Fourcroy were designated as commissioners for the formation of the Museum library.

All this was done without the aid or presence of Bernardin de Saint-Pierre, the Intendant. The Minister of the Interior, meanwhile, had communicated to him the decision of the National Convention, and invited him to continue his duties up to the moment when the new organization should be established. After remaining in his office until July 9th, he retired from the Museum August 7th following, and finally withdrew to the country at Essones.

The organization of the Museum is the same now as in 1793, having for over a century been the chief biological centre of France, and with its magnificent collections was never more useful in the advancement of science than at this moment.

Let us now look at the composition of the assembly of professors, which formed the Board of Administration of the Museum at the time of his appointment.

The associates of Lamarck and Geoffroy St. Hilaire, who had already been connected with the Royal Garden and Cabinet, were Daubenton, Thouin, Desfontaine, Portal, and Mertrude. The Nestor of the faculty was Daubenton, who was born in 1716. He was the collaborator of Buffon in the first part of his *Histoire Naturelle*, and the author of treatises on the mammals and of papers on the bats and other mammals, also on reptiles, together with embryological and anatomical essays. Thouin, the professor of horticulture, was the veteran gardener and architect of the Jardin des Plantes, and withal a most useful man. He was affable, modest, genial, greatly beloved by his students, a man of high character, and possessing much executive ability. A street near the Jardin was named after him. He was succeeded by Bosc. Desfontaine had the chair of botany, but his attainments as a botanist were mediocre, and his lectures were said to have been tame and uninteresting. Portal taught human anatomy, while Mertrude lectured on vertebrate anatomy; his chair was filled by Cuvier in 1795.

Of this group Lamarck was *facile princeps*, as he combined great sagacity and experience as a systematist with rare intellectual and philosophic traits. For this reason his fame has perhaps outlasted that of his young contemporary, Geoffroy St. Hilaire.

The necessities of the Museum led to the division of the chair of zoölogy, botany being taught by Desfontaine. And now began a new era in the life of Lamarck. After twenty-five years spent in botanical research he was compelled, as there seemed nothing else for him to undertake, to assume charge of the collection of invertebrate animals, and to him was assigned that enormous, chaotic mass of forms then known as molluscs, insects, worms, and microscopic animals. Had he continued to teach botany, we might never have had the Lamarck of biology and biological philosophy. But turned adrift in a world almost unexplored, he faced the task with his old-time bravery and dogged persistence, and at once showed the skill of a master mind in systematic work.

The two new professorships in zoölogy were filled, one by Lamarck, previously known as a botanist, and the other by the young Étienne Geoffroy St. Hilaire, then twenty-two years old, who was at that time a student of Haüy, and in charge of the minerals, besides teaching mineralogy with especial reference to crystallography.

To Geoffroy was assigned the four classes of vertebrates, but in reality he only occupied himself with the mammals and birds. Afterwards Lacépède * took charge of the reptiles and fishes. On the other hand, Lamarck's field comprised more than nine-tenths of the animal kingdom. Already the collections of insects, crustacea, worms, molluscs, echinoderms, corals, etc., at the Museum were enormous. At this time

---

* Bern. Germ. Étienne, Comte de Lacépède, born in 1756, died in 1825, was elected professor of the zoölogy of " quadrupedes ovipares, reptiles, et poissons," January 12, 1795 (Records of the Museum). He was the author of works on amphibia, reptiles, and mammals, forming continuations of Buffon's *Histoire Naturelle*. He also published *Histoire Naturelle des Poissons* (1798–1803), *Histoire des Cétacés* (1804), and *Histoire Naturelle de l'Homme* (1827), *Les Âges de la Nature et Histoire de l'Espèce Humaine*, tome 2, 1830.

France began to send out those exploring expeditions to all parts of the globe which were so numerous and fruitful during the first third of the nineteenth century. The task of arranging and classifying single-handed this enormous mass of material was enough to make a young man quail, and it is a proof of the vigor, innate ability, and breadth of view of the man that in this pioneer work he not only reduced to some order this vast horde of forms, but showed such insight and brought about such radical reforms in zoölogical classification, especially in the foundation and limitation of certain classes, an insight no one before him had evinced. To him and to Latreille much of the value of the *Règne Animal* of Cuvier, as regards invertebrate classes, is due.

The exact title of the chair held by Lamarck is given in the *État* of persons attached to the National Museum of Natural History at the date of the 1er messidor, an II. of the Republic (1794), where he is mentioned as follows: " LAMARCK—fifty years old; married for the second time; wife *enceinte;* six children; professor of zoölogy, of insects, of worms, and microscopic animals." His salary, like that of the other professors, was put at 2,868 livres, 6 sous, 8 deniers.[*]

Étienne Geoffroy St. Hilaire [†] has related how the professorship was given to Lamarck.

" The law of 1793 had prescribed that all parts of the natural sciences should be equally taught. The insects, shells, and an infinity of organisms—a portion

[*] Perrier, l. c., p. 14.
[†] *Fragments Biographiques*, p. 214.

of creation still almost unknown—remained to be
treated in such a course. A desire to comply with
the wishes of his colleagues, members of the administration, and without doubt, also, the consciousness
of his powers as an investigator, determined M.
de Lamarck: this task, so great, and which would
tend to lead him into numberless researches; this
friendless, unthankful task he accepted—courageous
resolution, which has resulted in giving us immense
undertakings and great and important works, among
which posterity will distinguish and honor forever the
work which, entirely finished and collected into seven
volumes, is known under the name of *Animaux sans
Vertèbres.*"

Before his appointment to this chair Lamarck had
devoted considerable attention to the study of conchology, and already possessed a rather large collection
of shells. His last botanical paper appeared in 1800,
but practically his botanical studies were over by
1793.

During the early years of the Revolution, namely,
from 1789 to and including 1791, Lamarck published
nothing. Whether this was naturally due to the
social convulsions and turmoil which raged around the
Jardin des Plantes, or to other causes, is not known.
In 1792, however, Lamarck and his friends and colleagues, Bruguière, Olivier, and the Abbé Haüy,
founded the *Journal d'Histoire Naturelle*, which
contains nineteen botanical articles, two on shells,
besides one on physics, by Lamarck. These, with
many articles by other men of science, illustrated by
plates, indicate that during the years of social unrest
and upheaval in Paris, and though France was also

engaged in foreign wars, the philosophers preserved in some degree, at least, the traditional calm of their profession, and passed their days and nights in absorption in matters biological and physical. In 1801 appeared his *Système des Animaux sans Vertèbres*, preceded by the opening discourse of his lectures on the lower animals, in which his views on the origin of species were first propounded. During the years 1793–1798, or for a period of six years, he published nothing on zoölogy, and during this time only one paper appeared, in 1798, on the influence of the moon on the earth's atmosphere. But as his memoirs on fire and on sound were published in 1798, it is evident that his leisure hours during this period, when not engaged in museum work and the preparation of his lectures, were devoted to meditations on physical and meteorological subjects, and most probably it was towards the end of this period that he brooded over and conceived his views on organic evolution.

It appears that he was led, in the first place, to conchological studies through his warm friendship for a fellow naturalist, and this is one of many proofs of his affectionate, generous nature. The touching story is told by Étienne Geoffroy St. Hilaire.*

" It was impossible to assign him a professorship of botany. M. de Lamarck, then forty-nine years old, accepted this change in his scientific studies to take charge of that which everybody had neglected; because it was, indeed, a heavy load, this branch of natural history, where, with so varied relations, every-

---

* *Fragments Biographiques*, p. 213.

thing was to be created. On one group he was a little prepared, but it was by accident; a self-sacrifice to friendship was the cause. For it was both to please his friend Bruguière as well as to penetrate more deeply into the affections of this very reserved naturalist, and also to converse with him in the only language which he wished to hear, which was restricted to conversations on shells, that M. de Lamarck had made some conchological studies. Oh, how, in 1793, did he regret that his friend had gone to Persia! He had wished, he had planned, that he should take the professorship which it was proposed to create. He would at least supply his place; it was in answer to the yearnings of his soul, and this affectionate impulse became a fundamental element in the nature of one of the greatest of zoölogical geniuses of our epoch."

Once settled in his new line of work, Lamarck, the incipient zoölogist, at a period in life when many students of less flexible and energetic natures become either hide-bound and conservative, averse to taking up a different course of study, or actually cease all work and rust out—after a half century of his life had passed, this rare spirit, burning with enthusiasm, charged like some old-time knight or explorer into a new realm and into "fresh fields and pastures new." His spirit, still young and fresh after nearly thirty years of mental toil, so unrequited in material things, felt a new stimulus as he began to investigate the lower animals, so promising a field for discovery.

He said himself :

" That which is the more singular is that the most important phenomena to be considered have been offered to our meditations only since the time when attention has been paid to the animals least perfect, and when researches on the different complications of the organization of these animals have become the principal foundation of their study. It is not less singular to realize that it was almost always from the examination of the smallest objects which nature presents to us, and that of considerations which seem to us the most minute, that we have obtained the most important knowledge to enable us to arrive at the discovery of her laws, and to determine her course."

After a year of preparation he opened his course at the Museum in the spring of 1794. In his introductory lecture, given in 1803, after ten years of work on the lower animals, he addressed his class in these words :

" Indeed it is among those animals which are the most multiplied and numerous in nature, and the most ready to regenerate themselves, that we should seek the most instructive facts bearing on the course of nature, and on the means she has employed in the creation of her innumerable productions. In this case we perceive that, relatively to the animal kingdom, we should chiefly devote our attention to the invertebrate animals, because their enormous multiplicity in nature, the singular diversity of their systems of organization and of their means of multiplication, their increasing simplification, and the extreme fugacity of those which compose the lowest orders of these animals, show us, much better than the higher animals, the true course of nature, and the means which she has used and which she still unceasingly employs to give existence to all the living bodies of which we have knowledge."

During this decade (1793–1803) and the one succeeding, Lamarck's mind grew and expanded. Before 1801, however much he may have brooded over the matter, we have no utterances in print on the transformation theory.   His studies on the lower animals, and his general knowledge of the vertebrates derived from the work of his contemporaries and his observations in the Museum and menagerie, gave him a broad grasp of the entire animal kingdom, such as no one before him had.   As the result, his comprehensive mind, with its powers of rapid generalization, enabled him to appreciate the series from monad (his *ébauche*) to man, the range of forms from the simple to the complex.   Even though not a comparative anatomist like Cuvier, he made use of the latter's discoveries, and could understand and appreciate the gradually increasing complexity of forms; and, unlike Cuvier, realize that they were blood relations, and not separate, piece-meal creations.   Animal life, so immeasurably higher than vegetable forms, with its highly complex physiological functions and varied means of reproduction, and the relations of its forms to each other and to the world around, affords facts for evolution which were novel to Lamarck, the descriptive botanist.

In accordance with the rules of the Museum, which required that all the professors should be lodged within the limits of the Jardin, the choice of lodgings being given to the oldest professors, Lamarck, at the time of his appointment, took up his abode in the house now known as the Maison de Buffon, situated on the opposite side of the Jardin des Plantes from the house afterwards inhabited by Cuvier, and in the angle between the Galerie de Zoologie and the Museum

BIRTHPLACE OF LAMARCK. REAR VIEW, FROM THE WEST

MAISON DE BUFFON, IN WHICH LAMARCK LIVED IN PARIS,
1793–1829

library.* With little doubt the windows of his study, where his earlier addresses, the *Recherches sur l'Organization des Corps Vivans*, and the *Philosophie Zoologique*, were probably written, looked out upon what is now the court on the westerly side of the house, that facing the Rue Geoffroy St. Hilaire.

At the time of his entering on his duties as professor of zoölogy, Lamarck was in his fiftieth year. He had married twice and was the father of six children, and without fortune. He married for a third, and afterwards for a fourth time, and in all,

---

*A few years ago, when we formed the plan of writing his life, we wrote to friends in Paris for information as to the exact house in which Lamarck lived, and received the answer that it was unknown ; another proof of the neglect and forgetfulness that had followed Lamarck so many years after his death, and which was even manifested before he died. Afterwards Professor Giard kindly wrote that by reference to the *procès verbaux* of the Assembly, it had been found by Professor Hamy that he had lived in the house of Buffon.

The house is situated at the corner of Rue de Buffon and Rue Geoffroy St. Hilaire. The courtyard facing Rue Geoffroy St. Hilaire bears the number 2 Rue de Buffon, and is in the angle between the Galerie de Zoologie and the Bibliothèque. The edifice is a large four-storied one. Lamarck occupied the second *étage*, what we should call the third story ; it was first occupied by Buffon. His bedroom, where he died, was on the *premier étage*. It was tenanted by De Quatrefages in his time, and is at present occupied by Professor G. T. Hamy ; Professor L. Vaillant living in the first *étage*, or second story, and Dr. J. Deniker, the *bibliothécaire* and learned anthropologist, in the third. The second *étage* was, about fifty years ago (1840-50), renovated for the use of Fremy the chemist, so that the exact room occupied by Lamarck as a study cannot be identified.

This ancient house was originally called *La Croix de Fer*, and was built about two centuries before the foundation of the Jardin du Roi. It appears from an inspection of the notes on the titles and copies of the original deeds, preserved in the Archives, and kindly shown me by Professor G. T. Hamy, the Archivist of the Museum, that this house was erected in 1468, the deed being dated 1xbre, 1468. The house is referred to as *maison ditte La Croix de Fer* in deeds of 1684, 1755, and 1768. It was sold by Charles Roger to M. le Compte de Buffon, March 23, 1771. One of the old gardens overlooked by it was called *de Jardin de la Croix*. It was originally the first structure erected on the south side of the Jardin du Roi.

seven children were born to him, as in the year (1794)
the minute referring to his request for an indemnity states: "Il est chargé de sept enfans dont un
est sur les vaisseaux de la République." Another
son was an artist, as shown by the records of the
Assembly of the Museum for September 23, 1814,
when he asked for a chamber in the lodgings of
Thouin, for the use of his son, "*peintre*."

Geoffroy St. Hilaire, in 1829, spoke of one of his
sons, M. Auguste de Lamarck, as a skilful and highly
esteemed engineer of Ponts-et-Chaussées, then advantageously situated.

But man cannot live by scientific researches and
philosophic meditations alone. The history of Lamarck's life is painful from beginning to end. With
his large family and slender salary he was never free
from carking cares and want. On the 30 fructidor,
an II. of the Republic, the National Convention voted
the sum of 300,000 livres, with which an indemnity
was to be paid to citizens eminent in literature and
art. Lamarck had sacrificed much time and doubtless some money in the preparation and publication
of his works, and he felt that he had a just claim to
be placed on the list of those who had been useful to
the Republic, and at the same time could give proof
of their good citizenship, and of their right to receive
such indemnity or appropriation.

Accordingly, in 1795 he sent in a letter, which possesses much autobiographical interest, to the Committee of Public Instruction, in which he says:

" During the twenty-six years that he has lived in
Paris the citizen Lamarck has unceasingly devoted

himself to the study of natural history, and particularly botany. He has done it successfully, for it is fifteen years since he published under the title of *Flore Française* the history and description of the plants of France, with the mention of their properties and of their usefulness in the arts; a work printed at the expense of the government, well received by the public, and which now is much sought after and very rare." He then describes his second great botanical undertaking, the *Encyclopædia and Illustration of Genera*, with nine hundred plates. He states that for ten years past he has kept busy "a great number of Parisian artists, three printing presses for different works, besides delivering a course of lectures."

The petition was granted. At about this period a pension of twelve hundred francs from the Academy of Sciences, and which had increased to three thousand francs, had ceased eighteen months previously to be paid to him. But at the time (an II.) Lamarck was "chargé de sept enfans," and this appropriation was a most welcome addition to his small salary.

The next year (an III.) he again applied for a similar allowance from the funds providing an indemnity for men of letters and artists "whose talents are useful to the Republic." Again referring to the *Flore Française*, and his desire to prepare a second edition of it, and his other works and travels in the interest of botanical science, he says:

"If I had been less overburdened by needs of all kinds for some years, and especially since the suppression of my pension from the aforesaid Academy of Sciences, I should prepare the second edition of this useful work; and this would be, without doubt, indeed, the opportunity of making a new present to my country.

"Since my return to France I have worked on the completion of my great botanical enterprises, and indeed for about ten years past my works have obliged me to keep in constant activity a great number of artists, such as draughtsmen, engravers, and printers. But these important works that I have begun, and have in a well-advanced state, have been in spite of all my efforts suspended and practically abandoned for the last ten years. The loss of my pension from the Academy of Sciences and the enormous increase in the price of articles of subsistence have placed me, with my numerous family, in a state of distress which leaves me neither the time nor the freedom from care to cultivate science in a fruitful way."

Lamarck's collection of shells, the accumulation of nearly thirty years,* was purchased by the government at the price of five thousand livres. This sum was used by him to balance the price of a national estate for which he had contracted by virtue of the law of 28 ventose de l'an IV.† This little estate, which was the old domain of Beauregard, was a modest farm-house or country-house at Héricourt-

---

* In the "avertissement" to his *Système des Animaux sans Vertèbres* (1801), after stating that he had at his disposition the magnificent collection of invertebrate animals of the museum, he refers to his private collection as follows: "Et une autre assez riche que j'ai formée moi-même par près de trente années de recherches," p. vii. Afterwards he formed another collection of shells named according to his system, and containing a part of the types described in his *Histoire Naturelle des Animaux sans Vertèbres* and in his minor articles. This collection the government did not acquire, and it is now in the museum at Geneva. The Paris museum, however, possesses a good many of the Lamarckian types, which are on exhibition (Perrier, l. c., p. 20).

† *Lettre du Ministre des Finances (de Ramel) au Ministre de l'Intérieur* (13 pr. an V.). See Perrier, l. c., p. 20.

Saint-Samson, in the Department of Seine-et-Oise, not far to the northward of Beauvais, and about fifty miles from Paris. It is probable that as a proprietor of a landed property he passed the summer season, or a part of it, on this estate.

This request was, we may believe, made from no unworthy or mercenary motive, but because he thought that such an indemnity was his due. Some years after (in 1809) the chair of zoölogy, newly formed by the Faculté des Sciences in Paris, was offered to him. Desirable as the salary would have been in his straitened circumstances, he modestly refused the offer, because he felt unable at that time of life (he was, however, but sixty-five years of age) to make the studies required worthily to occupy the position.

One of Lamarck's projects, which he was never able to carry out, for it was even then quite beyond the powers of any man single-handed to undertake, was his *Système de la Nature*. We will let him describe it in his own words, especially since the account is somewhat autobiographical. It is the second memoir he addressed to the Committee of Public Instruction of the National Convention, dated 4 vendémiaire, l'an III. (1795):

" In my first memoir I have given you an account of the works which I have published and of those which I have undertaken to contribute to the progress of natural history ; also of the travels and researches which I have made.

" But for a long time I have had in view a very important work—perhaps better adapted for education

in France than those I have already composed or undertaken—a work, in short, which the National Convention should without doubt order, and of which no
part could be written so advantageously as in Paris,
where are to be found abundant means for carrying
it to completion.

" This is a *Système de la Nature*, a work analogous
to the *Systema naturæ* of Linnæus, but written in
French, and presenting the picture complete, concise, and methodical, of all the natural productions
observed up to this day. This important work (of
Linnæus), which the young Frenchmen who intend
to devote themselves to the study of natural history
always require, is the object of speculations by foreign
authors, and has already passed through thirteen different editions. Moreover, their works, which, to our
shame, we have to use, because we have none written
expressly for us, are filled (especially the last edition
edited by Gmelin) with gross mistakes, omissions of
double and triple occurrence, and errors in synonymy,
and present many generic characters which are inexact or imperceptible and many series badly divided,
or genera too numerous in species, and difficulties insurmountable to students.

" If the Committee of Public Instruction had the
time to devote any attention to the importance of my
project, to the utility of publishing such a work, and
perhaps to the duty prescribed by the national honor,
I would say to it that, after having for a long time
reflected and meditated and determined upon the
most feasible plan, finally after having seen amassed
and prepared the most essential materials, I offer to
put this beautiful project into execution. I have
not lost sight of the difficulties of this great enterprise. I am, I believe, as well aware of them, and
better, than any one else ; but I feel that I can overcome them without descending to a simple and dis-
honorable compilation of what foreigners have writ-

ten on the subject. I have some strength left to sacrifice for the common advantage; I have had some experience and practice in writing works of this kind; my herbarium is one of the richest in existence; my numerous collection of shells is almost the only one in France the specimens of which are determined and named according to the method adopted by modern naturalists—finally, I am in a position to profit by all the aid which is to be found in the National Museum of Natural History. With these means brought together, I can then hope to prepare in a suitable manner this interesting work.

" I had at first thought that the work should be executed by a society of naturalists; but after having given this idea much thought, and having already the example of the new encyclopædia, I am convinced that in such a case the work would be very defective in arrangement, without unity or plan, without any harmony of principles, and that its composition might be interminable.

" Written with the greatest possible conciseness, this work could not be comprised in less than eight volumes in 8vo, namely: One volume for the quadrupeds and birds; one volume for the reptiles and fishes; two volumes for the insects; one volume for the worms (the molluscs, madrepores, lithophytes, and naked worms); two volumes for the plants; one volume for the minerals: eight volumes in all.

" It is impossible to prepare in France a work of this nature without having special aid from the nation, because the expense of printing (on account of the enormous quantity of citations and figures which it would contain) would be such that any arrangement with the printer or the manager of the edition could not remunerate the author for writing such an immense work.

" If the nation should wish to print the work at its own expense, and then give to the author the profits

4

of the sale of this edition, the author would be very much pleased, and would doubtless not expect any further aid. But it would cost the nation a great deal, and I believe that this useful project could be carried through with greater economy.

" Indeed, if the nation will give me twenty thousand francs, in a single payment, I will take the whole responsibility, and I agree, if I live, that before the expiration of seven years the *Système de la Nature* in French, with the complemental addition, the corrections, and the convenient explanations, shall be at the disposition of all those who love or study natural history."

CHAPTER V

LAST DAYS AND DEATH

LAMARCK'S life was saddened and embittered by the loss of four wives, and the pangs of losing three of his children; * also by the rigid economy he had to practise and the unending poverty of his whole existence. A very heavy blow to him and to science was the loss, at an advanced age, of his eyesight.

It was, apparently, not a sudden attack of blindness, for we have hints that at times he had to call in Latreille and others to aid him in the study of the insects. The continuous use of the magnifying lens and the microscope, probably, was the cause of enfeebled eyesight, resulting in complete loss of vision. Duval † states that he passed the last ten years of his life in darkness; that his loss of sight gradually came on until he became completely blind.

---

* I have been unable to ascertain the names of any of his wives, or of his children, except his daughter, Cornelie.

† "L'examen minutieux de petits animaux, analysés à l'aide d'instruments grossissants, fatigua, puis affaiblait, sa vue. Bientôt il fut complètement aveugle. Il passa les dix dernièrs années de sa vie plongé dans les ténèbres, entouré des soins de ses deux filles, à l'une desquelles il dictait le dernier volume de son *Histoire des Animaux sans Vertèbres.*"—*Le Transformiste Lamarck, Bull. Soc. Anthropologie*, xii., 1889, p. 341. Cuvier, also, in his history of the progress of natural science for 1819, remarks : " M. de La Marck, malgré l'affoiblissement total de sa vue, poursuit avec un courage inaltérable la continuation de son grand ouvrage sur les animaux sans vertèbres" (p. 406).

In the reports of the meetings of the Board of
Professors there is but one reference to his blindness. Previous to this we find that, at his last appearance at these sessions—*i.e.*, April 19, 1825—since
his condition did not permit him to give his course
of lectures, he had asked M. Latreille to fill his place;
but such was the latter's health, he proposed that
M. Audouin, sub-librarian of the French Institute,
should lecture in his stead, on the invertebrate animals. This was agreed to.

The next reference, and the only explicit one, is
that in the records for May 23, 1826, as follows:
" Vu la cécité dont M. de Lamarck est frappé, M.
Bosc * continuera d'exercer sur les parties confiert à
M. Audouin la surveillance attribuée au Professeur."

But, according to Duval, long before this he had
been unable to use his eyes. In his *Système analytique des Connoissances positives de l'Homme*, published
in 1820, he refers to the sudden loss of his eyesight.

---

* Louis Auguste Guillaume Bosc, born in Paris, 1759; died in 1828.
Author of now unimportant works, entitled : *Histoire Naturelle des
Coquilles* (1801); *Hist. Nat. des Vers* (1802); *Hist. Nat. des Crus-
tacés* (1828), and papers on insects and plants. He was associ-
ated with Lamarck in the publication of the *Journal d'Histoire
Naturelle*. During the Reign of Terror in 1793 he was a friend of
Madame Roland, was arrested, but afterwards set free and placed
first on the Directory in 1795. In 1798 he sailed for Charleston, S. C.
Nominated successively vice-consul at Wilmington and consul at New
York, but not obtaining his exequatur from President Adams, he
went to live with the botanist Michaux in Carolina in his botanical
garden, where he devoted himself to natural history until the quarrel
in 1800 between the United States and France caused him to return
to France. On his return he sent North American insects to his
friends Fabricius and Olivier, fishes to Lacépède, birds to Daudin,
reptiles to Latreille. Not giving all his time to public life, he devoted
himself to natural history, horticulture, and agriculture, succeeding
Thouin in the chair of horticulture, where he was most usefully employed until his death.—(Cuvier's *Éloge.*)

Even in advanced life Lamarck seems not to have suffered from ill-health, despite the fact that he apparently during the last thirty years of his life lived in a very secluded way. Whether he went out into the world, to the theatre, or even went away from Paris and the Museum into the country in his later years, is a matter of doubt. It is said that he was fond of novels, his daughters reading to him those of the best French authors. After looking with some care through the records of the sessions of the Assembly of Professors, we are struck with the evidences of his devotion to routine museum work and to his courses of lectures.

At that time the Museum sent out to the *Écoles centrales* of the different departments of France named collections made up from the duplicates, and in this sort of drudgery Lamarck took an active part. He also took a prominent share in the business of the Museum, in the exchange and in the purchase of specimens and collections in his department, and even in the management of the menagerie. Thus he reported on the dentition of the young lions (one dying from teething), on the illness and recovery of one of the elephants, on the generations of goats and kids in the park; also on a small-sized bull born of a small cow covered by a Scottish bull, the young animal having, as he states, all the characters of the original.

For one year (1794) he was secretary of the Board of Professors of the Museum.* The records of the

---

* The first director of the Board or Assembly of Professors-administrative of the Museum was Daubenton, Lacépède being the secretary, Thouin the treasurer. Daubenton was succeeded by Jussieu ; and Lacépède, first by Desfontaines and afterwards by Lamarck, who was elected secretary 18 fructidor, an II. (1794).

meetings from 4 vendémiaire, l'an III., until 4 vendé-
miaire, l'an IV., are each written in his bold, legible
handwriting or signed by him. He signed his name
Lamarck, this period being that of the first republic.
Afterwards, in the records, his name is written *De
Lamarck*. He was succeeded by É. Geoffroy St.
Hilaire, who signed himself plain *Geoffroy*.

In 1802 he acted as treasurer of the Assembly, and
again for a period of six years, until and including
1811, when he resigned, the reason given being : " Il
s'occupe depuis six ans et que ses travaux et son age
lui rendent penibles."

Lamarck was extremely regular in his attendance
at these meetings. From 1793 until 1818 he rarely,
if ever, missed a meeting. We have only observed in
the records of this long period the absence of his
name on two or three occasions from the list of those
present. During 1818 and the following year it was
his blindness which probably prevented his regular
attendance. July 15, 1818, he was present, and presented the fifth volume of his *Animaux sans Vertèbres ;* and August 31, 1819, he was present * and laid
before the Assembly the sixth volume of the same
great work.

From the observations of the records we infer that

---

* His attendance this year was infrequent. July 10, 1820, he was
present and made a report relative to madrepores and molluscs. In
the summer of 1821 he attended several of the meetings. August 7.
1821, he was present, and referred to the collection of shells of Struthi-
olaria. He was present May 23d and June 9th, when it was voted that
he should enjoy the garden of the house he occupied and that a chamber should be added to his lodgings. He was frequent in attendance
this year, especially during the summer months. He attended a few
meetings at intervals in 1822, 1823, and only twice in 1824.

At a meeting held April 19, 1825, he was present, and, stating that

Dessiné d'après Nature à Paris en 1824, et gravé par Ambroise Tardieu

PORTRAIT OF LAMARCK, WHEN OLD AND BLIND, IN THE COSTUME
OF A MEMBER OF THE INSTITUTE, ENGRAVED IN 1824

Lamarck never had any long, lingering illness or suffered from overwork, though his life had little sunshine or playtime in it. He must have had a strong constitution, his only infirmity being the terrible one (especially to an observer of nature) of total blindness.

Lamarck's greatest work in systematic zoölogy would never have been completed had it not been for the self-sacrificing spirit and devotion of his eldest daughter.

A part of the sixth and the whole of the last volume of the *Animaux sans Vertèbres* were presented to the Assembly of Professors September 10, 1822. This volume was dictated to and written out by one of his daughters, Mlle. Cornelie De Lamarck. On her the aged savant leaned during the last ten years of his life—those years of failing strength and of blindness finally becoming total. The frail woman accompanied him in his hours of exercise, and when he was confined to his house she never left him. It is stated by Cuvier, in his eulogy, that at her first walk out of doors after the end came she was nearly overcome by the fresh air, to which she had become so unaccustomed. She, indeed, practically sacrificed her life to her father. It is one of the rarest and most striking instances of filial devotion known in the annals of science or literature, and is a noticeable con-

his condition did not permit him to lecture, asked to have Audouin take his place, as Latreille's health did not allow him to take up the work. The next week (26th) he was likewise present. On May 10 he was present, as also on June 28, October 11, and also through December, 1825. His last appearance at these business meetings was on July 11, 1828.

trast to the daughters of the blind Milton, whose domestic life was rendered unhappy by their undutifulness, as they were impatient of the restraint and labors his blindness had imposed upon them.

Besides this, the seventh volume is a voluminous scientific work, filled with very dry special details, making the labor of writing out from dictation, of corrections and preparation for the press, most wearisome and exhausting, to say nothing of the corrections of the proof-sheets, a task which probably fell to her—work enough to break down the health of a strong man.

It was a natural and becoming thing for the Assembly of Professors of the Museum, in view of the " malheureuse position de la famille," to vote to give her employment in the botanical laboratory in arranging and pasting the dried plants, with a salary of 1,000 francs.

Of the last illness of Lamarck, and the nature of the sickness to which he finally succumbed, there is no account. It is probable that, enfeebled by the weakness of extreme old age, he gradually sank away without suffering from any acute disease.

The exact date of his death has been ascertained by Dr. Mondière,* with the aid of M. Saint-Joanny, archiviste du Dèpartment de la Seine, who made special search for the record. The " acte " states that December 28, 1829, Lamarck, then a widower, died in the Jardin du Roi, at the age of eighty-five years.

The obsequies, as stated in the *Moniteur Universel*

---

* See, for the *Acte de décès, L'Homme,* iv. p. 289, and *Lamarck. Par un Groupe de Transformistes,* etc., p. 24.

of Paris for December 23, 1829, were celebrated on the Sunday previous in the Church of Saint-Médard, his parish. From the church the remains were borne to the cemetery of Montparnasse. At the interment, which took place December 30, M. Latreille, in the name of the Academy of Sciences, and M. Geoffroy St. Hilaire, in the name and on behalf of his colleagues, the Professors of the Museum of Natural History, pronounced eulogies at the grave. The eulogy prepared by Cuvier, and published after his death, was read at a session of the Academy of Sciences, by Baron Silvestre, November 26, 1832.

With the exception of these formalities, the great French naturalist, "the Linné of France," was buried as one forgotten and unknown. We read with astonishment, in the account by Dr. A. Mondière, who made zealous inquiries for the exact site of the grave of Lamarck, that it is and forever will be unknown. It is a sad and discreditable, and to us inexplicable, fact that his remains did not receive decent burial. They were not even deposited in a separate grave, but were thrown into a trench apparently situated apart from the other graves, and from which the bones of those thrown there were removed every five years. They are probably now in the catacombs of Paris, mingled with those of the thousands of unknown or paupers in that great ossuary. *

---

* Dr. Mondière in *L'Homme*, iv. p. 291, and *Lamarck. Par un Groupe de Transformistes*, p. 271. A somewhat parallel case is that of Mozart, who was buried at Vienna in the common ground of St. Marx, the exact position of his grave being unknown. There were no ceremonies at his grave, and even his friends followed him no farther than the city gates, owing to a violent storm.—(*The Century Cyclopedia of Names.*)

Dr. Mondière's account is as follows. Having found in the *Moniteur* the notice of the burial services, as above stated, he goes on to say:

" Armed with this document, I went again to the cemetery of Montparnasse, where I fortunately found a conservator, M. Lacave, who is entirely *au courant* with the question of transformism. He therefore interested himself in my inquiries, and, thanks to him, I have been able to determine exactly where Lamarck had been buried. I say had been, because, alas! he had been simply placed in a *trench off on one side* (*fosse à part*), that is to say, one which should change its occupant at the end of five years. Was it negligence, was it the jealousy of his colleagues, was it the result of the troubles of 1830? In brief, there had been no permission granted to purchase a burial lot. The bones of Lamarck are probably at this moment mixed with those of all the other unknown which lie there. What had at first led us into an error is that we made the inquiries under the name of Lamarck instead of that of de Monnet. In reality, the register of inscription bears the following mention:

" ' De Monnet de Lamarck buried this 20 December 1829 (85 years, 3d square, 1st division, 2d line, trench 22.'

" At some period later, a friendly hand, without doubt, had written on the margin of the register the following information:

" ' To the left of M. Dassas.'

" M. Lacave kindly went with us to search for the place where Lamarck had been interred, and on the register we saw this:

" ' Dassas, 1st division, 4th line south, No. 6 to the west, concession 1165–1829.' On arriving at the spot designated, we found some new graves, but nothing to indicate that of M. Dassas, our only mark by which we could trace the site after the changes wrought since 1829. After several ineffectual attempts, I finally perceived a flat grave, surrounded by an iron railing, and covered with weeds. Its surface seemed to me very regular, and I probed this lot.

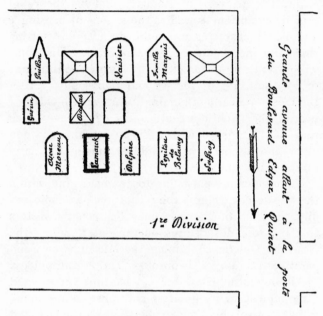

POSITION OF THE BURIAL PLACE OF LAMARCK IN THE CEMETERY OF MONTPARNASSE.

There was a gravestone there. The grave-digger who accompanied us cleared away the surface, and I confess that it was with the greatest pleasure and with deep emotion that we read the name Dassas.

"We found the place, but unfortunately, as I have

previously said, the remains of Lamarck are no longer there."

Mondière added to his letter a little plan (p. 59), which he drew on the spot.*

But the life-work of Lamarck and his theory of organic evolution, as well as the lessons of his simple and noble character, are more durable and lasting than any monument of stone or brass. His name will never be forgotten either by his own countrymen or by the world of science and philosophy. After the lapse of nearly a hundred years, and in this first year of the twentieth century, his views have taken root and flourished with a surprising strength and vigor, and his name is preëminent among the naturalists of his time.

No monument exists in Montparnasse, but within the last decade, though the reparation has come tardily, the bust of Lamarck may be seen by visitors to the Jardin des Plantes, on the outer wall of the Nouvelle Galerie, containing the Museums of Comparative Anatomy, Palæontology, and Anthropology.

Although the city of Paris has not yet erected a monument to its greatest naturalist, some public recognition of his eminent services to the city and nation was manifested when the Municipal Council of

---

* Still hoping that the site of the grave might have been kept open, and desiring to satisfy myself as to whether there was possibly space enough left on which to erect a modest monument to the memory of Lamarck, I took with me the *brochure* containing the letter and plan of Dr. Mondière to the cemetery of Montparnasse. With the aid of one of the officials I found what he told me was the site, but the entire place was densely covered with the tombs and grave-stones of later interments, rendering the erection of a stone, however small and simple, quite out of the question.

Paris, on February 10, 1875, gave the name Lamarck to a street.* This is a long and not unimportant street on the hill of Montmartre in the XVIIIᵉ *arrondisse-ment*, and in the zone of the old stone or gypsum quarries which existed before Paris extended so far out in that direction, and from which were taken the fossil remains of the early tertiary mammals described by Cuvier.

The city of Toulouse has also honored itself by naming one of its streets after Lamarck; this was due to the proposal of Professor Émile Cartailhac to the Municipal Council, which voted to this effect May 12, 1886.

In the meetings of the Assembly of Professors no one took the trouble to prepare and enter minutes, however brief and formal, relative to his decease. The death of Lamarck is not even referred to in the *Procès-verbaux*. This is the more marked because there is an entry in the same records for 1829, and about the same date, of an extraordinary *séance* held November 19, 1829, when "'the Assembly" was convoked to take measures regarding the death of Professor Vauquelin relative to the choice of a candidate, Chevreul being elected to fill his chair.

Lamarck's chair was at his death divided, and the

---

* The Rue Lamarck begins at the elevated square on which is situated the Church of the Sacré-Cœur, now in process of erection, and from this point one obtains a commanding and very fine view overlooking the city ; from there the street curves round to the westward, ending in the Avenue de Saint-Ouen, and continues as a wide and long thoroughfare, ending to the north of the cemetery of Montmartre. A neighboring street, Rue Becquerel, is named after another French savant, and parallel to it is a short street named Rue Darwin.

two professorships thus formed were given to Latreille and De Blainville.

At the session of the Assembly of Professors held December 8, 1829, Geoffroy St. Hilaire sent in a letter to the Assembly urging that the department of invertebrate animals be divided into two, and referred to the bad state of preservation of the insects, the force of assistants to care for these being insufficient. He also, in his usual tactful way, referred to the "*complaisance extrème de la parte de M. De Lamarck*" in 1793, in assenting to the reunion in a single professorship of the mass of animals then called "*insectes et vermes.*"

The two successors of the chair held by Lamarck were certainly not dilatory in asking for appointments. At a session of the Professors held December 22, 1829, the first meeting after his death, we find the following entry : " M. Latreille écrit pour exprimer son desir d'être présenté comme candidat à la chaire vacante par le décès de M. Lamarck et pour rappeler ses titres à cette place."

M. de Blainville also wrote in the same manner : " Dans le cas que la chaire serait divisée, il demande la place de Professeur de l'histoire des animaux inarticulés. Dans le cas contraire il se présente également comme candidat, voulant, tout en respectant les droits acquis, ne pas laisser dans l'oubli ceux qui lui appartiennent."

January 12, 1830, Latreille* was unanimously elected

---

* Latreille was born at Brives, November 29, 1762, and died February 6, 1833. He was the leading entomologist of his time, and to him Cuvier was indebted for the arrangement of the insects in the

by the Assembly a candidate to the chair of entomology, and at a following session (February 16th) De Blainville was unanimously elected a candidate for the chair of *Molluscs, Vers et Zoophytes*, and on the 16th of March the royal ordinance confirming those elections was received by the Assembly.

There could have been no fitter appointments made for those two positions. Lamarck had long known Latreille "and loved him as a son." De Blainville honored and respected Lamarck, and fully appreciated his commanding abilities as an observer and thinker.

Règne Animal. His bust is to be seen on the same side of the Nouvelle Galerie in the Jardin des Plantes as those of Lamarck, Cuvier, De Blainville, and D'Orbigny. His first paper was introduced by Lamarck in 1792. In the minutes of the session of 4 thermidor, l'an VI. (July, 1798), we find this entry : "The citizen Lamarck announces that the citizen Latreille offered to the administration to work under the direction of that professor in arranging the very numerous collection of insects of the Museum, so as to place them under the eye of the public." And here he remained until his appointment. Several years (1825) before Lamarck's death he had asked to have Latreille fill his place in giving instruction.

Audouin (1797–1841), also an eminent entomologist and morphologist, was appointed *aide-naturaliste-adjoint* in charge of Mollusca, Crustacea, Worms, and Zoöphytes. He was afterwards associated with H. Milne Edwards in works on annelid worms. December 26, 1827, Latreille asked to be allowed to employ Boisduval as a *préparateur ;* he became the author of several works on injurious insects and Lepidoptera.

CHAPTER VI

POSITION IN THE HISTORY OF SCIENCE; OPINIONS OF HIS CONTEMPORARIES AND SOME LATER BIOLOGISTS

DE BLAINVILLE, a worthy successor of Lamarck, in his posthumous book, *Cuvier et Geoffroy Saint-Hilaire*, pays the highest tribute to his predecessor, whose position as the leading naturalist of his time he fully and gratefully acknowledges, saying: "Among the men whose lectures I have had the advantage of hearing, I truly recognize only three masters, M. de Lamarck, M. Claude Richard, and M. Pinel" (p. 43). He also speaks of wishing to write the scientific biographies of Cuvier and De Lamarck, the two zoologists of this epoch whose lectures he most frequently attended and whose writings he studied, and "who have exercised the greatest influence on the zoölogy of our time" (p. 42). Likewise in the opening words of the preface he refers to the rank taken by Lamarck:

"The aim which I have proposed to myself in my course on the principles of zoölogy demonstrated by the history of its progress from Aristotle to our time, and consequently the plan which I have followed to attain this aim, have very naturally led me, so to speak, in spite of myself, to signalize in M. de Lamarck the expression of one of those phases through which the science of organization has to pass in order to arrive at its last term before showing its true aim. From my point of view this phase does not seem to me to have been represented by any other naturalist of our time, whatever may have been the reputation which he made during his life."

He then refers to the estimation in which Lamarck was held by Auguste Comte, who, in his *Cours de Philosophie Positive*, has anticipated and even surpassed himself in the high esteem he felt for "the celebrated author of the *Philosophie Zoologique*."

The eulogy by Cuvier, which gives most fully the details of the early life of Lamarck, and which has been the basis for all the subsequent biographical sketches, was unworthy of him. Lamarck had, with his customary self-abnegation and generosity, aided and favored the young Cuvier in the beginning of his career,* who in his *Règne Animal* adopted the classes founded by Lamarck. Thoroughly convinced of the erroneous views of Cuvier in regard to cataclysms, he criticised and opposed them in his writings in a courteous and proper way without directly mentioning Cuvier by name or entering into any public debate with him.

When the hour came for the great comparative anatomist and palæontologist, from his exalted position, to prepare a tribute to the memory of a naturalist of equal merit and of a far more thoughtful and

---

* For example, while Cuvier's chair was in the field of vertebrate zoölogy, owing to the kindness of Lamarck ("*par gracieuseté de la part de M. de Lamarck*") he had retained that of Mollusca, and yet it was in the special classification of the molluscs that Lamarck did his best work (Blainville, l. c., p. 116).

5

profound spirit, to be read before the French Academy of Sciences, what a eulogy it was—as De Blainville exclaims, *et quel éloge !* It was not printed until after Cuvier's death, and then, it is stated, portions were omitted as not suitable for publication.* This is, we believe, the only stain on Cuvier's life, and it was unworthy of the great man. In this *éloge*, so different in tone from the many others which are collected in the three volumes of Cuvier's eulogies, he indiscriminately ridicules all of Lamarck's theories. Whatever may have been his condemnation of Lamarck's essays on physical and chemical subjects, he might have been more reserved and less dogmatic and sarcastic in his estimate of what he supposed to be the value of Lamarck's views on evolution. It was Cuvier's adverse criticisms and ridicule and his anti-evolutional views which, more than any other single cause, retarded the progress of biological science and the adoption of a working theory of evolution for which the world had to wait half a century.

It even appears that Lamarck was in part instrumental in inducing Cuvier in 1795 to go to Paris from Normandy, and become connected with the Museum. De Blainville relates that the Abbé Tessier met the young zoölogist at Valmont near Fécamp, and wrote to Geoffroy that "he had just discovered in Nor-

---

* De Blainville states that "the Academy did not even allow it to be printed in the form in which it was pronounced" (p. 324) ; and again he speaks of the lack of judgment in Cuvier's estimate of Lamarck, "the naturalist who had the greatest force in the general conception of beings and of phenomena, although he might often be far from the path" (p. 323).

mandy a pearl," and invited him to do what he could to induce Cuvier to come to Paris. " I made," said Geoffroy, " the proposition to my *confrères*, but I was supported, and only feebly, by M. de Lamarck, who slightly knew M. Cuvier as the author of a memoir on entomology."

The eulogy pronounced by Geoffroy St. Hilaire over the remains of his old friend and colleague was generous, sympathetic, and heartfelt.

" Yes [he said, in his eloquent way], for us who knew M. de Lamarck, whom his counsels have guided, whom we have found always indefatigable, devoted, occupied so willingly with the most difficult labors, we shall not fear to say that such a loss leaves in our ranks an immense void. From the blessings of such a life, so rich in instructive lessons, so remarkable for the most generous self-abnegation, it is difficult to choose.

" A man of vigorous, profound ideas, and very often admirably generalized, Lamarck conceived them with a view to the public good. If he met, as often happened, with great opposition, he spoke of it as a condition imposed on every one who begins a reform. Moreover, the great age, the infirmities, but especially the grievous blindness of M. de Lamarck had reserved for him another lot. This great and strong mind could enjoy some consolation in knowing the judgment of posterity, which for him began in his own lifetime. When his last tedious days, useless to science, had arrived, when he had ceased to be subjected to rivalry, envy and passion became extinguished and justice alone remained. De Lamarck then heard impartial voices, the anticipated echo of posterity, which would judge him as history will judge him. Yes, the scientific world has pronounced its judgment in giving him the name of ' the French Linné,' thus linking together the two men who have both merited a triple crown by their works on general natural history, zoölogy and botany, and whose names, increasing in fame from age to age, will both be handed down to the remotest posterity."*

Also in his *Études sur la Vie, les Ouvrages, et les Doctrines de Buffon* (1838), Geoffroy again, with much warmth of affection, says:

" Attacked on all sides, injured likewise by odious ridicule, Lamarck, too indignant to answer these cutting epigrams, submitted to the indignity with a sorrowful patience. . . . Lamarck lived a long while poor, blind, and forsaken, but not by me; I shall ever love and venerate him." †

The following evidently heartfelt and sincere tribute to his memory, showing warm esteem and thorough respect for Lamarck, and also a confident feeling that his lasting fame was secure, is to be found in an obscure little book ‡ containing satirical, humorous, but perhaps not always fair or just, characterizations and squibs concerning the professors and aid-naturalists of the Jardin des Plantes.

" What head will not be uncovered on hearing pronounced the name of the man whose genius was ignored and who languished steeped in bitterness. Blind, poor, forgotten, he remained alone with a glory of whose extent he himself was conscious, but which only the coming ages will sanction, when. shall be revealed more clearly the laws of organization.

---

* *Fragments Biographiques*, pp. 209–219.
† L. c. p. 81.
‡ *Histoire Naturelle Drolatique et Philosophique des Professeurs du Jardin des Plantes*, etc.   *Par Isid. S. de Gosse.   Avec des Annotations de M. Frédéric Gerard.*   Paris, 1847.

" Lamarck, thy abandonment, sad as it was in thy old age, is better than the ephemeral glory of men who only maintain their reputation by sharing in the errors of their time.

" Honor to thee! Respect to thy memory! Thou hast died in the breach while fighting for truth, and the truth assures thee immortality."

Lamarck's theoretical views were not known in Germany until many years after his death. Had Goethe, his contemporary (1749–1832), known of them, he would undoubtedly have welcomed his speculations, have expressed his appreciation of them, and Lamarck's reputation would, in his own lifetime, have raised him from the obscurity of his later years at Paris.

Hearty appreciation, though late in the century, came from Ernst Haeckel, whose bold and suggestive works have been so widely read. In his *History of Creation* (1868) he thus estimates Lamarck's work as a philosopher:

" To him will always belong the immortal glory of having for the first time worked out the theory of descent, as an independent scientific theory of the first order, and as the philosophical foundation of the whole science of biology."

Referring to the *Philosophie Zoologique*, he says:

" This admirable work is the first connected exposition of the theory of descent carried out strictly into all its consequences. By its purely mechanical method of viewing organic nature, and the strictly philosophical proofs brought forward in it, Lamarck's work is raised far above the prevailing dualistic views of his time; and with the exception of Darwin's work, which appeared just half a century later, we know of none which we could, in this respect, place by the side of the *Philosophie Zoologique*. How far it was in advance of its time is perhaps best seen from the circumstance that it was not understood by most men, and for fifty years was not spoken of at all. Cuvier, Lamarck's greatest opponent, in his *Report on the Progress of Natural Science*, in which the most unimportant anatomical investigations are enumerated, does not devote a single word to this work, which forms an epoch in science. Goethe, also, who took such a lively interest in the French nature-philosophy and in the 'thoughts of kindred minds beyond the Rhine,' nowhere mentions Lamarck, and does not seem to have known the *Philosophie Zoologique* at all."

Again in 1882 Haeckel writes: *

" We regard it as a truly tragic fact that the *Philosophie Zoologique* of Lamarck, one of the greatest productions of the great literary period of the beginning of our century, received at first only the slightest notice, and within a few years became wholly forgotten. . . . Not until fully fifty years later, when Darwin breathed new life into the transformation views founded therein, was the buried treasure again recovered, and we cannot refrain from regarding it as the most complete presentation of the development theory before Darwin.

" While Lamarck clearly expressed all the essential fundamental ideas of our present doctrine of descent; and excites our admiration at the depth of his morphological knowledge, he none the less surprises us by the prophetic (*vorausschauende*) clearness of his physiological conceptions."

---

* *Die Naturanschauung von Darwin, Goethe und Lamarck*, Jena, 1882.

In his views on life, the nature of the will and reason, and other subjects, Haeckel declares that Lamarck was far above most of his contemporaries, and that he sketched out a programme of the biology of the future which was not carried out until our day.

J. Victor Carus * also claims for Lamarck "the lasting merit of having been the first to have placed the theory (of descent) on a scientific foundation."

The best, most catholic, and just exposition of Lamarck's views, and which is still worth reading, is that by Lyell in Chapters XXXIV.–XXXVI. of his *Principles of Geology*, 1830, and though at that time one would not look for an acceptance of views which then seemed extraordinary and, indeed, far-fetched, Lyell had no words of satire and ridicule, only a calm, able statement and discussion of his principles. Indeed, it is well known that when, in after years, his friend Charles Darwin published his views, Lyell expressed some leaning towards the older speculations of Lamarck.

Lyell's opinions as to the interest and value of Lamarck's ideas may be found in his *Life and Letters*, and also in the *Life and Letters of Charles Darwin*. In the chapter, *On the Reception of the Origin of Species*, by Huxley, are the following extracts from Lyell's *Letters* (ii., pp. 179–204). In a letter addressed to Mantell (dated March 2, 1827), Lyell speaks of having just read Lamarck; he expresses his delight at Lamarck's theories, and his personal freedom from any objections based on theological

* *Geschichte der Zoologie bis auf Joh. Müller und Charles Darwin*, 1872.

grounds. And though he is evidently alarmed at the pithecoid origin of man involved in Lamarck's doctrine, he observes: " But, after all, what changes species may really undergo! How impossible will it be to distinguish and lay down a line beyond which some of the so-called extinct species have never passed into recent ones?"

He also quotes a remarkable passage in the postscript to a letter written to Sir John Herschel in 1836: "In regard to the origination of new species, I am very glad to find that you think it probable it may be carried on through the intervention of intermediate causes."

How nearly Lyell was made a convert to evolution by reading Lamarck's works may be seen by the following extracts from his letters, quoted by Huxley:

"I think the old ' creation ' is almost as much.required as ever, but of course it takes a new form if Lamarck's views, improved by yours, are adopted." (To Darwin, March 11, 1863, p. 363.)

"As to Lamarck, I find that Grove, who has been reading him, is wonderfully struck with his book. I remember that it was the conclusion he (Lamarck) came to about man, that fortified me thirty years ago against the great impression which his argument at first made on my mind—all the greater because Constant Prevost, a pupil of Cuvier forty years ago, told me his conviction ' that Cuvier thought species not real, but that science could not advance without assuming that they were so.'"

"When I came to the conclusion that after all Lamarck was going to be shown to be right, that we must ' go the whole orang,' I re-read his book, and remembering when it was written, I felt I had done him injustice.

" Even as to man's gradual acquisition of more and more ideas, and then of speech slowly as the ideas multiplied, and then his persecution of the beings most nearly allied and competing with him—all this is very Darwinian.

" The substitution of the variety-making power for ' volition,' ' muscular action,' etc. (and in plants even volition was not called in), is in some respects only a change of names. Call a new variety a new creation, one may say of the former, as of the latter, what you say when you observe that the creationist explains nothing, and only affirms ' it is so because it is so.'

" Lamarck's belief in the slow changes in the organic and inorganic world in the year 1800 was surely above the standard of his times, and he was right about progression in the main, though you have vastly advanced that doctrine. As to Owen in his ' Aye Aye ' paper, he seems to me a disciple of Pouchet, who converted him at Rouen to ' spontaneous generation.'

" Have I not, at p. 412, put the vast distinction between you and Lamarck as to ' necessary progression ' strongly enough?" (To Darwin, March 15, 1863. *Lyell's Letters*, ii., p. 365.)

Darwin, in the freedom of private correspondence, paid scant respect to the views of his renowned predecessor, as the following extracts from his published letters will show :

" Heaven forfend me from Lamarck nonsense of a ' tendency to progression,' ' adaptations from the slow willing of animals,' etc. But the conclusions I am led to are not widely different from his ; though the means of change are wholly so." (Darwin's *Life and Letters*, ii., p. 23, 1844.)

" With respect to books on this subject, I do not know of any systematical ones, except Lamarck's, which is veritable rubbish. . . . Is it not strange that the author of such a book as the *Animaux sans Vertèbres* should have written that insects, which never see their eggs, should *will* (and plants, their seeds) to be of particular forms, so as to become attached to particular objects." * (ii., p. 29, 1844.)

" Lamarck is the only exception, that I can think of, of an accurate describer of species, at least in the Invertebrate Kingdom, who has disbelieved in permanent species, but he in his absurd though clever work has done the subject harm." (ii., p. 39, no date.)

" To talk of climate or Lamarckian habit producing such adaptions to other organic beings is futile." (ii., p. 121, 1858.)

On the other hand, another great English thinker and naturalist of rare breadth and catholicity, and despite the fact that he rejected Lamarck's peculiar evolutional views, associated him with the most eminent biologists.

In a letter to Romanes, dated in 1882, Huxley thus estimates Lamarck's position in the scientific world :

" I am not likely to take a low view of Darwin's position in the history of science, but I am disposed to think that Buffon and Lamarck would run him hard in both genius and fertility. In breadth of view and in extent of knowledge these two men were giants, though we are apt to forget their services.

---

* We have been unable to find these statements in any of Lamarck's writings.

Von Bär was another man of the same stamp; Cuvier, in a somewhat lower rank, another; and J. Müller another." (*Life and Letters of Thomas Henry Huxley*, ii., p. 42, 1900.

The memory of Lamarck is deeply and warmly cherished throughout France. He gave his country a second Linné. One of the leading botanists in Europe, and the greatest zoölogist of his time, he now shares equally with Geoffroy St. Hilaire and with Cuvier the distinction of raising biological science to that eminence in the first third of the nineteenth century which placed France, as the mother of biologists, in the van of all the nations. When we add to his triumphs in pure zoölogy the fact that he was in his time the philosopher of biology, it is not going too far to crown him as one of the intellectual glories, not only of France, but of the civilized world.

How warmly his memory is now cherished may be appreciated by the perusal of the following letter, with its delightful reminiscences, for which we are indebted to the venerable and distinguished zoölogist and comparative anatomist who formerly occupied the chair made illustrious by Lamarck, and by his successor, De Blainville, and who founded the Laboratoire Arago on the Mediterranean, also that of Experimental Zoölogy at Roscoff, and who still conducts the *Journal de Zoologie Expérimentale*.

PARIS LE 28 *Décembre*, 1899.

M. le PROFESSEUR PACKARD.

Cher Monsieur: Vous m'avez fait l'honneur de me demander des renseignements sur la famille de De Lamarck, et sur ses relations, afin de vous en servir dans la biographie que vous préparez de notre grand naturaliste.

Je n'ai rien appris de plus que ce que vous voulez bien me rappeler comme l'ayant trouvé dans mon adresse de 1889. Je ne connais plus ni les noms ni les adresses des parents de De Lamarck, et c'est avec regret qu'il ne m'est pas possible de répondre à vos désirs.

Lorsque je commençai mes études à Paris, on ne s'occupait guère des idées générales de De Lamarck que pour s'en moquer. Excepté Geoffroy St. Hilaire et De Blainville, dont j'ai pu suivre les belles leçons et qui le citaient souvent, on parlait peu de la philosophie zoologique.

Il m'a été possible de causer avec des anciens collègues du grand naturaliste ; au Jardin des Plantes de très grands savants, dont je ne veux pas écrire le nom, le traitaient *de fou !*

Il avait loué un appartement sur le haut d'une maison, et là cherchait d'après la direction des nuages à prévoir l'état du temps.

On riait de ces études. N'est-ce pas comme un observatoire de météorologie que ce savant zoologiste avait pour ainsi dire fondé avant que la science ne se fut emparée de l'idée ?

Lorsque j'eus l'honneur d'être nommé professeur au Jardin des Plantes en 1865, je fis l'historique de la chaire que j'occupais, et qui avait été illustrée par De Lamarck et De Blainville. Je crois que je suis le premier à avoir fait l'histoire de notre grand naturaliste dans un cours public. Je dus travailler pas mal pour arriver à bien saisir l'idée fondamentale de la philosophie. Les définitions de la nature et des forces qui président aux changements qui modifient les êtres d'après les conditions auxquelles ils sont soumis ne sont pas toujours faciles à rendre claires pour un public souvent difficile.

Ce qui frappe surtout dans ses raisonnements, c'est

que De Lamarck est parfaitement logique. Il comprend très bien ce que plus d'un transformiste de nos jours ne cherche pas à éclairer, que le premier pas, le pas difficile à faire pour arriver à expliquer la création par des modifications successives, c'est le passage de la matière inorganique à la matière organisée, et il imagine la chaleur et l'électricité comme étant les deux facteurs qui par attraction ou répulsion finissent par former ces petits amas organisés qui seront le point de départ de toutes les transformations de tous les organismes.

Voilà le point de départ—la génération spontanée se trouve ainsi expliquée !

De Lamarck était un grand et profond observateur. On me disait au Museum (des contemporains) qu'il avait l'Instinct de l'Espèce.—Il y aurait beaucoup à dire sur cette expression—l'instinct de l'espèce—il m'est difficile dans une simple lettre de développer des idées philosophiques que j'ai sur cette question,—laquelle suppose la notion de l'individu parfaitement définie et acquis.

Je ne vous citerai qu'un exemple. Je ne l'ai vu signalé nulle part dans les ouvrages anciens sur De Lamarck.

Qu'étaient nos connaissances à l'époque de De Lamarck sur les Polypiers ? Les Hydraires étaient loin d'avoir fourni les remarquables observations qui parurent dans le milieu à peu près du siècle qui vient de finir, et cependant De Lamarck déplace hardiment la Lucernaire—l'éloigne des Coralliaires, et la rapproche des êtres qui forment le grand groupe des Hydraires. Ce trait me paraît remarquable et le rapporte à cette réputation qu'il avait au Museum de jouir de l'instinct de l'espèce.

De toute part on acclame le grand naturaliste, et'il n'y a pas même une rue portant son nom aux environs du Jardin des Plantes ? J'ai eu beau réclamer le conseil municipal de Paris à d'autres favoris que De Lamarck.

Lorsque le Jardin des Plantes fut réorganisé par la Convention, De Lamarck avait 50 ans. Il ne s'était jusqu'alors occupé que de botanique. Il fut à cet age chargé de l'histoire de la partie du règne animal renfermant les animaux invertèbres sauf les Insectes et les Crustacés. La chaire est restée la méme ; elle comprend les vers, les helminthes, les mollusques, et ce qu'on appelait autrefois les Zoophytes ou Rayonnées, enfin les Infusoires. Quelle puissance de travail ! Ne fallait-il pas pour passer de la Botanique, à 50 ans, à la Zoologie, et laisser un ouvrage semblable à celui qui illustre encore le nom du Botaniste devenue Zoologiste par ordre de la Convention !

Sans doute dans cet ouvrage il y a bien des choses qui ne sont plus acceptables—mais pour le juger avec équité, il faut se porter a l'époque où il fut fait, et alors on est pris d'admiration pour l'auteur d'un aussi immense travail.

J'ai une grande admiration pour le génie de De Lamarck, et je ne puis que vous louer de le faire encore mieux connaître de nos contemporains.

Recevez, mon cher collègue, l'expression de mes sentiments d'estime pour vos travaux remarquables et croyez-moi—tout à vous,

H. DE LACAZE DUTHIERS.

CHAPTER VII

LAMARCK'S WORK IN METEOROLOGY AND PHYSICAL SCIENCE

WHEN a medical student in Paris, Lamarck, from day to day watching the clouds from his attic windows, became much interested in meteorology, and, indeed, at first this subject had nearly as much attraction for him as botany. For a long period he pursued these studies, and he was the first one to foretell the probabilities of the weather, thus anticipating by over half a century the modern idea of making the science of meteorology of practical use to mankind.

His article, " De l'influence de la lune sur l'atmosphère terrestre," appeared in the *Journal de Physique* for 1798, and was translated in two English journals. The titles of several other essays will be found in the Bibliography at the close of this volume.

From 1799 to 1810 he regularly published an annual meteorological report containing the statement of probabilities acquired by a long series of observations on the state of the weather and the variations of the atmosphere at different times of the year, giving indications of the periods when to expect pleasant weather, or rain, storms, tempests, frosts, thaws, etc.; finally the citations of these probabilities of times favorable to fêtes, journeys, voyages, harvesting crops, and other enterprises dependent on good weather.

Lamarck thus explained the principles on which he based his probabilities: Two kinds of causes, he says, displace the fluids which compose the atmosphere, some being variable and irregular, others constant, whose action is subject to progressive and fixed laws.

Between the tropics constant causes exercise an action so considerable that the irregular effects of variable causes are there in some degree lost; hence result the prevailing winds which in these climates become established and change at determinate epochs.

Beyond the tropics, and especially toward the middle of the temperate zones, variable causes predominate. We can, however, still discover there the effects of the action of constant causes, though much weakened; we can assign them the principal epochs, and in a great number of cases make this knowledge turn to our profit. It is in the elevation and depression (*abaissement*) of the moon above and below the celestial equator that we should seek for the most constant of these causes.

With his usual facility in such matters, he was not long in advancing a theory, according to which the atmosphere is regarded as resembling the sea, having a surface, waves, and storms; it ought likewise to have a flux and reflux, for the moon ought to exercise the same influence upon it that it does on the ocean. In the temperate and frigid zones, therefore, the wind, which is only the tide of the atmosphere, must depend greatly on the declination of the moon;

it ought to blow toward the pole that is nearest to it, and advancing in that direction only, in order to reach every place, traversing dry countries or extensive seas, it ought then to render the sky serene or stormy. If the influence of the moon on the weather is denied, it is only that it may be referred to its phases, but its position in the ecliptic is regarded as affording probabilities much nearer the truth.*

In each of these annuals Lamarck took great care to avoid making any positive predictions. " No one," he says, " could make these predictions without deceiving himself and abusing the confidence of persons who might place reliance on them." He only intended to propose simple probabilities.

After the publication of the first of these annuals, at the request of Lamarck, who had made it the subject of a memoir read to the Institute in 1800 (9 ventose, l'an IX.), Chaptal, Minister of the Interior, thought it well to establish in France a regular correspondence of meteorological observations made daily at different points remote from each other, and he conferred the direction of it on Lamarck. This system of meteorological reports lasted but a short time, and was not maintained by Chaptal's successor. After three of these annual reports had appeared, Lamarck rather suddenly stopped publishing them, and an incident occurred in connection with their cessation which led to the story that he had suffered ill treatment and neglect from Napoleon I.

---

* " On the Influence of the Moon on the Earth's Atmosphere," *Journal de Physique*, prairial, l'an VI. (1798).

6

It has been supposed that Lamarck, who was frank and at times brusque in character, had made some enemies, and that he had been represented to the Emperor as a maker of almanacs and of weather predictions, and that Napoleon, during a reception, showing to Lamarck his great dissatisfaction with the annuals, had ordered him to stop their publication.

But according to Bourguin's statement this is not the correct version. He tells us:

" According to traditions preserved in the family of Lamarck things did not happen so at all. During a reception given to the Institute at the Tuileries, Napoleon, who really liked Lamarck, spoke to him in a jocular way about his weather probabilities, and Lamarck, very much provoked (*très contrarié*) at being thus chaffed in the presence of his colleagues, resolved to stop the publication of his observations on the weather. What proves that this version is the true one is that Lamarck published another annual which he had in preparation for the year 1810. In the preface he announced that his age, ill health, and his circumstances placed him in the unfortunate necessity of ceasing to busy himself with this periodical work. He ended by inviting those who had the taste for meteorological observations, and the means of devoting their time to it, to take up with confidence an enterprise good in itself, based on a genuine foundation, and from which the public would derive advantageous results."

These opuscles, such as they were, in which Lamarck treated different subjects bearing on the winds, great droughts, rainy seasons, tides, etc., became the precursors of the *Annuaires du Bureau des Longitudes*.

An observation of Lamarck's on a rare and curious form of cloud has quite recently been referred to by a French meteorologist. It is probable, says M. E. Durand-Greville in *La Nature*, November 24, 1900, that Lamarck was the first to observe the so-called pocky or festoon cloud, or mammato-cirrus cloud, which at rare intervals has been observed since his time.*

Full of over confidence in the correctness of his views formed without reference to experiments, although Lavoisier, by his discovery of oxygen in the years 1772–85, and other researches, had laid the foundations of the antiphlogistic or modern chemistry, Lamarck quixotically attempted to substitute his own speculative views for those of the discoverers of oxygen—Priestley (1774) and the great French chemist Lavoisier. Lamarck, in his *Hydrogéologie* (1802), went so far as to declare:

" It is not true, and it seems to me even absurd to believe that pure air, which has been justly called *vital air*, and which chemists now call *oxygen gas*, can be the radical of saline matters—namely, can be the principle of acidity, of causticity, or any salinity whatever. There are a thousand ways of refuting this error without the possibility of a reply. . . . This hypothesis, the best of all those which had been imagined when Lavoisier conceived it, cannot now be longer held, since I have discovered what is really *caloric*" (p. 161).

---

* *Nature*, Dec. 6, 1900.

After paying his respects to Priestley, he asks: "What, then, can be the reason why the views of chemists and mine are so opposed?" and complains that the former have avoided all written discussion on this subject. And this after his three physico-chemical works, the *Refutation*, the *Recherches*, and the *Mémoires* had appeared, and seemed to chemists to be unworthy of a reply.

It must be admitted that Lamarck was on this occasion unduly self-opinionated and stubborn in adhering to such views at a time when the physical sciences were being placed on a firm and lasting basis by experimental philosophers. The two great lessons of science—to suspend one's judgment and to wait for more light in theoretical matters on which scientific men were so divided—and the necessity of adhering to his own line of biological study, where he had facts of his own observing on which to rest his opinions, Lamarck did not seem ever to have learned.

The excuse for his rash and quixotic course in respect to his physico-chemical vagaries is that he had great mental activity. Lamarck was a synthetic philosopher. He had been brought up in the encyclopædic period of learning. He had from his early manhood been deeply interested in physical subjects. In middle age he probably lived a very retired life, did not mingle with his compeers or discuss his views with them. So that when he came to publish them, he found not a single supporter. His speculations were received in silence and not deemed worthy of discussion.

A very just and discriminating judge of Lamarck's work, Professor Cleland, thus refers to his writings on physics and chemistry:

"The most prominent defect in Lamarck must be admitted, quite apart from all consideration of the famous hypothesis which bears his name, to have been want of control in speculation. Doubtless the speculative tendency furnished a powerful incentive to work, but it outran the legitimate deductions from observation, and led him into the production of volumes of worthless chemistry without experimental basis, as well as into spending much time in fruitless meteorological predictions." (*Encyc. Brit.*, Art. LA-MARCK.)

How a modern physicist regards Lamarck's views on physics may be seen by the following statement kindly written for this book by Professor Carl Barus of Brown University, Providence:

"Lamarck's physical and chemical speculations, made throughout on the basis of the alchemistic philosophy of the time, will have little further interest to-day than as evidence showing the broadly philosophic tendencies of Lamarck's mind. Made without experiment and without mathematics, the contents of the three volumes will hardly repay perusal, except by the historian interested in certain aspects of pre-Lavoisierian science. The temerity with which physical phenomena are referred to occult static molecules, permeated by subtle fluids, the whole mechanism left without dynamic quality, since the mass of the molecule is to be non-essential, is markedly in contrast with the discredit into which such hypotheses have now fallen. It is true that an explanation of natural phenomena in terms " le feu éthéré, le feu calorique, et le feu fixé " might be interpreted with reference to the modern doctrine of energy; but it is certain that Lamarck, antedating Fresnel, Carnot, Ampère, not to mention their great followers, had not the faintest inkling of the possibility of such an interpretation. Indeed, one may readily account for the resemblance to modern views, seeing that all speculative systems of science must to some extent run in parallel, inasmuch as they begin with the facts of common experience. Nor were his speculations in any degree stimulating to theoretical science. Many of his mechanisms in which the ether operates on a plane of equality with the air can only be regarded with amusement. The whole of his elaborate schemes of color classification may be instanced as forerunners of the methods commercially in vogue to-day; they are not the harbingers of methods scientifically in vogue. One looks in vain for research adequate to carry the load of so much speculative text.

" Even if we realize that the beginnings of science could but be made amid such groping in the dark, it is a pity that a man of Lamarck's genius, which seems to have been destitute of the instincts of an experimentalist, should have lavished so much serious thought in evolving a system of chemical physics out of himself."

The chemical status of Lamarck's writings is thus stated by Professor H. Carrington Bolton in a letter dated Washington, D. C., February 9, 1900 :

" Excuse delay in replying to your inquiry as to the chemical status of the French naturalist, Lamarck. Not until this morning have I found it convenient to go to the Library of Congress. That Library has not the *Recherches* nor the *Mémoires*, but the position of Lamarck is well known. He had no influence on chemistry, and his name is not mentioned in the principal histories of chemistry. He made no experiments, but depended upon his imagination for his facts; he opposed the tenets of the new French school founded by Lavoisier, and proposed a fanciful scheme of abstract principles that remind one of alchemy.

"Cuvier, in his *Éloge* (*Mémoires Acad. Royale des Sciences*, 1832), estimates Lamarck correctly as respects his position in physical science."

Lamarck boldly carried the principle of change and evolution into inorganic nature by the same law of change of circumstances producing change of species.

Under the head, "De l'espèce parmi les minéraux," p. 149, the author states that he had for a long time supposed that there were no species among minerals. Here, also, he doubts, and boldly, if not rashly, in this case, opposes accepted views, and in this field, as elsewhere, shows, at least, his independence of thought.

"They teach in Paris," he says, "that the integrant molecule of each kind of compound is invariable in nature, and consequently that it is as old as nature, hence, mineral species are constant.

"For myself, I declare that I am persuaded, and even feel convinced, that the integrant molecule of every compound substance whatever, may change its nature, namely, may undergo changes in the number and in the proportions of the principles which compose it."

He enlarges on this subject through eight pages. He was evidently led to take this view from his assumption that everything, every natural object, organic or inorganic, undergoes a change. But it may be objected that this view will not apply to minerals, because those of the archæan rocks do not differ, and have undergone no change since then to the present time, unless we except such minerals as are alteration products due to metamorphism. The primary laws of nature, of physics, and of chemistry are unchangeable, while change, progression from the generalized to the specialized, is distinctly characteristic of the organic as opposed to the inorganic world.

CHAPTER VIII

LAMARCK'S WORK IN GEOLOGY

WHATEVER may be said of his chemical and physical lucubrations, Lamarck in his geological and palæontological writings is, despite their errors, always suggestive, and in some most important respects in advance of his time. And this largely for the reason that he had once travelled, and to some extent observed geological phenomena, in the central regions of France, in Germany, and Hungary ; visiting mines and collecting ores and minerals, besides being in a degree familiar with the French cretaceous fossils, but more especially those of the tertiary strata of Paris and its vicinity. He had, therefore, from his own experience, slight as it was, some solid grounds of facts and observations on which to meditate and from which to reason.

He did not attempt to touch upon cosmological theories—chaos and creation—but, rather, confined himself to the earth, and more particularly to the action of the ocean, and to the changes which he believed to be due to organic agencies. The most impressive truth in geology is the conception of the immensity of past time, and this truth Lamarck fully realized. His views are to be found in a little book of 268 pages, entitled *Hydrogéologie*. It appeared in 1802 (an X.), or ten years before the first publication of Cuvier's famous *Discours sur les Revolutions de la Surface du Globe* (1812). Written in his popular and attractive style, and thoroughly in accord with the cosmological and theological prepossessions of the age, the *Discours* was widely read, and passed through many editions. On the other hand, the *Hydrogéologie* died stillborn, with scarcely a friend or a reader, never reaching a second edition, and is now, like most of his works, a bibliographical rarity.

The only writer who has said a word in its favor, or contrasted it with the work of Cuvier, is the judicious and candid Huxley, who, though by no means favorable to Lamarck's factors of evolution, frankly said :

"The vast authority of Cuvier was employed in support of the traditionally respectable hypotheses of special creation and of catastrophism ; and the wild speculations of the *Discours sur les Revolutions de la Surface du Globe* were held to be models of sound scientific thinking, while the really much more sober and philosophic hypotheses of the *Hydrogéologie* were scouted." *

Before summarizing the contents of this book, let us glance at the geological atmosphere—thin and tenuous as it was then—in which Lamarck lived. The credit of being the first observer, before Steno (1669), to state that fossils are the remains of animals which were once alive, is due to an Italian, Frascatero, of Verona, who wrote in 1517.

---

* *Evolution in Biology*, in *Darwiniana*, New York, 1896, p. 212.

" But," says Lyell,* " the clear and philosophical views of Frascatero were disregarded, and the talent and argumentative powers of the learned were doomed for three centuries to be wasted in the discussion of these two simple and preliminary questions : First, whether fossil remains had ever belonged to living creatures ; and, secondly, whether, if this be admitted, all the phenomena could not be explained by the deluge of Noah."

Previous to this the great artist, architect, engineer, and musician, Leonardo da Vinci (1452–1519), who, among other great works, planned and executed some navigable canals in Northern Italy, and who was an observer of rare penetration and judgment, saw how fossil shells were formed, saying that the mud of rivers had covered and penetrated into the interior of fossil shells at a time when these were still at the bottom of the sea near the coast.†

That versatile and observing genius, Bernard Palissy, as early as 1580, in a book entitled *The Origin of Springs from Rain-water*, and in other writings, criticized the notions of the time, especially of Italian writers, that petrified shells had all been left by the universal deluge.

" It has happened," said Fontenelle, in his eulogy on Palissy, delivered before the French Academy a century and a half later, " that a potter who knew neither Latin nor Greek dared, toward the end of the sixteenth century, to say in Paris, and in the presence of all the doctors, that fossil shells were veritable shells deposited at some time by the sea in the places

---

* *Principles of Geology.*
† Lyell's *Principles of Geology*, 8th edit., p. 22.

where they were then found ; that the animals had
given to the figured stones all their different shapes,
and that he boldly defied all the school of Aristotle
to attack his proofs." *

Then succeeded, at the end of the seventeenth
century, the forerunners of modern geology : Steno
(1669), Leibnitz (1683), Ray (1692), Woodward (1695),
Vallisneri (1721), while Moro published his views in
1745. In the eighteenth century Réaumur † (1720)
presented a paper on the fossil shells of Touraine.

Cuvier ‡ thus pays his respects, in at least an un-
sympathetic way, to the geological essayists and
compilers of the seventeenth century :

" The end of the seventeenth century lived to see
the birth of a new science, which took, in its infancy,
the high-sounding name of ' Theory of the Earth.'
Starting from a small number of facts, badly observed,
connecting them by fantastic suppositions, it pretended to go back to the origin of worlds, to, as it
were, play with them, and to create their history.
Its arbitrary methods, its pompous language, alto-
gether seemed to render it foreign to the other
sciences, and, indeed, the professional savants for a
long time cast it out of the circle of their studies."

Their views, often premature, composed of half-
truths, were mingled with glaring errors and fantastic
misconceptions, but were none the less germinal.
Leibnitz was the first to propose the nebular hypothesis, which was more fully elaborated by Kant and
Laplace. Buffon, influenced by the writing of Leib-

---

* Quoted from Flouren's *Éloge Historique de Georges Cuvier*,
Hoefer's edition. Paris, 1854.

† *Remarques sur les Coquilles fossiles de quelques Cantons de la
Touraine.* Mém. Acad. Sc. Paris, 1720, pp. 400–417.

‡ *Éloge Historique de Werner*, p. 113.

nitz, in his *Théorie de la Terre*, published in 1749, adopted his notion of an original volcanic nucleus and a universal ocean, the latter as he thought leaving the land dry by draining into subterranean caverns. He also dimly saw, or gathered from his reading, that the mountains and valleys were due to secondary causes; that fossiliferous strata had been deposited by ocean currents, and that rivers had transported materials from the highlands to the lowlands. He also states that many of the fossil shells which occur in Europe do not live in the adjacent seas, and that there are remains of fishes and of plants not now living in Europe, and which are either extinct or live in more southern climates, and others in tropical seas. Also that the bones and teeth of elephants and of the rhinoceros and hippopotamus found in Siberia and elsewhere in northern Europe and Asia indicate that these animals must have lived there, though at present restricted to the tropics. In his last essay, *Époques de la Nature* (1778), he claims that the earth's history may be divided into epochs, from the earliest to the present time. The first epoch was that of fluidity, of incandescence, when the earth and the planets assumed their form; the second, of cooling; the third, when the waters covered the earth, and volcanoes began to be active; the fourth, that of the retreat of the seas, and the fifth the age when the elephants, the hippopotamus, and other southern animals lived in the regions of the north; the sixth, when the two continents, America and the old world, became separate; the seventh and last being the age of man.

Above all, by his attractive style and bold suggestions he popularized the subjects and created an interest in these matters and a spirit of inquiry which spread throughout France and the rest of Europe.

But notwithstanding the crude and uncritical nature of the writings of the second half of the eighteenth century, resulting from the lack of that more careful and detailed observation which characterizes our day, there was during this period a widespread interest in physical and natural science, and it led up to that more exact study of nature which signalizes the nineteenth century. " More new truths concerning the external world," says Buckle, " were discovered in France during the latter half of the eighteenth century than during all preceding periods put together." * As Perkins † says : " Interest in scientific study, as in political investigation, seemed to rise suddenly from almost complete inactivity to extraordinary development.   In both departments English thinkers had led the way, but if the impulse to such investigations came from without, the work done in France in every branch of scientific research during the eighteenth century was excelled by no other nation, and England alone could assert any claim to results of equal importance.   The researches of Coulomb in electricity, of Buffon in geology, of Lavoisier in chemistry, of Daubenton in comparative anatomy, carried still farther by their illustrious successors towards the close of the century, did much to establish conceptions of the universe and its laws

---

* *History of Civilization*, i. p. 627.
† *France under Louis XV.*, p. 359.

upon a scientific basis." And not only did Rousseau
make botany fashionable, but Goldsmith wrote from
Paris in 1755 : " I have seen as bright a circle of
beauty at the chemical lectures of Rouelle as gracing
the court of Versailles." Petit lectured on astronomy to crowded houses, and among his listeners were
gentlemen and ladies of fashion, as well as professional students.* The popularizers of science during
this period were Voltaire, Montesquieu, Alembert,
Diderot, and other encyclopædists.

Here should be mentioned one of Buffon's contemporaries and countrymen ; one who was the first true
field geologist, an observer rather than a compiler or
theorist. This was Jean E. Guettard (1715–1786).
He published, says Sir Archibald Geikie, in his valuable work, *The Founders of Geology*, about two hundred papers on a wide range of scientific subjects,
besides half a dozen quarto volumes of his observations, together with many excellent plates. Geikie
also states that he is undoubtedly entitled to rank
among the first great pioneers of modern geology.
He was the first (1751) to make a geological map of
northern France, and roughly traced the limits of his
three bands or formations from France across the
southeastern English counties. In his work on " The
degradation of mountains effected in our time by
heavy rains, rivers, and the sea,"† he states that the

---

* *France under Louis XV.*, p. 360.

† See vol. iii. of his *Mémoires sur différentes Parties des
Sciences et des Arts*, pp. 209–403. Geikie does not give the date
of the third volume of his work, but it was apparently about 1771,
as vol. ii. was published in 1770. I copy Geikie's account of Guettard's observations often in his own words.

sea is the most potent destroyer of the land, and that
the material thus removed is deposited either on the
land or along the shores of the sea. He thought that
the levels of the valleys are at present being raised,
owing to the deposit of detritus in them. He points
out that the deposits laid down by the ocean do not
extend far out to sea, " that consequently the elevations of new mountains in the sea, by the deposition
of sediment, is a process very difficult to conceive ;
that the transport of the sediment as far as the equator is not less improbable ; and that still more difficult to accept is the suggestion that the sediment
from our continent is carried into the seas of the
New World. In short, we are still very little advanced towards the theory of the earth as it now
exists." Guettard was the first to discover the volcanoes of Auvergne, but he was " hopelessly wrong "
in regard to the origin of basalt, forestalling Werner
in his mistakes as to its aqueous origin. He was
thus the first Neptunist, while, as Geikie states, his
" observations in Auvergne practically started the
Vulcanist camp."

We now come to Lamarck's own time. He must
have been familiar with the results of Pallas's travels
in Russia and Siberia (1793–94). The distinguished
German zoölogist and geologist, besides working out
the geology of the Ural Mountains, showed, in 1777,
that there was a general law in the formation of all
mountain chains composed chiefly of primary rocks ; *
the granitic axis being flanked by schists, and these

---

* Lyell's *Principles of Geology.*

by fossiliferous strata. From his observations made on the Volga and about its mouth, he presented proofs of the former extension, in comparatively recent times, of the Caspian Sea. But still more pregnant and remarkable was his discovery of an entire rhinoceros, with its flesh and skin, in the frozen soil of Siberia. His memoir on this animal places him among the forerunners of, if not within the ranks of, the founders of palæontology.

Meanwhile Soldani, an Italian, had, in 1780, shown that the limestone strata of Italy had accumulated in a deep sea, at least far from land, and he was the first to observe the alternation of marine and fresh-water strata in the Paris basin.

Lamarck must have taken much interest in the famous controversy between the Vulcanists and Neptunists. He visited Freyburg in 1771; whether he met Werner is not known, as Werner began to lecture in 1775. He must have personally known Faujas of Paris, who, in 1779, published his description of the volcanoes of Vivarais and Velay; while Desmarest's (1725–1815) elaborate work on the volcanoes of Auvergne, published in 1774, in which he proved the igneous origin of basalt, was the best piece of geological exploration which had yet been accomplished, and is still a classic.*

Werner (1750–1817), the propounder of the Neptunian theory, was one of the founders of modern geology and of palæontology. His work entitled

---

* Geikie states that the doctrine of the origin of valleys by the erosive action of the streams which flow through them, though it has been credited to various writers, was first clearly taught from actual concrete examples by Desmarest. L. c., p. 65.

7

Ueber die äussern Kennzeichen der Fossilien appeared in 1774; his *Kurze Klassifikation und Beschreibung der Gebirgsarten* in 1787. He discovered
the law of the superposition of stratified rocks,
though he wrongly considered volcanic rocks, such as
basalt, to be of aqueous origin, being as he supposed
formed of chemical precipitates from water. But he
was the first to state that the age of different formations can be told by their fossils, certain species
being confined to particular beds, while others ranged
throughout whole formations, and others seemed to
occur in several different formations; "the original
species found in these formations appearing to have
been so constituted as to live through a variety of
changes which had destroyed hundreds of other
species which we find confined to particular beds." *
His views as regards fossils, as Jameson states, were
probably not known to Cuvier, and it is more than
doubtful whether Lamarck knew of them. He
observed that fossils appear first in " transition " or
palæozoic strata, and were mainly corals and molluscs;
that in the older carboniferous rocks the fossils are
of higher types, such as fish and amphibious animals;
while in the tertiary or alluvial strata occur the remains of birds and quadrupeds. He thought that
marine plants were more ancient than land plants.
His studies led him to infer that the fossils contained in the oldest rocks are very different from any
of the species of the present time; that the newer the
formation, the more do the remains approach in form

---

* Jameson's *Cuvier's Theory of the Earth*, New York, 1818.

to the organic beings of the present creation, and that in the very latest formations, fossil remains of species now existing occur. Such advanced views as these would seem to entitle Werner to rank as one of the founders of palæontology.*

Hutton's *Theory of the Earth* appeared in 1785, and in a more developed state, as a separate work, in 1795.† "The ruins of an older world," he said, "are visible in the present structure of our planet, and the strata which now compose our continents have been once beneath the sea, and were formed out of the waste of preëxisting continents. The same forces are still destroying, by chemical decomposition or mechanical violence, even the hardest rocks, and transporting the materials to the sea, where they are spread out and form strata analogous to those of more ancient date. Although loosely deposited along the bottom of the ocean, they became afterwards altered and consolidated by volcanic heat, and were then heaved up, fractured, and contorted." Again he said: "In the economy of the world I can find no traces of a beginning, no prospect of an end." As Lyell remarks: "Hutton imagined that the continents were first gradually destroyed by aqueous degradation, and when their ruins had furnished materials for new

---

* J. G. Lehmann of Berlin, in 1756, first formally stated that there was some regular succession in the strata, his observations being based on profiles of the Hartz and the Erzgebirge. He proposed the names Zechstein, Kupferschiefer, rothes Todtliegendes, which still linger in German treatises. G. C. Fuchsel (1762) wrote on the stratigraphy of the coal measures, the Permian and the later systems in Thuringia. (Zittel.)

† James Hutton was born at Edinburgh, June 3, 1726, where he died March 26, 1797.

continents, they were upheaved by violent convulsions. He therefore required alternate periods of general disturbance and repose."

To Hutton, therefore, we are indebted for the idea of the immensity of the duration of time. He was the forerunner of Lyell and of the uniformitarian school of geologists.

Hutton observed that fossils characterized certain strata, but the value of fossils as time-marks and the principle of the superposition of stratified fossiliferous rocks were still more clearly established by William Smith, an English surveyor, in 1790. Meanwhile the Abbé Haüy, the founder of crystallography, was in 1802 Professor of Mineralogy in the Jardin des Plantes.

Lamarck's Contributions to Physical Geology; his Theory of the Earth.

Such were the amount and kind of knowledge regarding the origin and structure of our earth which existed at the close of the eighteenth century, while Lamarck was meditating his *Hydrogéologie*, and had begun to study the invertebrate fossils of the Paris tertiary basin.

His object, he says in his work, is to present certain considerations which he believed to be new and of the first order, which had escaped the notice of physicists, and which seemed to him should serve as the foundations for a good theory of the earth. His theses are :

1. What are the natural consequences of the influence and the movements of the waters on the surface of the globe?

2. Why does the sea constantly occupy a basin within the limits which contain it, and there separate the dry parts of the surface of the globe always projecting above it?

3. Has the ocean basin always existed where we actually see it, and if we find proofs of the sojourn of the sea in places where it no longer remains, by what cause was it found there, and why is it no longer there?

4. What influence have living bodies exerted on the substances found on the surface of the earth and which compose the crust which invests it, and what are the general results of this influence?

Lamarck then disclaims any intentions of framing brilliant hypotheses based on supposititious principles, but nevertheless, as we shall see, he falls into this same error, and like others of his period makes some preposterous hypotheses, though these are far less so than those of Cuvier's *Discours*. He distinguishes between the action of rivers or of fresh-water currents, torrents, storms, the melting of snow, and the work of the ocean. The rivers wear away and bear materials from the highlands to the lowlands, so that the plains are gradually elevated; ravines form and become immense valleys, and their sides form elevated crests and pass into mountains ranges.

He brings out and emphasizes the fact, now so well known, that the erosive action of rain and rivers has formed mountains of a certain class.

" It is then evident to me, that every mountain which is not the result of a *volcanic irruption* or of some local catastrophe, has been carved out from a plain, where its mass is gradually formed, and was a part of it ; hence what in this case are the summits of the mountains are only the remains of the former level of the plain unless the process of washing away and other means of degradation have not since reduced its height."

Now this will apply perfectly well to our table-lands, mesas, the mountains of our bad-lands, even to our Catskills and to many elevations of this nature in France and in northern Africa. But Lamarck unfortunately does not stop here, but with the zeal of an innovator, by no means confined to his time alone, claims that the mountain masses of the Alps and the Andes were carved out of plains which had been raised above the sea-level to the present heights of those mountains.

Two causes, he says, have concurred in forming these elevated plains.

"One consists in the continual accumulation of material filling the portion of the ocean-basin from which the same seas slowly retreat ; for it does not abandon those parts of the ocean-basin which are situated nearer and nearer to the shores that it tends to leave, until after having filled its bottom and having gradually raised it. It follows that the coasts which the sea is abandoning are never made by a very deep-lying formation, however often it appears to be such, for they are continually elevated as the result of the perpetual balancing of the sea, which casts off from its shores all the sediments brought down by the rivers ; in such a way that the great depths of the ocean are not near the shore from which the sea retreats, but out in the middle of the ocean and near the opposite shores which the sea tends to invade.

"The other cause, as we shall see, is found in the

detritus of organic bodies successively accumulated, which perpetually elevates, although with extreme slowness, the soil of the dry portions of the globe, and which does it all the more rapidly, as the situation of these parts gives less play to the degradation of the surface caused by the rivers.

" Doubtless a plain which is destined some day to furnish the mountains which the rivers will carve out from its mass would have, when still but a little way from the sea, but a moderate elevation above its river channels; but gradually as the ocean basin removed from this plain, this basin constantly sinking down into the interior (*épaisseur*) of the external crust of the globe, and the soil of the plain perpetually rising higher from the deposition of the detritus of organic bodies, it results that, after ages of elevation of the plain in question, it would be in the end sufficiently thick for high mountains to be shaped and carved out of its mass.

" Although the ephemeral length of life of man prevents his appreciation of this fact, it is certain that the soil of a plain unceasingly acquires a real increase in its elevation in proportion as it is covered with different plants and animals. Indeed the débris successively heaped up for numerous generations of all these beings which have by turns perished, and which, as the result of the action of their organs, have, during the course of this life, given rise to combinations which would never have existed without this means, most of the principles which have formed them not being borrowed from the soil; this débris, I say, wasting successively on the soil of the plain in question, gradually increases the thickness of its external bed, multiplies there the mineral matters of all kinds and gradually elevates the formation."

Our author, as is evident, had no conception, nor had any one else at the time he wrote, of the slow secular elevation of a continental plateau by crust-movements, and Lamarck's idea of the formation of elevated plains on land by the accumulation of débris of organisms is manifestly inadequate, our aërial or eolian rocks and loess being wind-deposits of sand and silt rather than matters of organic origin. Thus he cites as an example of his theory the vast elevated plains of Tartary, which he thought had been dry land from time immemorable, though we now know that the rise took place in the quaternary or present period. On the other hand, given these vast elevated plains, he was correct in affirming that rivers flowing through them wore out enormous valleys and carved out high mountains, left standing by atmospheric erosion, for examples of such are to be seen in the valley of the Nile, the Colorado, the Upper Missouri, etc.

He then distinguishes between granitic or crystalline mountains, and those composed of stratified rocks and volcanic mountains.

The erosive action of rivers is thus discussed ; they tend first, he says, to fill up the ocean basins, and second, to make the surface of the land broken and mountainous, by excavating and furrowing the plains.

Our author did not at all understand the causes of the inclination or tilting up of strata. Little close observation or field work had yet been done, and the rocks about Paris are but slightly if at all disturbed. He attributes the dipping down of strata to the inclination of the shores of the sea, though he adds that nevertheless it is often due to local subsidences. And then he remarks that " indeed in many mountains, and especially in the Pyrenees, in the very centre of these mountains, we observe that the strata are for the most part either vertical or so inclined that they more or less approach this direction."

"But," he asks, "should we conclude from this that there has necessarily occurred a universal catastrophe, a general overturning? This assumption, so convenient for those naturalists who would explain all the facts of this kind without taking the trouble to observe and study the course which nature follows, is not at all necessary here; for it is easy to conceive that the inclined direction of the beds in the mountains may have been produced by other causes, and especially by causes more natural and less hypothetical than a general overturning of strata."

While streams of fresh water tend to fill up and destroy the ocean basins, he also insists that the movements of the sea, such as the tides, currents, storms, submarine volcanoes, etc., on the contrary, tend to unceasingly excavate and reëstablish these basins. Of course we now know that tides and currents have no effect in the ocean depths, though their scouring effects near shore in shallow waters have locally had a marked effect in changing the relations of land and sea. Lamarck went so far as to insist that the ocean basin owes its existence and its preservation to the scouring action of the tides and currents.

The earth's interior was, in Lamarck's opinion, solid, formed of quartzose and silicious rocks, and its centre of gravity did not coincide with its geographical centre, or what he calls the *centre de forme*. He imagined also that the ocean revolved around the globe from east to west, and that this movement, by its continuity, displaced the ocean basin and made it pass successively over all the surface of the earth.

Then, in the third chapter, he asks if the basin of the sea has always been where we now actually see it, and whether we find proofs of the sojourn of the sea in the place where it is now absent; if so, what are the causes of these changes. He reiterates his strange idea of a general movement of the ocean from east to west, at the rate of at least three leagues in twenty-four hours and due to the moon's influence. And here Lamarck, in spite of his uniformitarian principles, is strongly cataclysmic. What he seems to have in mind is the great equatorial current between Africa and the West Indies. To this perpetual movement of the waters of the Atlantic Ocean he ventures to attribute the excavation of the Gulf of Mexico, and presumes that at the end of ages it will break through the Isthmus of Panama, and transform America into two great islands or two small continents. Not understanding that the islands are either the result of upheaval, or outliers of continents, due to subsidence, Lamarck supposed that his westward flow of the ocean, due to the moon's attraction, eroded the eastern shores of America, and the currents thus formed "in their efforts to move westward, arrested by America and by the eastern coasts of China, were in great part diverted towards the South Pole, and seeking to break through a passage across the ancient continent have, a long time since, reduced the portion of this continent which united New Holland to Asia into an archipelago which comprises the Molucca, Philippine, and Mariana Islands." The West Indies and Windward Islands were formed by the same means, and the sea not breaking through the Isthmus of Panama was turned southward, and the action of its currents resulted in detaching the island of Tierra del Fuego from South America. In like manner New Zealand was separated from New Holland, Madagascar from Africa, and Ceylon from India.

He then refers to other "displacements of the ocean basin," to the shallowing of the Straits of Sunda, of the Baltic Sea, the ancient subsidence of the coast of Holland and Zealand, and states that Sweden offers all the appearance of having recently emerged from the sea, while the Caspian Sea, formerly much larger than at present, was once in communication with the Black Sea, and that some day the Straits of Sunda and the Straits of Dover will be dry land, so that the union of England and France will be formed anew.

Strangely enough, with these facts known to him, Lamarck did not see that such changes were due to changes of level of the land rather than to their being abandoned or invaded by the sea, but explained these by his bizarre hypothesis of westward-flowing currents due to the moon's action; though it should be in all fairness stated that down to recent times there have been those who believed that it is the sea and not the land which has changed its level.

This idea, that the sea and not the land has changed its level, was generally held at the time Lamarck wrote, though Strabo had made the shrewd observation that it was the land which moved. The Greek geographer threw aside the notion of some of his contemporaries, and with wonderful prevision, considering the time he wrote and the limited observations he could make, claimed that it is not the sea which has risen or fallen, but the land itself which is sometimes raised up and sometimes depressed, while the sea-bottom may also be elevated or sunk down. He refers to such facts as deluges, earthquakes, and volcanic eruptions, and sudden swellings of the land beneath the sea.

"And it is not merely the small, but the large islands also, not merely the islands, but the continents which can be lifted up together with the sea ; and, too, the large and small tracts may subside, for habitations and cities, like Bure, Bizona, and many others, have been engulfed by earthquakes." *

But it was not until eighteen centuries later that this doctrine, under the teachings of Playfair, Leopold von Buch, and Élie de Beaumont (1829–30) became generally accepted. In 1845 Humboldt remarked, " It is a fact to-day recognized by all geologists, that the rise of continents is due to an actual upheaval, and not to an apparent subsidence occasioned by a general depression of the level of the sea " (*Cosmos*, i). Yet as late as 1869 we have an essay by H. Trautschold † in which is a statement of the arguments which can be brought forward in favor of the doctrine that the increase of the land above sea level is due to the retirement of the sea.‡

---

* Quoted from Lyell's *Principles of Geology*, eighth edit., p. 17.

† *Bulletin Société Imp. des Naturalistes de Moscou*, xlii. (1869), pt. 1, p. 4, quoted from Geikie's *Geology*, p. 276, footnote.

‡ Suess also, in his *Anlitz*, etc., substitutes for the folding of the earth's crust by tangential pressure the subsidence by gravity of portions of the crust, their falling in obliging the sea to follow.   Suess

As authentic and unimpeachable proofs of the former existence of the sea where now it is absent, Lamarck cites the occurrence of fossils in rocks inland. Lamarck's first paper on fossils was read to the Institute in 1799, or about three years previous to the publication of the *Hydrogéologie*. He restricts the term " fossils " to vegetable and animal remains, since the word in his time was by some loosely applied to minerals as well as fossils; to anything dug out of the earth. " We find fossils," he says, " on dry land, even in the middle of continents and large islands; and not only in places far removed from the sea, but even on mountains and in their bowels, at considerable heights, each part of the earth's surface having at some time been a veritable ocean bottom." He then quotes at length accounts of such instances from Buffon, and notices their prodigious number, and that while the greater number are marine, others are fresh-water and terrestrial shells, and the marine shells may be divided into littoral and pelagic.

" This distinction is very important to make, because the consideration of fossils is, as we have already said, one of the principal means of knowing well the revolutions which have taken place on the surface of our globe. This subject is of great importance, and under this point of view it should lead naturalists to study fossil shells, in order to compare them with their analogues which we can discover in the sea; finally, to carefully seek the places where each species

---

also explains the later transgressions of the sea by the progressive accumulation of sediments which raise the level of the sea by their deposition at its bottom. Thus he believes that the true factor in the deformation of the globe is vertical descent, and not, as Neumayr had previously thought, the folding of the crust.

lives, the banks which are formed of them, the different beds which these banks may present, etc., etc., so that we do not believe it out of place to insert here the principal considerations which have already resulted from that which is known in this respect.

"*The fossils which are found in the dry parts of the surface of the globe are evident indications of a long sojourn of the sea in the very places where we observe them.*" Under this heading, after repeating the statement previously made that fossils occur in all parts of the dry land, in the midst of the continents and on high mountains, he inquires *by what cause* so many marine shells could be found in the explored parts of the world. Discarding the old idea that they are monuments of the deluge, transformed into fossils, he denies that there was such a general catastrophe as a universal deluge, and goes on to say in his assured, but calm and philosophic way :

"On the globe which we inhabit, everything is submitted to continual and inevitable changes, which result from the essential order of things : they take place, in truth, with more or less promptitude or slowness, according to the nature, the condition, or the situation of the objects ; nevertheless they are wrought in some time or other.

" To nature, time is nothing, and it never presents a difficulty ; she always has it at her disposal, and it is for her a means without limit, with which she has made the greatest as well as the least things.

" The changes to which everything in this world is subjected are changes not only of form and of nature, but they are changes also of bulk, and even of situation.

" All the considerations stated in the preceding chapters should convince us that nothing on the surface of the terrestrial globe is immutable. They teach us that the vast ocean which occupies so great a part of the surface of our globe cannot have its bed constantly fixed in the same place; that the dry or exposed parts of this surface themselves undergo perpetual changes in their condition, and that they are in turn successively invaded and abandoned by the sea.

" There is, indeed, every evidence that these enormous masses of water continually displace themselves, both their bed and their limits.

" In truth these displacements, which are never interrupted, are in general only made with extreme and almost inappreciable slowness, but they are in ceaseless operation, and with such constancy that the ocean bottom, which necessarily loses on one side while it gains on another, has already, without doubt, spread over not only once, but even several times, every point of the surface of the globe.

" If it is thus, if each point of the surface of the terrestrial globe has been in turn dominated by the seas—that is to say, has contributed to form the bed of those immense masses of water which constitute the ocean—it should result (1) that the insensible but uninterrupted transfer of the bed of the ocean over the whole surface of the globe has given place to deposits of the remains of marine animals which we should find in a fossil state; (2) that this translation of the ocean basin should be the reason why the dry portions of the earth are always more elevated than the level of the sea; so that the old ocean bed should become exposed without being elevated above the sea, and without consequently giving rise to the formation of mountains which we observe in so many different regions of the naked parts of our globe."

Thus littoral shells of many genera, such as Pectens, Tellinæ, cockle shells, turban shells (*sabots*), etc.,

madrepores and other littoral polyps, the bones of
marine or of amphibious animals which have lived
near the sea, and which occur as fossils, are then unimpeachable monuments of the sojourn of the sea on
the points of the dry parts of the globe where we
observe their deposits, and besides these occur deep-
water forms. " Thus the encrinites, the belemnites,
the orthoceratites, the ostracites, the terebratules,
etc., all animals which habitually live at the bottom,
found for the most part among the fossils deposited
on the point of the globe in question, are unimpeachable witnesses which attest that this same place was
once part of the bottom or great depths of the sea."
He then attempts to prove, and does so satisfactorily,
that the shells he refers to are what he calls deep-
water (pélagiennes).   He proves the truth of his thesis
by the following facts :

1. We are already familiar with a marine Gryphæa,
and different Terebratulæ, also marine shell-fish, which
do not, however, live near shore.   2. Also the greatest
depth which has been reached with the rake or the
dredge is not destitute of molluscs, since we find
there a great number which only live at this depth,
and without instruments to reach and bring them up
we should know nothing of the *cones, olives,* Mitra,
many species of Murex, Strombus, etc.   3. Finally,
since the discovery of a living Encrinus, drawn up on
a sounding line from a great depth, and where lives
the animal or polyp in question, it is not only possible to assure ourselves that at this depth there are
other living animals, but on the contrary we are
strongly bound to think that other species of the
same genus, and probably other animals of different
genera, also live at the same depths.   All this leads

one to admit, with Bruguière,* the existence of deep-water shell-fish and polyps, which, like him, I distinguish from littoral shells and polyps.

" The two sorts of monuments of which I have above spoken, namely, littoral and deep-sea fossils, may be, and often should be, found separated by different beds in the same bank or in the same moun-

---

* Bruguière (1750–1799), a conchologist of great merit. His descriptions of new species were clear and precise. In his paper on the coal mines of the mountains of Cevennes (Choix de Mémoires d'Hist. Nat., 1792) he made the first careful study of the coal formation in the Cevennes, including its beds of coal, sandstone, and shale. A. de Jussieu had previously supposed that the immense deposits of coal were due to sudden cataclysms or to one of the great revolutions of the earth during which the seas of the East or West Indies, having been driven as far as into Europe, had deposited on its soil all these exotic plants to be found there, after having torn them up on their way.

But Bruguière, who is to be reckoned among the early uniformitarians, says that " the capacity for observation is now too well-informed to be contented with such a theory," and he explains the formation of coal deposits in the following essentially modern way :

" The stores of coal, although formed of vegetable substances, owe their origin to the sea. It is when the places where we now find them were covered by its waters that these prodigious masses of vegetable substances were gathered there, and this operation of nature, which astonishes the imagination, far from depending on any extraordinary commotion of the globe, seems, on the contrary, to be only the result of time, of an order of things now existing, and especially that of slow changes" (i, pp. 116, 117).

The proofs he brings forward are the horizontality of the beds, both of coal and deposits between them, the marine shells in the sandstones, the fossil fishes intermingled with the plant remains in the shales ; moreover, some of the coal deposits are covered by beds of limestone containing marine shells which lived in the sea at a very great depth. The alternation of these beds, the great mass of vegetable matter which lived at small distances from the soil which conceals them, and the occurrence of these beds so high up, show that at this time Europe was almost wholly covered by the sea, the summits of the Alps and the Pyrenees being then, as he says, so many small islands in the midst of the ocean. He also intimates that the climate when these ferns ("bamboo" and "banana") lived was warmer than that of Europe at present.

In this essay, then, we see a great advance in correctness of geological observation and reasoning over any previous writers, while its suggestions were appreciated and adopted by Lamarck.

tains, since they have been deposited there at very different epochs. But they may often be found mixed together, because the movements of the water, the currents, submarine volcanoes, etc., have overturned the beds, yet some regular deposits in water always tranquil would be left in quite distant beds . . . Every dry part of the earth's surface, when the presence or the abundance of marine fossils prove that formerly the sea has remained in that place, has necessarily twice received, for a single incursion of the sea, littoral shells, and once deep-sea shells, in three different deposits—this will not be disputed. But as such an incursion of the sea can only be accomplished by a period of immense duration, it follows that the littoral shells deposited at the first sojourn of the edge of the sea, and constituting the first deposit, have been destroyed—that is to say, have not been preserved to the present time ; while the deep-water shells form the second deposit, and there the littoral shells of the third deposit are, in fact, the only ones which now exist, and which constitute the fossils that we see."

He again asserts that these deposits could not be the result of any sudden catastrophe, because of the necessarily long sojourn of the sea to account for the extensive beds of fossil shells, the remains of " infinitely multiplied generations of shelled animals which have lived in this place, and have there successively deposited their débris." He therefore supposes that these remains, " continually heaped up, have formed these shell banks, become fossilized after the lapse of considerable time, and in which it is often possible to distinguish different beds." He then continues his line of anti-catastrophic reasoning, and we must remember that in his time facts in biology and geology were feebly grasped, and scientific reasoning or induction was in its infancy.

" I would again inquire how, in the supposition of a universal çatastrophe, there could have been pre-served an infinity of delicate shells which the least shock would break, but of which we now find a great number uninjured among other fossils. How also could it happen that bivalve shells, with which cal-careous rocks and even those changed into a silicious condition are interlarded, should be all still provided with their two valves, as I have stated, if the animals of these shells had not lived in these places?

" There is no doubt but that the remains of so many molluscs, that so many shells deposited and consequently changed into fossils, and most of which were totally destroyed before their substance became silicified, furnished a great part of the calcareous matter which we observe on the surface and in the upper beds of the earth.

" Nevertheless there is in the sea, for the formation of calcareous matter, a cause which is greater than shelled molluscs, which is consequently still more powerful, and to which, must be referred ninety-nine hundredths, and indeed more, of the calcareous matter occurring in nature. This cause, so important to consider, is the existence of *coralligenous polyps*, which we might therefore call *testaceous polyps*, because, like the testaceous molluscs, these polyps have the faculty of forming, by a transudation or a continual secretion of their bodies, the stony and calcareous polypidom on which they live.

" In truth these polyps are animals so small that a single one only forms a minute quantity of calca-reous matter. But in this case what nature does not obtain in any volume or in quantity from any one individual, she simply receives by the number of ani-mals in question, through the enormous multiplicity

of these animals, and their astonishing fecundity—
namely, by the wonderful faculty they have of
promptly regenerating, of multiplying in a short time
their generations successively, and rapidly accumulat-
ing ; finally, by the total amount of reunion of the
products of these numerous little animals.

"Moreover, it is a fact now well known and well
established that the coralligenous polyps, namely,
this great family of animals with coral stocks, such as
the millepores, the madrepores, astræ, meandrinæ,
etc., prepare on a great scale at the bottom of the
sea, by a continual secretion of their bodies, and as
the result of their enormous multiplication and their
accumulated generations, the greatest part of the calcareous matter which exists. The numerous coral
stocks which these animals produce, and whose bulk
and numbers perpetually increase, form in certain
places islands of considerable extent, fill up extensive
bays, gulfs, and roadsteads ; in a word, close harbors,
and entirely change the condition of coasts.

"These enormous banks of madrepores and millepores, heaped upon each other, covered and intermingled with serpulæ, different kinds of oysters,
patellæ, barnacles, and other shells fixed by their
base, form irregular mountains of an almost limitless
extent.

"But when, after the lapse of considerable time, the
sea has left the places where these immense deposits
are laid down, then the slow but combined alteration
that these great masses undergo, left uncovered and
exposed to the incessant action of the air, light, and a
variable humidity, changes them gradually into fossils
and destroys their membranous or gelatinous part,
which is the readiest to decompose. This alteration,
which the enormous masses of the corals in question continued to undergo, caused their structure to
gradually disappear, and their great porosity unceasingly diminished the parts of these stony masses

by displacing and again bringing together the molecules composing them, so that, undergoing a new aggregation, these calcareous molecules obtained a number of points of contact, and constituted harder and more compact masses. It finally results that instead of the original masses of madrepores and millepores there occurs only masses of a compact calcareous rock, which modern mineralogists have improperly called *primitive limestone*, because, seeing in it no traces of shells or corals, they have mistaken these stony masses for deposits of a matter primitively existing in nature."

He then reiterates the view that these deposits of marble and limestones, often forming mountain ranges, could not have been the result of a universal catastrophe, and in a very modern way goes on to specify what the limits of catastrophism are. The only catastrophes which a naturalist can reasonably admit as having taken place are partial or local ones, those dependent on causes acting in isolated places, such as the disturbances which are caused by volcanic eruptions, by earthquakes, by local inundations, by violent storms, etc. These catastrophes are with reason admissible, because we observe their analogues, and because we know that they often happen. He then gives examples of localities along the coast of France, as at Manche, where there are ranges of high hills made up of limestones containing Gryphææ, ammonites, and other deep-water shells.

In the conclusion of the chapter, after stating that the ocean has repeatedly covered the greater part of the earth, he then claims that "the displacement of the sea, producing a constantly variable inequality

in the mass of the terrestrial radii, has necessarily
caused the earth's centre of gravity to vary, as also
its two poles.* Moreover, since it appears that this
variation, very irregular as it is, not being subjected
to any limits, it is very probable that each point of
the surface of the planet we inhabit is really in
the case of successively finding itself subjected to
different climates." He then exclaims in eloquent,
profound, and impassioned language:

" How curious it is to see that such suppositions
receive their confirmation from the consideration of
the state of the earth's surface and of its external
crust, from that of the nature of certain fossils found
in abundance in the northern regions of the earth,
and whose analogues now live in warm climates;
finally, in that of the ancient astronomical observations of the Egyptians.

"Oh, how great is the antiquity of the terrestrial
globe, and how small are the ideas of those who attribute to the existence of this globe a duration of
six thousand and some hundred years since its origin
down to our time!

"The physico-naturalist and the geologist in this
respect see things very differently; for if they have
given the matter the slightest consideration—the one,
the nature of fossils spread in such great numbers in
all the exposed parts of the globe, both in elevated
situations and at considerable depths in the earth; the
other, the number and disposition of the beds, as also
the nature and order of the materials which compose
the external crust of this globe studied throughout

---

* Hooke had previously, in order to explain the presence of tropical fossil shells in England, indulged in a variety of speculations
concerning changes in the position of the axis of the earth's rotation,
" a shifting of the earth's centre of gravity analogous to the revolutions of the magnetic pole, etc." (Lyell's *Principles*). See also p. 132.

a great part of its thickness and in the mountain masses—have they not had opportunities to convince themselves that the antiquity of this same globe is so great that it is absolutely beyond the power of man to appreciate it in an adequate way!

" Assuredly our chronologies do not extend back very far, and they could only have been made by propping them up by fables. Traditions, both oral and written, become necessarily lost, and it is in the nature of things that this should be so.

" Even if the invention of printing had been more ancient than it is, what would have resulted at the end of ten thousand years? Everything changes, everything becomes modified, everything becomes lost or destroyed. Every living language insensibly changes its idiom; at the end of a thousand years the writings made in any language can only be read with difficulty; after two thousand years none of these writings will be understood. Besides wars, vandalism, the greediness of tyrants and of those who guide religious opinions, who always rely on the ignorance of the human race and are supported by it, how many are the causes, as proved by history and the sciences, of epochs after epochs of revolutions, which have more or less completely destroyed them.

" How many are the causes by which man loses all trace of that which has existed, and cannot believe nor even conceive of the immense antiquity of the earth he inhabits!

" How great will yet seem this antiquity of the terrestrial globe in the eyes of man when he shall form a just idea of the origin of living bodies, as also of the causes of the development and of the gradual process of perfection of the organization of these bodies, and especially when it will be conceived that, time and favorable circumstances having been necessary to give existence to all the living species such as we actually see, he is himself the last result and the actual maximum of this process of perfecting, the limit (*terme*) of which, if it exists, cannot be known."

In the fourth chapter of the book there is less to interest the reader, since the author mainly devotes it to a reiteration of the ideas of his earlier works on physics and chemistry. He claims that the minerals and rocks composing the earth's crust are all of organic origin, including even granite. The thickness of this crust he thinks, in the absence of positive knowledge, to be from three to four leagues, or from nine to twelve miles.

After describing the mode of formation of minerals, including agates, flint, geodes, etc., he discusses the process of fossilization by molecular changes, silicious particles replacing the vegetable or animal matter, as in the case of fossil wood.

While, then, the products of animals such as corals and molluscs are limestones, those of vegetables are humus and clay; and all of these deposits losing their less fixed principles pass into a silicious condition, and end by being reduced to quartz, which is the earthy element in its purest form. The salts, pyrites, and metals only differ from other minerals by the different circumstances under which they were accumulated, in their different proportions, and in their much greater amount of carbonic or acidific fire.

Regarding granite, which, he says, naturalists very erroneously consider as *primitive*, he begins by observing that it is only by conjecture that we should designate as primitive any matter whatever. He recognizes the fact that granite forms the highest mountains, which are generally arranged in more or less regular chains. But he strangely assumes that the constituents of granite, *i.e.*, felspar, quartz, and mica, did not exist before vegetables, and that these minerals and their aggregation into granite were the result of slow deposition in the ocean.* He goes so far as to assert that the porphyritic rocks were not thus formed in the sea, but that they are the result of deposits carried down by streams, especially torrents flowing down from mountains. Gneiss, he thinks, resulted from the detritus of granitic rocks, by means of an inappreciable cement, and formed in a way analogous to that of the porphyries.

Then he attacks the notion of Leibnitz of a liquid globe, in which all mineral substances were precipitated tumultuously, replacing this idea by his chemical notion of the origin of the crystalline and volcanic rocks.

He is on firmer ground in explaining the origin of chalk and clay, for the rocks of the region about Paris, with which he was familiar, are sedimentary and largely of organic origin.

In the "Addition" (pp. 173–188) following the fourth chapter Lamarck states that, allowing for the variations in the intensity of the cause of elevation of the land as the result of the accumulations of organic

---

* Cuvier, in a footnote to his *Discours* (sixth edition, p. 49), in referring to this view, states that it originated with Rodig (*La Physique*, p. 106, Leipzig, 1801) and De Maillet (*Telliamed*, tome ii, p. 169), "also an infinity of new German works." He adds : " M. de Lamarck has recently expanded this system in France at great length in his *Hydrogéologie* and in his *Philosophie zoologique*." Is the Rodig referred to Ih. Chr. Rodig, author of *Beiträge zur Naturwissenschaft* (Leipzig, 1803. 8°)? We have been unable to discover this view in De Maillet ; Cuvier's reference to p. 169 is certainly incorrect, as quite a different subject is there discussed.

matter, he thinks he can, without great error, consider the mean rate as 324 mm. (1 foot) a century. As a concrete example it has been observed, he says, that one river valley has risen a foot higher in the space of eleven years.

Passing by his speculations on the displacement of the poles of the earth, and on the elevations of the equatorial regions, which will dispense with the necessity of considering the earth as originally in a liquid condition, he allows that " the terrestrial globe is not at all a body entirely and truly solid, but that it is a combination (*réunion*) of bodies more or less solid, displaceable in their mass or in their separate parts, and among which there is a great number which undergo continual changes in condition."

It was, of course, too early in the history of geology for Lamarck to seize hold of the fact, now so well known, that the highest mountain ranges, as the Alps, Pyrenees, the Caucasus, Atlas ranges, and the Mountains of the Moon (he does not mention the Himalayas) are the youngest, and that the lowest mountains, especially those in the more northern parts of the continents, are but the roots or remains of what were originally lofty mountain ranges. His idea, on the contrary, was, that the high mountain chains above mentioned were the remains of ancient equatorial elevations, which the fresh waters, for an enormous multitude of ages, were in the process of progressively eroding and wearing down.

What he says of the formation of coal is noteworthy:

" Wherever there are masses of fossil wood buried

in the earth, the enormous subterranean beds of coal that are met with in different countries, these are the witnesses of ancient encroachments of the sea, over a country covered with forests ; it has overturned them, buried them in deposits of clay, and then after a time has withdrawn."

In the appendix he briefly rehearses the laws of evolution as stated in his opening lecture of his course given in the year IX. (1801), and which would be the subject of his projected work, *Biologie*, the third and last part of the Terrestrial Physics, a work which was not published, but which was probably comprised in his *Philosophie zoologique*.

The *Hydrogéologie* closes with a "*Mémoire sur la matière du feu*" and one "*sur la matière du son*," both being reprinted from the *Journal de Physique*.

CHAPTER IX

LAMARCK THE FOUNDER OF INVERTEBRATE PALÆ-ONTOLOGY

It was fortunate for palæontology that the two greatest zoölogists of the end of the eighteenth and the beginning of the nineteenth centuries, Lamarck and Cuvier, lived in the Paris basin, a vast cemetery of corals, shells, and mammals; and not far from extensive deposits of cretaceous rocks packed with fossil invertebrates. With their then unrivalled knowledge of recent or existing forms, they could restore the assemblages of extinct animals which peopled the cretaceous ocean, and more especially the tertiary seas and lakes.

Lamarck drew his supplies of tertiary shells from the tertiary beds situated within a radius of from twenty-five to thirty miles from the centre of Paris, and chiefly from the village of Grignon, about ten miles west of Paris, beyond Versailles, and still a rich collecting ground for the students of the Museum and Sorbonne. He acknowledges the aid received from Defrance,* who had already collected at Grignon five hundred species of fossil shells, three-fourths of which, he says, had not then been described.

Lamarck's first essay (" *Sur les fossiles*") on fossils

---

* Although Defrance (born 1759, died in 1850) aided Lamarck in collecting tertiary shells, his earliest palæontological paper (on Hipponyx) did not appear until the year 1819.

in general was published at the end of his *Système des Animaux sans Vertèbres* (pp. 401–411), in 1801, a year before the publication of the *Hydrogéologie.* " I give the name *fossils*," he says, " to remains of living beings, changed by their long sojourn in the earth or under water, but whose forms and structure are still recognizable.

" From this point of view, the bones of vertebrate animals and the remains of testaceous molluscs, of certain crustacea, of many echinoderms, coral polyps, when after having been for a long time buried in the earth or hidden under the sea, will have undergone an alteration which, while changing their substance, has nevertheless destroyed neither their forms, their figures, nor the special features of their structures."

He goes on to say that the animal parts having been destroyed, the shell remains, being composed of calcareous matter. This shell, then, has lost its lustre, its colors, and often even its nacre, if it had any ; and in this altered condition it is usually entirely white. In some cases where the shells have remained for a long period buried in a mud of some particular color, the shell receives the same color.

" In France, the fossil shells of Courtagnon near Reims, Grignon near Versailles, of what was formerly Touraine, etc., are almost all still in this calcareous state, having more or less completely lost their animal parts—namely, their lustre, their peculiar colors, and their nacre.

" Other fossils have undergone such an alteration that not only have they lost their animal portion, but their substance has been changed into a silicious matter. I give to this second kind of fossil the name of *silicious fossils*, and examples of this kind are the different oysters ('des ostracites'), many terebratulæ ('des terebratulites'), trigoniæ, ammonites, echinites, encrinites, etc.

"The fossils of which I have just spoken are in part buried in the earth, and others lie scattered over its surface. They occur in all the exposed parts of our globe, in the middle even of the largest continents, and, what is very remarkable, they occur on mountains up to very considerable altitudes. In many places the fossils buried in the earth form banks extending several leagues in length." *

Conchologists, he says, did not care to collect or study fossil shells, because they had lost their lustre, colors, and beauty, and they were rejected from collections on this account as "dead" and uninteresting. "But," he adds, "since attention has been drawn to the fact that these fossils are extremely valuable *monuments* for the study of the revolutions which have taken place in different regions of the earth, and of the changes which the beings living there have themselves successively undergone (in my lectures I have always insisted on these considerations), consequently the search for and study of fossils have excited special interest, and are now the objects of the greatest interest to naturalists."

Lamarck then combats the views of several naturalists, undoubtedly referring to Cuvier, that the fos-

---

* In a footnote Lamarck refers to an unpublished work, which probably formed a part of the *Hydrogéologie*, published in the following year. "*Voyez à ce sujet mon ouvrage intitulé: De l'influence du mouvement des eaus sur la surface du globe terrestre, et des indices du déplacement continuel du bassin des mers, ainsi que de son transport successif sur les différens points de la surface du globe*" (no date).

sils are extinct species, and that the earth has passed through a general catastrophe (*un bouleversement universel*) with the result that a multitude of species of animals and plants were consequently absolutely lost or destroyed, and remarks in 'the following telling and somewhat derisive language :

"A universal catastrophe (*bouleversement*) which necessarily regulates nothing, mixes up and disperses everything, is a very convenient way to solve the problem for those naturalists who wish to explain everything, and who do not take the trouble to observe and investigate the course followed by nature as respects its production and everything which constitutes its domain. I have already elsewhere said what should be thought of this so-called universal overturning of the globe? I return to fossils.

"It is very true that, of the great quantity of fossil shells gathered in the different countries of the earth, there are yet but a very small number of species whose living or marine analogues are known. Nevertheless, although this number may be very small, which no one will deny, it is enough to suppress the universality announced in the proposition cited above.

"It is well to remark that among the fossil shells whose marine or living analogues are not known, there are many which have a form closely allied to shells of the same genera known to be now living in the sea. However, they differ more or less, and cannot be rigorously regarded as the same species as those known to be living, since they do not perfectly resemble them. These are, it is said, extinct species.

"I am convinced that it is possible never to find, among fresh or marine shells, any shells perfectly similar to the fossil shells of which I have just spoken. I believe I know the reason; I proceed to succinctly indicate, and I hope that it will then be seen, that although many fossil shells are different from all the marine shells known, this does not prove that the species of these shells are extinct, but only that these species have changed as the result of time, and that actually they have different forms from those individuals whose fossil remains we have found."

Then he goes on in the same strain as in the opening discourse, saying that nothing terrestrial remains constant, that geological changes are continually occurring, and that these changes produce in living organisms a diversity of habits, a different mode of life, and as the result modifications or developments in their organs and in the shape of their parts.

"We should still realize that all the modifications which the organism undergoes in its structure and form as the result of the influence of circumstances which would influence this being, are propagated by generation, and that after a long series of ages not only will it be able to form new species, new genera, and even new orders, but also each species will even necessarily vary in its organization and in its forms.

"We should not be more surprised then if, among the numerous fossils which occur in all the dry parts of the globe and which offer us the remains of so many animals which have formerly existed, there should be found so few of which we know the living analogues. If there is in this, on the contrary, anything which should astonish us, it is to find that among these numerous fossil remains of beings which have lived there should be known to us some whose analogues still exist, from a germ to a vast multitude of living forms, of different and ascending grades of perfection, ending in man.

"This fact, as our collection of fossils proves, should lead us to suppose that the fossil remains of the animals whose living analogues we know are the less ancient fossils. The species to which each of them belongs had doubtless not yet time to vary in any of its forms.

" We should, then, never expect to find among the living species the totality of those that we meet with in the fossil state, and yet we cannot conclude that any species can really be lost or extinct. It is undoubtedly possible that among the largest animals some species have been destroyed as a result of the multiplication of man in the regions where they live. But this conjecture cannot be based on the consideration of fossils alone; we can only form an opinion in this respect when all the inhabited parts of the globe will have become perfectly known."

Lamarck did not have, as we now have, a knowledge of the geological succession of organic forms. The comparatively full and detailed view which we possess of the different vast assemblages of plant and animal life which have successively peopled the surface of our earth is a vision on which his eyes never rested. His slight, piecemeal glimpse of the animal life of the Paris Basin, and of the few other extinct forms then known, was all he had to depend upon or reason from. He was not disposed to believe that the thread of life once begun in the earliest times could be arbitrarily broken by catastrophic means; that there was no relation whatever between the earlier and later faunas. He utterly opposed Cuvier's view that species once formed could ever be lost or become extinct without ancestors or descendants. He on the contrary believed that species underwent a slow modification, and that the fossil forms are the ancestors of the animals now living. Moreover, Lamarck was the inventor of

9

the first genealogical tree; his phylogeny, in the second volume of his *Philosophie zoologique* (p. 463), proves that he realized that the forms leading up to the existing ones were practically extinct, as we now use the word. Lamarck in theory was throughout, as Houssay well says, at one with us who are now living, but a century behind us in knowledge of the facts needed to support his theory.

In this first published expression of his views on palæontology, we find the following truths enumerated on which the science is based : (1) The great length of geological time ; (2) The continuous existence of animal life all through the different geological periods without sudden total extinctions and as sudden re-creations of new assemblages ; (3) The physical environment remaining practically the same throughout in general, but with (4) continual gradual but not catastrophic changes in the relative distribution of land and sea and other modifications in the physical geography, changes which (5) caused corresponding changes in the habitat, and (6) consequently in the habits of the living beings ; so that there has been all through geological history a slow modification of life-forms.

Thus Lamarck's idea of creation is *evolutional* rather than *uniformitarian*. There was, from his point of view, not simply a uniform march along a dead level, but a progression, a change from the lower or generalized to the higher or specialized—an evolution or unfolding of organic life. In his effort to disprove catastrophism he failed to clearly see that species, as we style them, became extinct, though really the changes in the species practically amounted to extinctions of the earlier species as such. The little that was known to Lamarck at the time he wrote, prevented his knowing that species became extinct, as we say, or recognizing the fact that while some species, genera, and even orders may rise, culminate, and die, others are modified, while a few persist from one period to another. He did, however, see clearly that, taking plant and animal life as a whole, it underwent a slow modification, the later forms being the descendants of the earlier; and this truth is the central one of modern palæontology.

Lamarck's first memoir on fossil shells, in which he described many new species, was published in 1802, after the appearance of his *Hydrogéologie*, to which he refers. It was the first of a series of descriptive papers, which appeared at intervals from 1802 to 1806. He does not fail to open the series of memoirs with some general remarks, which prove his broad, philosophic spirit, that characterizing the founder of a new science. He begins by saying that the fossil forms have their analogues in the tropical seas. He claims that there was evident proof that these molluscs could not have lived in a climate like that of places in which they now occur, instancing *Nautilius pompilius*, which now lives in the seas of warm countries; also the presence of exotic ferns, palms, fossil amber, fossil gum-elastic, besides the occurrence of fossil crocodiles and elephants both in France and Germany.*

---

* It should be stated that the first observer to inaugurate the comparative method was that remarkable forerunner of modern palæontologists, Steno the Dane, who was for a while a professor at Padua.

Hence there have been changes of climate since these forms flourished, and, he adds, the intervals between these changes of climate were stationary periods, whose duration was practically without limit. He assigns a duration to these station-

---

In 1669, in his treatise entitled *De Solido intra Solidum naturaliter contento*, which Lyell translates "On gems, crystals, and organic petrefactions inclosed within solid rocks," he showed, by dissecting a shark from the Mediterranean, that certain fossil teeth found in Tuscany were also those of some shark. "He had also compared the shells discovered in the Italian strata with living species, pointed out their resemblance, and traced the various gradations from shells merely calcined, or which had only lost their animal gluten, to those petrefactions in which there was a perfect substitution of stony matter" (Lyell's *Principles*, p. 25). About twenty years afterwards, the English philosopher Robert Hooke, in a discourse on earthquakes, written in 1688, but published posthumously in 1705, was aware that the fossil ammonites, nautili, and many other shells and fossil skeletons found in England, were of different species from any then known ; but he doubted whether the species had become extinct, observing that the knowledge of naturalists of all the marine species, especially those inhabiting the deep sea, was very deficient. In some parts of his writings, however, he leans to the opinion that species had been lost. Some species, he observes with great sagacity, "are *peculiar to certain places*, and not to be found elsewhere." Turtles and such large ammonites as are found in Portland seem to have been the productions of hotter countries, and he thought that England once lay under the sea within the torrid zone (Lyell's *Principles*).

Gesner the botanist, of Zurich, also published in 1758 an excellent treatise on petrefactions and the changes of the earth which they testify. He observed that some fossils, "such as ammonites, gryphites, belemnites, and other shells, are either of unknown species or found only in the Indian and other distant seas" (Lyell's *Principles*).

Geikie estimates very highly Guettard's labors in palæontology, saying that "his descriptions and excellent drawings entitle him to rank as the first great leader of the palæontological school of France." He published many long and elaborate memoirs containing brief descriptions, but without specific names, and figured some hundreds of fossil shells. He was the first to recognize trilobites (Illænus) in the Silurian slates of Angers, in a memoir published in 1762. Some of his generic names, says Geikie, "have passed into the languages of modern palæontology, and one of the genera of chalk sponges which he described has been named after him, *Guettardia*. In his memoir "On the accidents that have befallen fossil shells compared with those which are found to happen to shells now living in the sea" (Trans. Acad. Roy. Sciences, 1765, pp. 189, 329, 399) he shows that the

ary or intermediate periods of from three to five
million years each — "a duration infinitely small
relative to those required for all the changes of the
earth's surface."

He refers in an appreciative way to the first special
treatise on fossil shells ever published, that of an
Englishman named Brander,* who collected the shells
"out of the cliffs by the sea-coast between Christ
Church and Lymington, but more especially about
the cliffs by the village of Hordwell," where the strata
are filled with these fossils. Lamarck, working upon
collections of tertiary shells from Grignon and also
from Courtagnon near Reims, with the aid of Brander's work showed that these beds, not known to
be Eocene, extended into Hampshire, England; thus
being the first to correlate by their fossils, though
in a limited way to be sure, the tertiary beds of
France with those of England.

How he at a later period (1805) regarded fossils

---

beds of fossil shells on the land present the closest possible analogy
to the flow of the present sea, so that it becomes impossible to doubt
that the accidents, such as broken and worn shells, which have affected
the fossil organisms, arose from precisely the same causes as those of
exactly the same nature that still befall their successors on the existing
ocean bottom. On the other hand, Geikie observes that it must be
acknowledged "that Guettard does not seem to have had any clear
ideas of the sequence of formations and of geological structures."

* Scheuchzer's "Complaint and Vindication of the Fishes" (*Piscium
Querelae et Vindiciae*, Germany, 1708), "a work of zoölogical merit,
in which he gave some good plates and descriptions of fossil fish"
(Lyell). Gesner's treatise on pretrefactions preceded Lamarck's work
in this direction, as did Brander's *Fossillia Hantoniensia*, published
in 1766, which contained "excellent figures of fossil shells from the
more modern (or Eocene) marine strata of Hampshire. In his opinion
fossil animals and testacea were, for the most part, of unknown
species, and of such as were known the living analogues now belonged
to southern latitudes" (Lyell's *Principles*, eighth edition, p. 46).

and their relations to geology may be seen in his later memoirs, *Sur les Fossiles des environs de Paris.**

" The determination of the characters, both generic and specific, of animals of which we find the fossil remains in almost all the dry parts of the continents and large islands of our globe will be, from several points of view, a thing extremely useful to the progress of natural history. At the outset, the more this determination is advanced, the more will it tend to complete our knowledge in regard to the species which exist in nature and of those which have existed, as it is true that some of them have been lost, as we have reason to believe, at least as concerns the large animals. Moreover, this same determination will be singularly advantageous for the advancement of geology ; for the fossil remains in question may be considered, from their nature, their condition, and their situation, as authentic monuments of the revolutions which the surface of our globe has undergone, and they can throw a strong light on the nature and character of these revolutions."

This series of papers on the fossils of the Paris tertiary basin extended through the first eight volumes of the *Annales*, and were gathered into a volume published in 1806. In his descriptions his work was comparative, the fossil species being compared with their living representatives. The thirty plates, containing 483 figures representing 184 species (exclusive of those figured by Brard), were afterwards published, with the explanations, but not the descriptions, as a separate volume in 1823.† This (the text

---

* *Annales du Muséum d'Histoire Naturelle*, vi., 1805, pp. 222–228.

† *Recueil de Planches des Coquilles fossiles des environs de Paris* (Paris, 1823). There are added two plates of fossil fresh-water shells (twenty-one species of Limnæa, etc.) by Brard, with sixty-two figures.

published in 1806) is the first truly scientific palæontological work ever published, preceding Cuvier's
Ossemens fossiles by six years.

When we consider Lamarck's—at his time unrivalled—knowledge of molluscs, his philosophical
treatment of the relations of the study of fossils to
geology, his correlation of the tertiary beds of England with those of France, and his comparative descriptions of the fossil forms represented by the existing shells, it seems not unreasonable to regard him
as the founder of invertebrate palæontology, as Cuvier
was of vertebrate or mammalian palæontology.

We have entered the claim that Lamarck was one
of the chief founders of palæontology, and the first
French author of a genuine, detailed palæontological
treatise. It must be admitted, therefore, that the
statement generally made that Cuvier was the founder
of this science should be somewhat modified, though
he may be regarded as the chief founder of vertebrate
palæontology.

In this field, however, Cuvier had his precursors
not only in Germany and Holland, but also in France.

Our information as to the history of the rise of
vertebrate palæontology is taken from Blainville's
posthumous work entitled *Cuvier et Geoffroy Saint-
Hilaire.** In this work, a severe critical and perhaps
not always sufficiently appreciative account of Cuvier's
character and work, we find an excellent history of
the first beginnings of vertebrate palæontology. Blainville has little or nothing to say of the first steps in

---

* *Cuvier et Geoffroy Saint-Hilaire. Biographies scientifiques*, par
Ducrotay de Blainville (Paris, 1890, p. 446).

invertebrate palæontology, and, singularly enough, not
a word of Lamarck's principles and of his papers and
works on fossil shells—a rather strange oversight,
because he was a friend and admirer of Lamarck, and
succeeded him in one of the two departments of invertebrates created at the Museum d'Histoire Naturelle after Lamarck's death.

Blainville, who by the way was the first to propose
the word *palæontology*, shows that the study of the
great extinct mammals had for forty years been held
in great esteem in Germany, before Faujas and Cuvier took up the subject in France. Two Frenchmen,
also before 1789, had examined mammalian bones.
Thus Bernard de Jussieu knew of the existence in a
fossil state of the teeth of the hippopotamus. Guettard * published in 1760 a memoir on the fossil bones
of Aix en Provence. Lamanon (1780–1783) † in a
beautiful memoir described a head, almost entire,
found in the gypsum beds of Paris. Daubenton had
also slightly anticipated Cuvier's law of correlation,
giving "a very remarkable example of the mode of
procedure to follow in order to solve these kinds of
questions by the way in which he had recognized a
bone of a giraffe whose skeleton he did not possess"
(De Blainville).

---

* " Mémoire sur des os fossiles découverts auprès de la ville d'Aix
en Provence " (Mém. Acad. Sc., Paris, 1760, pp. 209–220).

† " Sur un os d'une grosseur énorme qu'on a trouvé dans une couche
de glaise au milieu de Paris ; et en général sur les ossemens fossiles
qui ont appartenu à de grands animaux " (*Journal de Physique*, tome
xvii, 1781, pp. 393–405). Lamanon also, in 1780, published in the
same *Journal* an article on the nature and position of the bones found
at Aix en Provence ; and in 1783 another article on the fossil bones
belonging to gigantic animals.

" But it was especially in Germany, in the hands of Pallas, Camper, Blumenbach, anatomists and physicians, also those of Walch, Merck, Hollmann, Esper, Rosenmüller, and Collini (who was not, however, occupied with natural history), of Beckman, who had even discussed the subject in a general way (*De reductione rerum fossilium ad genera naturalia prototyporum — Nov. Comm. Soc. Scient. Goettingensis*, t. ii.), that palæontology applied to quadrupeds had already settled all that pertained to the largest species."

As early as 1764, Hollmann * had admirably identified the bones of a rhinoceros found in a bone-deposit of the Hartz, although he had no skeleton of this animal for comparison.

Pallas, in a series of memoirs dating from 1773, had discovered and distinguished the species of Siberian elephant or mammoth, the rhinoceros, and the large species of oxen and buffalo whose bones were found in such abundance in the quaternary deposits of Siberia ; and, as Blainville says, if he did not distinguish the species, it was because at this epoch the question of the distinction of the two species of rhinoceros and of elephants, in the absence of material, could not be solved. This solution, however, was made by the Dutch anatomist Camper, in 1777, who had brought together at Amsterdam a collection of skeletons and skulls of the existing species which enabled him for the first time to make the necessary comparisons between the extinct and living species. A few years

---

* Hollmann had still earlier published a paper entitled *De corporum marinorum, aliorumque peregrinorum in terra continente origine* (*Commentarii Soc. Goettingen.*, tom. iii., 1753, pp. 285-374).

later (1780) Blumenbach confirmed Camper's identifi-
cation, and gave the name of *Elephas primigenius* to
the Siberian mammoth.

"Beckman" [says Blainville] "as early as 1772 had
even published a very good memoir on the way in
which we should consider fossil organic bodies; he
was also the first to propose using the name *fossilia*
instead of *petrefacta*, and to name the science which
studies fossils *Oryctology*. It was also he who admitted that these bodies should be studied with reference
to the class, order, genus, species, as we would do with
a living being, and he compared them, which he called
prototypes,* with their analogues. He then passes in
review, following the zoölogical order, the fossils which
had been discovered by naturalists. He even described
one of them as a new species, besides citing, with an
erudition then rare, all the authors and all the works
where they were described. He did no more than to
indicate but not name each species. Thus he was
the means of soon producing a number of German
authors who made little advance from lack of anatomical knowledge; but afterwards the task fell into
the hands of men capable of giving to the newly
created palæontology a remarkable impulse, and one
which since then has not abated."

Blumenbach,† the most eminent and all-round German anatomist and physiologist of his time, one of
the founders of anthropology as well as of palæontol-

---

* *Novi Commentarii Soc. Sc. Goettingensis*, tom. ii., *Commentat.*,
tom. i.

† His first palæontological article appears to have been one entitled
Beiträge zur Naturgeschichte der Vorwelt (Lichtenberg, *Voigt's
Magaz.*, Bd. vi, S. 4, 1790, pp. 1–17). I have been unable to ascertain in which of his publications he describes and names the cave-
bear.

ogy, had meanwhile established the fact that there were two species of fossil cave-bear, which he named *Ursus spelæus* and *U. arctoideus.* He began to publish his *Archæologia telluris,** the first part of which appeared in 1803.

From Blainville's useful summary we learn that Blumenbach, mainly limiting his work to the fossils of Hanover, aimed at studying fossils in order to explain the revolutions of the earth.

" Hence the order he proposed to follow was not that commonly followed in treatises on oryctology, namely, systematic, following the classes and the orders of the animal and vegetable kingdom, but in a chronological order, in such a way as to show that the classes, so far as it was possible to conjecture with any probability, were established after or in consequence of the different revolutions of the earth.

" Thus, as we see, all the great questions, more or less insoluble, which the study of fossil organic bodies can offer, were raised and even discussed by the celebrated professor of Göttingen as early as 1803, before anything of the sort could have arisen from the essays of M. G. Cuvier ; the errors of distribution in the classes committed by Blumenbach were due to the backward state of geology."

The political troubles of Germany, which also bore heavily upon the University of Göttingen, probably brought Blumenbach's labors to an end, for after a second " specimen " of his work, of less importance than the first, the *Archæologia telluris* was discontinued.

---

* *Specimen archæologia telluris terrarumque imprimis Hannoverana*, pts. i., ii. *Cum* 4 *tabl. aen.* 4 *maj.* Gottingæ, 1803.

The French geologist Faujas,* who also published several articles on fossil animals, ceased his labors, and now Cuvier began his memorable work.

The field of the labors and triumphs of palæontology were now transferred to France. We have seen that the year 1793, when Lamarck and Geoffroy Saint-Hilaire were appointed to fill the new zoölogical chairs, and the latter had in 1795 called Cuvier from Normandy to Paris, was a time of renascence of the natural sciences in France. Cuvier began a course of lectures on comparative anatomy at the Museum of Natural History. He was more familiar than any one else in France with the progress in natural science in Germany, and had felt the stimulus arising from this source; besides, as Blainville stated, he was also impelled by the questions boldly raised by Faujas in his geological lectures, who was somewhat of the school of Buffon. Cuvier, moreover, had at his disposition the collection of skeletons of the Museum, which was frequently increased by those of the animals which died in the menagerie. With his knowledge of comparative anatomy, of which, after Vicq-d'Azyr, he was the chief founder, and with the gypsum quarry of Montmartre, that rich cemetery of tertiary mammals, to draw from, he had the whole field before him, and rapidly

---

* Faujas Saint-Fond wrote articles on fossil bones (1794) ; on fossil plants both of France (1803) and of Monte Bolca (1820) ; on a fish from Nanterre (1802) and a fossil turtle (1803) ; on two species of fossil ox, whose skulls were found in Germany, France, and England (1803), and on an elephant's tusk found in the volcanic tufa of Darbres (1803) ; on the fossil shells of Mayence (1806) ; and on a new genus (*Clotho*) of bivalve shells.

built up his own vast reputation and thus added to the glory of France.

His first contribution to palæontology * appeared in 1798, in which he announced his intention of publishing an extended work on fossil bones of quadrupeds, to restore the skeletons and to compare them with those now living, and to determine their relations and differences; but, says Blainville, in the list of thirty or forty species which he enumerates in his tableau, none was apparently discovered by him, unless it was the species of " dog " of Montmartre, which he afterward referred to his new genera Palæotherium and Anaplotherium. In 1801 (le 26 brumaire, an IX.) he published, by order of the Institut, the programme of a work on fossil quadrupeds, with an increased number of species; but, as Blainville states, " It was not until 1804, and in tome iii. of the *Annales du Muséum*, namely, more than three years after his programme, that he began his publications by fragments and without any order, while these publications lasted more than eight years before they were collected into a general work"; this " *corps d'ouvrage* " being the *Ossemens fossiles*, which was issued in 1812 in four quarto volumes, with an atlas of plates.

It is with much interest, then, that we turn to Cuvier's great work, which brought him such immediate and widespread fame, in order to see how he treated his subject. His general views are contained

---

* *Sur les ossemens qui se trouvent dans le gyps de Montmartre* (*Bulletin des sciences pour la Société philomatique*, tomes 1, 2, 1798, pp. 154–155).

in the preliminary remarks in his well-known " Essay on the Theory of the Earth " (1812), which was followed in 1821 by his *Discours sur les Révolutions de la Surface du Globe.*

It was written in a more attractive and vigorous style than the writings of Lamarck, more elegant, concise, and with less repetition, but it is destitute of the philosophic grasp, and is not the work of a profound thinker, but rather of a man of talent who was an industrious collector and accurate describer of fossil bones, of a high order to be sure, but analytical rather than synthetical, of one knowing well the value of carefully ascertained and demonstrated facts, but too cautious, if he was by nature able to do so, to speculate on what may have seemed to him too few facts.   It is also the work of one who fell in with the current views of the time as to the general bearing of his discoveries on philosophy and theology, believing as he did in the universality of the Noachian deluge.

Like Lamarck, Cuvier independently made use of the comparative method, the foundation method in palæontology ; and Cuvier's well-known " law of correlation of structures," so well exemplified in the vertebrates, was a fresh, new contribution to philosophical biology.

In his *Discours,* speaking of the difficulty of determining the bones of fossil quadrupeds, as compared with fossil shells or the remains of fishes, he remarks : *

---

* The following account is translated from the fourth edition of the *Ossemens fossiles,* vol. I., 1834, also the sixth edition of the *Discours,*

" Happily comparative anatomy possessed a principle which, well developed, was capable of overcoming every difficulty ; it was that of the correlation of forms in organic beings, by means of which each kind of organism can with exactitude be recognized by every fragment of each of its parts.—Every organized being," he adds, " forms an entire system, unique and closed, whose organs mutually correspond, and concur in the same definite action by a reciprocal reaction. Hence none of these parts can change without the other being also modified, and consequently each of them, taken separately, indicates and produces (*donne*) all the others.

" A claw, a shoulder-blade, a condyle, a leg or arm-bone, or any other bone separately considered, enables us to discover the kind of teeth to which they have belonged ; so also reciprocally we may determine the form of the other bones from the teeth. Thus, commencing our investigation by a careful survey of any one bone by itself, a person who is sufficiently master of the laws of organic structure can reconstruct the entire animal. The smallest facet of bone, the smallest apophysis, has a determinate character, relative to the class, the order, the genus, and the species to which it belongs, so that even when one has only the extremity of a well-preserved bone, he can, with careful examination, assisted by analogy and exact comparison, determine all these things as surely as if he had before him the entire animal."

Cuvier adds that he has enjoyed every kind of advantage for such investigations owing to his fortunate situation in the Museum of Natural History,

---

separately published in 1830. It does not differ materially from the first edition of the *Essay on the Theory of the Earth*, translated by Jameson, and republished in New York, with additions by Samuel L. Mitchell, in 1818.

and that by assiduous researches for nearly thirty years * he has collected skeletons of all the genera and sub-genera of quadrupeds, with those of many species in certain genera, and several individuals of certain species. With such means it was easy for him to multiply his comparisons, and to verify in all their details the applications of his laws.

Such is the famous law of correlation of parts, of Cuvier. It could be easily understood by the layman, and its enunciation added vastly to the popular reputation and prestige of the young science of comparative anatomy.†   In his time, and applied to the forms

---

* In the first edition of the *Théorie* he says fifteen years, writing in 1812.   In the later edition he changed the number of years to thirty.

† De Blainville is inclined to make light of Cuvier's law and of his assumptions ; and in his somewhat cynical, depreciatory way, says :

" Thus for the thirty years during which appeared the works of M. G. Cuvier on fossil bones, under the most favorable circumstances, in a kind of renascence of the science of organization of animals, then almost effaced in France, aided by the richest osteological collections which then existed in Europe, M. G. Cuvier passed an active and a comparatively long life, in a region abounding in fossil bones, without having established any other principle in osteology than a witticism which he had been unable for a moment to take seriously himself, because he had not yet investigated or sufficiently studied the science of organization, which I even doubt, to speak frankly, if he ever did. Otherwise, he would himself soon have perceived the falsity of his assertion that a single facet of a bone was sufficient to reconstruct a skeleton from the observation that everything is harmoniously correlated in an animal.   It is a great thing if the memory, aided by a strong imagination, can thus pass from a bone to the entire skeleton, even in an animal well known and studied even to satiety ; but for an unknown animal, there is no one except a man but slightly acquainted with the anatomy of animals who could pretend to do it.   It is not true anatomists like Hunter, Camper, Pallas, Vicq-d'Azyr, Blumenbach, Soemmering, and Meckel who would be so presuming, and M. G. Cuvier would have been himself much embarrassed if he had been taken at his word, and besides it is this assertion which will remain formulated in the mouths of the ignorant, and which has already made many persons believe that it is possible to answer the most difficult and often insoluble problems in palæontology, without having made any preliminary study, with the aid of dividers, and, on the other hand,

occurring in the Paris Basin, it was a most valuable, ingenious, and yet obvious method, and even now is the principal rule the palæontologist follows in identifying fragments of fossils of any class. But it has its limitations, and it goes without saying that the more complete the fossil skeleton of a vertebrate, or the remains of an arthropod, the more complete will be our conception of the form of the extinct organism. It may be misleading in the numerous cases of convergence and of generalized forms which now abound in our palæontological collections. We can well understand how guarded one must be in working out the restorations of dinosaurs and fossil birds, of the Permian and Triassic theromorphs, and the Tertiary creodonts as compared with existing çarnivora.

As the late O. C. Marsh* observed:

" We know to-day that unknown extinct animals cannot be restored from a single tooth or claw unless they are very similar to forms already known. Had

---

discouraging the Blumenbachs and Soemmerings from giving their attention to this kind of work."

Huxley has, *inter alia*, put the case in a somewhat similar way, to show that the law should at least be applied with much caution to unknown forms :

" Cuvier, in the *Discours sur les Révolutions de la Surface du Globe*, strangely credits himself, and has ever since been credited by others, with the invention of a new method of paleontological research. But if you will turn to the *Recherches sur les Ossemens fossiles*, and watch Cuvier not speculating, but working, you will find that his method is neither more nor less than that of Steno. If he was able to make his famous prophecy from the jaw which lay upon the surface of a block of stone to the pelvis which lay hidden in it, it was not because either he or any one else knew, or knows, why a certain form of jaw is, as a rule, constantly accompanied by the presence of marsupial bones, but simply because experience has shown that these two structures are coördinated " (*Science and Hebrew Tradition. Rise and Progress of Paleontology* 1881, p. 23).

* *History and Methods of Paleontological Discovery* (1879).

10

Cuvier himself applied his methods to many forms from the early tertiary or older formations he would have failed. If, for instance, he had had before him the disconnected fragments of an eocene tillodont he would undoubtedly have referred a molar tooth to one of his pachyderms, an incisor tooth to a rodent, and a claw bone to a carnivore. The tooth of a Hesperornis would have given him no possible hint of the rest of the skeleton, nor its swimming feet the slightest clue to the ostrich-like sternum or skull. And yet the earnest belief in his own methods led Cuvier to some of his most important discoveries."

Let us now examine from Cuvier's own words in his *Discours*, not relying on the statements of his expositors or followers, just what he taught notwithstanding the clear utterances of his older colleague, Lamarck, whose views he set aside and either ignored or ridiculed.*

He at the outset affirms that nature has, like mankind, also had her intestine wars, and that "the surface of the globe has been much convulsed by successive revolutions and various catastrophes."

As first proof of the revolutions on the surface of the earth he instances fossil shells, which in the lowest and most level parts of the earth are "almost everywhere in such a perfect state of preservation that even the smallest of them retain their most

---

* The following statement of Cuvier's views is taken from Jameson's translation of the first *Essay on the Theory of the Earth*, "which formed the introduction to his *Recherches sur les Ossemens fossiles*," the first edition of which appeared in 1812, or ten years after the publication of the *Hydrogéologie*. The original I have not seen, but I have compared Jameson's translation with the sixth edition of the *Discours* (1820).

delicate parts, their sharpest ridges, and their finest and tenderest processes."

" We are therefore forcibly led to believe not only that the sea has at one period or another covered all our plains, but that it must have remained there for a long time and in a state of tranquillity, which circumstance was necessary for the formation of deposits so extensive, so thick, in part so solid, and filled with the exuviæ of aquatic animals."

But the traces of revolutions become still more marked when we ascend a little higher and approach nearer to the foot of the great mountain chains. Hence the strata are variously inclined, and at times vertical, contain shells differing specifically from those of beds on the plains below, and are covered by horizontal later beds. Thus the sea, previous to the formation of the horizontal strata, had formed others, which by some means have been broken, lifted up, and overturned in a thousand ways. There had therefore been also at least one change in the basin of that sea which preceded ours; it had also experienced at least one revolution.

He then gives proofs that such revolutions have been numerous.

" Thus the great catastrophes which have pro-duced revolutions in the basins of the sea were pre-ceded, accompanied, and followed by changes in the nature of the fluid and of the substances which it held in solution, and when the surface of the seas came to be divided by islands and projecting ridges, different changes took place in every separate basin."

We now come to the Cuvierian doctrine *par excellence*, one in which he radically differs from Lamarck's views as to the genetic relations between the organisms of successive strata.

" Amid these changes of the general fluid it must have been almost impossible for the same kind of animals to continue to live, nor did they do so in fact. Their species, and even their genera, change with the strata, and although the same species occasionally recur at small distances, it is generally the case that the shells of the ancient strata have forms peculiar to themselves; that they gradually disappear till they are not to be seen at all in the recent strata, still less in the existing seas, in which, indeed, we never discover their corresponding species, and where several even of their genera are not to be found; that, on the contrary, the shells of the recent strata resemble, as regards the genus, those which still exist in the sea, and that in the last formed and loosest of these strata there are some species which the eye of the most expert naturalists cannot distinguish from those which at present inhabit the ocean.

" In animal nature, therefore, there has been a succession of changes corresponding to those which have taken place in the chemical nature of the fluid; and when the sea last receded from our continent its inhabitants were not very different from those which it still continues to support."

He then refers to successive irruptions and retreats of the sea, " the final result of which, however, has been a universal depression of the level of the sea."

" These repeated irruptions and retreats of the sea have neither been slow nor gradual; most of the catastrophes which have occasioned them have been sudden."

He then adds his proofs of the occurrence of revolutions before the existence of living beings. Like Lamarck, Cuvier was a Wernerian, and in speaking of the older or primitive crystalline rocks which contain no vestige of fossils, he accepted the view of the German theorist in geology, that granites forming the axis of mountain chains were formed in a fluid.

We must give Cuvier the credit of fully appreciating the value of fossils as being what he calls "historical documents," also for appreciating the fact that there were a number of revolutions marking either the incoming or end of a geological period; but as he failed to perceive the unity of organization in organic beings, and their genetic relationship, as had been indicated by Lamarck and by Geoffroy St. Hilaire, so in geological history he did not grasp, as did Lamarck, the vast extent of geological time, and the general uninterrupted continuity of geological events. He was analytic, thoroughly believing in the importance of confining himself to the discovery of facts, and, considering the multitude of fantastic hypotheses and suggestions of previous writers of the eighteenth century, this was sound, sensible, and thoroughly scientific. But unfortunately he did not stop here. Master of facts concerning the fossil mammals of the Paris Basin, he also—usually cautious and always a shrewd man of the world—fell into the error of writing his "theory of the world," and of going to the extreme length of imagining universal catastrophes where there are but local ones, a universal Noachian deluge when there was none, and of assuming that there were at successive periods thoroughgoing total

and sudden extinctions of life, and as sudden recreations. Cuvier was a natural leader of men, a ready
debater, and a clear, forcible writer, a man of great
executive force, but lacking in insight and imagination ; he dominated scientific Paris and France, he was
the law-giver and autocrat of the laboratories of Paris,
and the views of quiet, thoughtful, profound scholars
such as Lamarck and Geoffroy St. Hilaire were dis-
dainfully pushed aside, overborne, and the progress
of geological thought was arrested, while, owing to
his great prestige, the rising views of the Lamarckian
school were nipped in the bud. Every one, after the
appearance of Cuvier's great work on fossil mammals
and of his *Règne Animal,* was a Cuvierian, and down
to the time of Lyell and of Charles Darwin all naturalists, with only here and there an exception, were pronounced Cuvierians in biology and geology—catas-
trophists rather than uniformitarians. We now, with
the increase of knowledge of physical and historical
geology, of the succession of life on the earth, of the
unity of organization pervading that life from monad
to man all through the ages from the Precambrian to
the present age, know that there were vast periods
of preparation followed by crises, perhaps geologically
brief, when there were widespread changes in physical geography, which reacted on the life-forms, rendering certain ones extinct, and modifying others; but
this conception is entirely distinct from the views of
Cuvier and his school, * which may, in the light of

---

* Cuvier, in speaking of these revolutions, " which have changed
the surface of our earth," correctly reasons that they must have excited a more powerful action upon terrestrial quadrupeds than upon

our present knowledge, properly be deemed not only totally inadequate, but childish and fantastic.

Cuvier cites the view of Dolomieu, the well-known geologist and mineralogist (1770–1801), only, however, to reject it, who went to the extent of supposing that "tides of seven or eight hundred fathoms have carried off from time to time the bottom of the ocean, throwing it up in mountains and hills on the primitive valleys and plains of the continents" (Dolomieu in *Journal de Physique*).

Cuvier met with objections to his extreme views. In his discourse he thus endeavors to answer "the following objection" which "has already been stated against my conclusions":

"Why may not the non-existing races of mammiferous land quadrupeds be mere modifications or varieties of those ancient races which we now find in the fossil state, which modifications may have been produced by change of climate and other local circumstances, and since raised to the present excessive differences by the operation of similar causes during a long succession of ages?

"This objection may appear strong to those who believe in the indefinite possibility of change of forms

---

marine animals. "As these revolutions," he says, "have consisted chiefly in changes of the bed of the sea, and as the waters must have destroyed all the quadrupeds which they reached if their irruption over the land was general, they must have destroyed the entire class, or, if confined only to certain continents at one time, they must have destroyed at least all the species inhabiting these continents, without having the same effect upon the marine animals. On the other hand, millions of aquatic animals may have been left quite dry, or buried in newly formed strata or thrown violently on the coasts, while their races may have been still preserved in more peaceful parts of the sea, whence they might again propagate and spread after the agitation of the water had ceased."

in organized bodies, and think that during a succession of ages, and by alternations of habits, all the
species may change into each other, or one of them
give birth to all the rest. Yet to these persons the
following answer may be given from their own system : If the species have changed by degrees, as they
assume, we ought to find traces of this gradual modification. Thus, between the Palæotherium and the
species of our own days, we should be able to discover some intermediate forms ; and yet no such
discovery has ever been made. Since the bowels of
the earth have not preserved monuments of this
strange genealogy, we have a right to conclude that
the ancient and now extinct species were as permanent in their forms and characters as those which exist
at present ; or, at least, that the catastrophe which
destroyed them did not have sufficient time for the
production of the changes that are alleged to have
taken place."

Cuvier thus emphatically rejects all idea that any
of the tertiary mammals could have been the ancestral
forms of those now existing.

" From all these well-established facts, there does
not seem to be the smallest foundation for supposing
that the new genera which I have discovered or established among extraneous fossils, such as the *palæotherium, anaplotherium, megalonynx, mastodon, ptero-
dactylis,* etc., have ever been the sources of any of
our present animals, which only differ as far as they
are influenced by time or climate. Even if it should
prove true, which I am far from believing to be the
case, that the fossil elephants, rhinoceroses, elks, and
bears do not differ further from the present existing
species of the same genera than the present races of
dogs differ among themselves, this would by no
means be a sufficient reason to conclude that they

were of the same species; since the races or varieties of dogs have been influenced by the trammels of domestication, which these other animals never did and indeed never could experience." *

The extreme views of Cuvier as to the frequent renewal and extinction of life were afterward (in 1850) carried out to an exaggerated extent by D'Orbigny, who maintained that the life of the earth must have become extinct and again renewed twenty-seven times. Similar views were held by Agassiz, who, however, maintained the geological succession of animals and the parallelism between their embryonic development and geological succession, the two foundation stones of the biogenetic law of Haeckel. But immediately after the publication of Cuvier's *Ossemens fossiles*, as early as 1813, Von Schlotheim, the founder of vegetable palæontology, refused to admit that each set of beds was the result of such a thoroughgoing revolution.†

At a later date Bronn " demonstrated that certain species indeed really passed from one formation to

---

* *Discours*, etc.   Sixth edition.

† Felix Bernard, *The Principles of Paleontology*, Paris, 1895, translated by C. E. Brooks, edited by J. M. Clark, from 14th Annual Report New York State Geologist, 1895, pp. 127–217 (p. 16).   Bernard gives no reference to the work in which Schlotheim expressed this opinion.   E. v. Schlotheim's first work, *Flora der Vorwelt*, appeared in 1804, entitled *Beschreibung merkwürdiger Kraüterabdrücke und Pflanzenversteinerungen. Ein Beytrag zur Flora der Vorvelt*.   1 Abtheil.   Mit 14 Kpfrn.   4°.   Gotha, 1804.   A later work was *Beyträge zur Naturgeschichte der Versteinerungen in geognostischer Hinsicht (Denkschrift d. k. Academie d. Wissenschaften zu München für den Jahren 1816 und 1817.   8 Taf.   München, 1819).   He was followed in Germany by Sternberg (*Versuch einer geognostischbotanischen Darstellung der Flora der Vorvelt*.   1–8.   1811.   Leipzig, 1820–38) ; and in France by A. T. Brongniart, 1801–1876 (*Histoire des Végétaux fossiles*, 1828).   These were the pioneers in palæophytology.

another, and though stratigraphic boundaries are
often barriers confining the persistence of some form,
still this is not an absolute rule, since the species in
nowise appear in their entirety." *   At present the
persistence of genera like Saccamina, Lingula, Cera-
todus, etc., from one age to another, or even through
two or more geological ages, is well known, while
Atrypa reticulatus, a species of world-wide distribution, lived from near the beginning of the Upper
Silurian to the Waverly or beginning of the Carboniferous age.

Such were the views of the distinguished founder
of vertebrate palæontology. When we compare the
Hydrogéologie of Lamarck with Cuvier's *Discours*, we
see, though some erroneous views, some very fantastic conceptions are held, in common with others of
his time, in regard to changes of level of the land
and the origin of the crystalline rocks, that it did
contain the principles upon which modern palæontology is founded, while those of Cuvier are now in
the limbo—so densely populated—of exploded, ill-
founded theories.

Our claim that Lamarck should share with Cuvier
the honor of being a founder of palæontology † is

---

* Bernard's *History and Methods of Paleontological Discovery*
(1879), p. 23.

† In his valuable and comprehensive *Geschichte der Geologie und
Paläontologie* (1899), Prof. K. von Zittel, while referring to Lamarck's
works on the tertiary shells of Paris and his *Animaux sans Vertèbres*,
also giving a just and full account of his life, practically gives him the
credit of being one of the founders of invertebrate palæontology. He
speaks of him as " the reformer and founder of scientific conchology,"
and states that " he defined with wonderful acuteness the numerous
genera and species of invertebrate animals, and created thereby for
the ten years following an authoritative foundation." Zittel, how-

substantiated by the philosophic Lyell, who as early as 1836, in his *Principles of Geology*, expresses the same view in the following words: "The labors of Cuvier in comparative osteology, and of Lamarck in recent and fossil shells, had raised these departments of study to a rank of which they had never previously been deemed susceptible."

Our distinguished American palæontologist, the late O. C. Marsh, takes the same view, and draws the following parallel between the two great French naturalists:

"In looking back from this point of view, the philosophical breadth of Lamarck's conclusions, in comparison with those of Cuvier, is clearly evident. The invertebrates on which Lamarck worked offered less striking evidence of change than the various animals investigated by Cuvier; yet they led Lamarck directly to evolution, while Cuvier ignored what was before him on this point, and rejected the proof offered by others. Both pursued the same methods, and had an abundance of material on which to work, yet the facts observed induced Cuvier to believe in catastrophes, and Lamarck in the uniform course of nature. Cuvier declared species to be permanent; Lamarck, that they were descended from others. Both men stand in the first rank in science; but Lamarck was the prophetic genius, half a century in advance of his time.*

---

ever, does not mention the *Hydrogéologie.* Probably so rare a book was overlooked by the eminent German palæontologist.

* *History and Methods of Paleontological Discovery* (1879), p. 23.

CHAPTER X

LAMARCK'S OPINIONS ON GENERAL PHYSIOLOGY AND BIOLOGY

LAMARCK died before the rise of the sciences of morphology, embryology, and cytology. As to palæontology, which he aided in founding, he had but the slightest idea of the geological succession of life-forms, and not an inkling of the biogenetic law or recapitulation theory. Little did he know or foresee that the main and strongest support of his own theory was to be this same science of the extinct forms of life. Yet it is a matter of interest to know what were his views or opinions on the nature of life; whether he made any suggestions bearing on the doctrine of the unity of nature; whether he was a vitalist or not; and whether he was a follower of Haller and of Bonnet,* as was Cuvier, or pronounced in favor of epigenesis.

---

* Charles Bonnet (1720–1793), a Swiss naturalist, is famous for his work on Aphides and their parthenogenetic generation, on the mode of reproduction in the Polyzoa, and on the respiration of insects. After the age of thirty-four, when his eyesight became impaired, he began his premature speculations, which did not add to his reputation. Judging, however, by an extract from his writings by D'Archiac (*Introduction à l'Étude de la Paléontologie stratigraphique*, ii., p. 49), he had sound ideas on the theory of descent, claiming that "la diversité et la multitude des conjunctions, peut-être même la diversité des climats et des nourritures, ont donné naissance à de nouvelles espèces ou à des individus intermédiaires" (*Œuvres d'Hist. nat. et de Philosophie*, in-8vo, p. 230, 1779).

We know that he was a firm believer in spontaneous generation, and that he conceived that it took place not only in the origination of his primeval germs or *ébauches*, but at all later periods down to the present day.

Yet Lamarck accepted Harvey's doctrine, published in 1651, that all living beings arose from germs or eggs.*

He must have known of Spallanzani's experiments, published in 1776, even if he had not read the writings of Treviranus (1802–1805), both of whom had experimentally disproved the theory of the spontaneous generation of animalcules in putrid infusions, showing that the lowest organisms develop only from germs.

The eighteenth century, though one of great intellectual activity, was, however, as regards cosmology, geology, general physiology or biology, a period of groping in the dim twilight, when the whole truth or even a part of it was beyond the reach of the greatest geniuses, and they could only seize on half-truths. Lamarck, both a practical botanist, systematic zoölogist, and synthetic philosopher, had done his best work before the rise of the experimental and inductive methods, when direct observation and experiments had begun to take the place of vague *à priori* thinking and reasoning, so that he labored under a disadvantage due largely to the age in which he lived.

---

* See his remark : " *On a dit avec raison que tout ce qui a vie provient d'un œuf* " (*Mémoires de Physique*, etc., 1797, p. 272). He appears, however, to have made the simplest organisms exceptions to this doctrine.

Only the closing years of the century witnessed the rise of the experimental methods in physics and chemistry, owing to the brilliant work of Priestley and of Lavoisier. The foundations of general physiology had been laid by Haller,[*] those of embryology to a partial extent by Wolff,[†] Von Baer's work not appearing until 1829, the year in which Lamarck died.

Spontaneous Generation.—Lamarck's views on spontaneous generation are stated in his *Recherches sur l'Organisation des Corps vivans* (1802). He begins by referring to his statement in a previous work[‡] that life may be suspended for a time and then go on again.

" Here I would remark it (life) can be produced (*préparée*) both by an organic act and by nature herself, without any act of this kind, in such a way that certain bodies without possessing life can be prepared to receive it, by an impression *which indicates in these bodies the first traces of organization.*"

We will not enter upon an exposition of his views on the nature of sexual generation and of fecundation, the character of his *vapeur subtile* (*aura vitalis*) which he supposes to take an active part in the act of fertilization, because the notion is quite as objectionable as that of the vital force which he rejects. He goes on to say, however, that we cannot penetrate farther into the wonderful mystery of fecundation, but the opinions he expresses lead to the view that " nature

---

[*] *Elementa physiologiae corporis humani*, iv.   Lausanne, 1762.
[†] *Theoria generationis*, 1774.
[‡] *Mémoires de Physique* (1797), p. 250.

herself imitates her procedures in fecundation in another state of things, without having need of the union or of the products of any preëxistent organization."

He proceeds to observe that in the places where his *aura vitalis*, or subtle fluid, is very abundant, as in hot climates or in heated periods, and especially in humid places, life seems to originate and to multiply itself everywhere and with a singular rapidity.

" In this high temperature the higher animals and mankind develop and mature more rapidly, and diseases run their courses more swiftly; while on the other hand these conditions are more favorable to the simpler forms of life, for the reason that in them the orgasm and irritability are entirely dependent on external influences, and all plants are in the same case, because heat, moisture, and light complete the conditions necessary to their existence.

" Because heat is so advantageous to the simplest animals, let us examine whether there is not occasion for believing that it can itself form, with the concourse of favorable circumstances, the first germs of animal life.

" *Nature necessarily forms generations, spontaneous or direct, at the extremity of each organic kingdom or where the simplest organic bodies occur.*"

This proposition, he allows, is so far removed from the view generally held, that it will be for a long time, and perhaps always, regarded as one of the errors of the human mind.

" I do not," he adds, " ask any one to accord it the least confidence on my word alone. But as surely it will happen, sooner or later, that men on the one hand independent of prejudices even the most wide-spread, and on the other profound observers of nature, may have a glimpse of this truth, I am very content that we should know that it is of the number of those views which, in spite of the prejudices of my age, I have thought it well to accept."

"Why," he asks, "should not heat and electricity act on certain matters under favorable conditions and circumstances?" He quotes Lavoisier as saying (*Chémie*, i., p. 202) "that God in creating light had spread over the world the principle of organization of feeling and of thought"; and Lamarck suggests that heat, "this mother of generation, this material soul of organized bodies," may be the chief one of the means which nature directly employs to produce in the appropriate kind of matter an act of arrange-ment of parts, of a primitive germ of organization, and consequently of vitalization analogous to sexual fecundation.

"Not only the direct formation of the simplest living beings could have taken place, as I shall at-tempt to demonstrate, but the following considera-tions prove that it is necessary that such germ-forma-tions should be effected and be repeated under favorable conditions, without which the state of things which we observe could neither exist nor subsist."

His argument is that in the lower polyps (the Protozoa) there is no sexual reproduction, no eggs. But they perish (as he strangely thought, without apparently attempting to verify his belief) in the winter. How, he asks, can they reappear? Is it not

more likely that these simple organisms are themselves regenerated? After much verbiage and repetition, he concludes:

"We may conceive that the simplest organisms
can arise from a minute mass of substances which
possess the following conditions—namely, which will
have solid parts in a state nearest the fluid conditions,
consequently having the greatest suppleness and
only sufficient consistence to be susceptible of constituting the parts contained in it. Such is the
condition of the most gelatinous organized bodies.

"Through such a mass of substances the subtile and
expansive fluids spread, and, always in motion in the
milieu environing it, unceasingly penetrate it and
likewise dissipate it, arranging while traversing this
mass the internal disposition of its parts, and rendering it suitable to continually absorb and to exhale
the other environing fluids which are able to penetrate
into its interior, and which are susceptible of being
contained.

"These other fluids, which are water charged with
dissolved (*dissous*) gas, or with other tenuous substances, the atmospheric air, which contains water,
etc., I call containable fluids, to distinguish them from
subtile fluids, such as caloric, electricity, etc., which
no known bodies are believed to contain.

"The containable fluids absorbed by the small
gelatinous mass in question remain almost motionless
in its different parts, because the non-containable
subtile fluids which always penetrate there do not
permit it.

"In this way the uncontainable fluids at first mark
out the first traces of the simplest organization, and
consequently the containable fluids by their movements and their other influences develop it, and
with time and all the favorable circumstances complete it."

11

This is certainly a sufficiently vague and unsatisfactory theory of spontaneous generation. This sort of guess-work and hypothetical reasoning is not entirely confined to Lamarck's time. Have we not, even a century later, examples among some of our biologists, and very eminent ones, of whole volumes of *à priori* theorizing and reasoning, with scarcely a single new fact to serve as a foundation? And yet this is an age of laboratories, of experimentations and of trained observers. The best of us indulge in far-fetched hypotheses, such as pangenesis, panmixia, the existence of determinants, and if this be so should we not excuse Lamarck, who gave so many years to close observation in systematic botany and zoölogy, for his flights into the empyrean of subtle fluids, containable and uncontainable, and for his invocation of an *aura vitalis*, at a time when the world of demonstrated facts in modern biology was undiscovered and its existence unsuspected?

The Preëxistence of Germs and the Encasement Theory.—Lamarck did not believe in Bonnet's idea of the "preëxistence of germs." He asks whether there is any foundation for the notion that germs "successively develop in generations, *i.e.* in the multiplication of individuals for the preservation of species," and says:

"I am not inclined to believe it if this preëxistence is taken in a general sense; but in limiting it to individuals in which the unfertilized embryos or germs are formed before generation, I then believe that it has some foundation.—They say with good reason," he adds, "that every living being originates from

an egg. . . . But the eggs being the envelope
of every kind of germ, they preëxist in the individuals which produce them, before fertilization has
vivified them. The seeds of plants (which are vegetable eggs) actually exist in the ovaries of flowers
before the fertilization of these ovaries." *

From whom did he get this idea that seeds or eggs
are envelopes of all sorts of germs? It is not the
" evolution " of a single germ, as, for example, an
excessively minute but complete chick in the hen's
egg, in the sense held by Bonnet. Who it was he
does not mention. He evidently, however, had the
Swiss biologist in mind, who held that all living things
proceed from preëxisting germs.†

Whatever may have been his views as to the germs
in the egg before fertilization, we take it that he believed in the epigenetic development of the plant or
animal after the seed or egg was once fertilized. ‡

Lamarck did not adopt the encasement theory of
Swammerdam and of Heller. We find nothing in
Lamarck's writings opposed to epigenesis. The following passage, which bears on this subject, is translated from his *Mémoires de Physique* (p. 250), where

---

* *Mémoires de Physique*, etc. (1797), p. 272.
† Huxley's " Evolution in Biology " (*Darwiniana*, p. 192), where
he quotes from Bonnet's statements, which " bear no small resemblance to what is understood by evolution at the present day."
‡ Buffon did not accept Bonnet's theory of preëxistent germs, but
he assumed the existence of "*germes accumulés*" which reproduced
parts or organs, and for the production of organisms he imagined
"*molécules organiques*." Réaumur had previously (1712) conjectured
that there were "*germes cachés et accumulés*" to account for the regeneration of the limbs of the crayfish. The ideas of Bonnet on
germs are stated in his *Mémoires sur les Salamandres* (1777-78-80)
and in his *Considérations sur les corps organisés* (1762.)

he contrasts the growth of organic bodies with that of minerals.

" The body of this living being not having been formed by *juxtaposition*, as most mineral substances, that is to say, by the external and successive apposition of particles aggregated *en masse* by attraction, but essentially formed by generation, in its principle, it has then grown by intussusception—namely, by the introduction, the transportation, and the internal apposition of molecules borne along and deposited between its parts ; whence have resulted the successive developments of parts which compose the body of this living individual, and from which afterwards also result the repairs which preserve it during a limited time."

Here, as elsewhere in his various works, Lamarck brings out the fact, for the first time stated, that all material things are either non-living or mineral, inorganic ; or living, organic.   A favorite phrase with him is living bodies, or, as we should say, organisms. He also is the first one to show that minerals increase by juxtaposition, while organisms grow by intussusception.

No one would look in his writings for an idea or suggestion of the principle of differentiation of parts or organs as we now understand it, or for the idea of the physiological division of labor ; these were reserved for the later periods of embryology and morphology.

Origin of the First Vital Function.—We will now return to the germ.   After it had begun spontaneous existence, Lamarck proceeds to say :

" Before the containable fluids absorbed by the small, jelly-like mass in question have been expelled by the new portions of the same fluids which reach there, they can then deposit certain of the contained fluids they carry along, and the movements of the contained fluids may apply these substances to the containing parts of the newly organized microscopic being. In this way originates the first of the vital functions which becomes established in the simplest organism, *i.e.*, nutrition. The environing containable fluids are, then, for the living body of very great simplicity, a veritable chyle entirely prepared by nature.

" Mutilation cannot operate without gradually increasing the consistence of the parts contained within the minute new organism and without extending its dimensions. Hence soon arose the second of the vital functions, *growth or internal development.*"

First Faculty of Animal Nature.—Then gradually as the continuity of this state of things within the same minute living mass in question increases the consistence of its parts enclosed within and extends its dimensions, a vital orgasm, at first very feeble, but becoming progressively more intense, is formed in these enclosed parts and renders them susceptible of *reaction* against the slight impression of the fluids in motion which they contain, and at the same time renders them capable of contraction and of distention. Hence the origin of *animal irritability* and the basis of feeling, which is developed wherever a nervous fluid, susceptible of locating the effects in one of several special centres, can be formed.

" Scarcely will the living corpuscle, newly animalized, have received any increase in consistence and in dimensions of the parts contained, when, as the result of the organic movement which it enjoys, it will be subjected to successive changes and losses of its substance.

"It will then be obliged to take nourishment not only to obtain any development whatever, but also to preserve its individual existence, because it is necessary that it repair its losses under penalty of its destruction.

"But as the individual in question has not yet any special organ for nutrition, it therefore absorbs by the pores of its internal surface the substance adapted for its nourishment. Thus the first mode of taking food in a living body so simple can be no other than by absorption or a sort of suction, which is accomplished by the pores of its outer surface.

"This is not all; up to the present time the animalized corpuscle we are considering is still only a primitive animalcule because it as yet has no special organ. Let us see then how nature will come to furnish it with any primitive special organ, and what will be the organ that nature will form before any others, and which in the simplest animal is the only one constantly found; this is the alimentary canal, the principal organ of digestion common to all except colpodes, vibrios, proteus (amœba), volvoces, monads, etc.

"This digestive canal is," he says—proceeding with his *à priori* morphology—"a little different from that of this day, produced by contractions of the body, which are stronger in one part of the body than in another, until a little crease is produced on the surface of the body. This furrow or crease will receive the food. Insensibly this little furrow by the habit of being filled, and by the so frequent use of its pores, will gradually increase in depth; it will soon assume the form of a pouch or of a tubular cavity with porous walls, a blind sac, or with but a single opening. Behold the primitive alimentary

canal created by nature, the simplest organ of digestion."

In like *à priori* manner he describes the creation
of the faculty of reproduction. The next organ, he
says, is that of reproduction due to the regenerative
faculty. He describes fission and budding. Finally
(p. 122) he says:

"Indeed, we perceive that if the first germs of
living bodies are all formed in one day in such great
abundance and facility under favorable circumstances,
they ought to be, nevertheless, by reason of the
antiquity of the causes which make them exist, the
most ancient organisms in nature."

In 1794 he rejected the view once held of a continuous chain of being, the *échelle des êtres* suggested
by Locke and by Leibnitz, and more fully elaborated
by Bonnet, from the inorganic to the organic worlds,
from minerals to plants, from plants to polyps (our
Infusoria), polyps to worms, and so on to the higher
animals. He, on the contrary, affirms that nature
makes leaps, that there is a wide gap between minerals
and living bodies, that everything is not gradated and
shaded into each other. One reason for this was
possibly his strange view, expressed in 1794, that all
brute bodies and inorganic matters, even granite,
were not formed at the same epoch but at different
times, and were derived from organisms.*

The mystical doctrine of a vital force was rife in

---

* *Mémoires de Physique*, etc., pp. 318, 319, 324–359. Yet the idea
of a sort of continuity between the inorganic and the organic world
is expressed by Verworn.

Lamarck's time. The chief starting point of the
doctrine was due to Haller, and, as Verworn states,
it is a doctrine which has confused all physiology down
to the middle of the present century, and even now
emerges again here and there in varied form.*

Lamarck was not a vitalist. Life, he says,† is usually
supposed to be a particular being or entity ; a sort of
principle whose nature is unknown, and which possesses
living bodies. This notion he denies as absurd, saying
that life is a very natural phenomenon, a physical fact ;
in truth a little complicated in its principles, but not in
any sense a particular or special being or entity.

He then defines life in the following words : " Life
is an order and a state of things in the parts of every
body possessing it, which permits or renders possible
in it the execution of organic movement, and which,
so long as it exists, is effectively opposed to death.
Derange this order and this state of things to the point
of preventing the execution of organic movement, or
the possibility of its reëstablishment, then you cause
death." Afterwards, in the *Philosophie zoologique*, he
modifies this definition, which reads thus : " Life, in
the parts of a body which possesses it, is an order and
a state of things which permit organic movements ;

---

* *General Physiology* (English trans., 1899, p. 17). In France
vitalism was founded by Bordeu (1722–1766), developed further by
Barthez (1734–1806) and Chaussier (1746–1828), and formulated most
distinctly by Louis Dumas (1765–1813). Later vitalists gave it a thoroughly mystical aspect, distinguishing several varieties, such as the
nisus formativus or formative effort, to explain the forms of organisms,
accounting for the fact that from the egg of a bird, a bird and no other
species always develops (*l. c.*, p. 18).

† *Recherches sur l'organisation des corps vivans* (1802), p. 70. The
same view was expressed in *Mémoires de physique* (1797), pp. 254–
257, 386.

and these movements, which constitute active life, result from the action of a stimulating cause which excites them." *

For the science of all living bodies Lamarck proposed the word " Biology," which is so convenient a term at the present day. The word first appears in the preface to the *Hydrogéologie*, published in 1802. It is worthy of note that in the same year the same word was proposed for the same science by G. R. Treviranus as the title of a work, *Biologie, der Philosophie der lebenden Natur*, published in 1802–1805 (vols. i.–vi., 1802–1822), the first volume appearing in 1802.

In the second part of the *Philosophie zoologique* he considers the physical causes of life, and in the introduction he defines nature as the *ensemble* of objects which comprise : (1) All existing physical bodies ; (2) the general and special laws which regulate the changes of condition and situation of these bodies ; (3) finally, the movement everywhere going on among them resulting in the wonderful order of things in nature.

To regard nature as eternal, and consequently as having existed from all time, is baseless and unreason-

---

* Here might be quoted for comparison other famous definitions of life :

" Life is the sum of the functions by which death is resisted." —Bichat.

" Life is the result of organization."—(?)

" Life is the principle of individuation."—Coleridge ex. Schelling.

" Life is the twofold internal movement of composition and decomposition, at once general and continuous."—De Blainville, who wisely added that there are "two fundamental and correlative conditions inseparable from the living being—an organism and a medium."

" Life is the continuous adjustment of internal relations to external relations."—Herbert Spencer.

able. He prefers to think that nature is only a result, " whence, I suppose, and am glad to admit, a first cause, in a word, a supreme power which has given existence to nature, which has made it as a whole what it is."

As to the source of life in bodies endowed with it, he considers it a problem more difficult than to determine the course of the stars in space, or the size, masses, and movements of the planets belonging to our solar system ; but, however formidable the problem, the difficulties are not insurmountable, as the phenomena are purely physical—*i.e.*, essentially resulting from acts of organization.

After defining life, in the third chapter (beginning vol. ii.) he treats of the exciting cause of organic movements. This exciting cause is foreign to the body which it vivifies, and does not perish, like the latter. " This cause resides in invisible, subtile, expansive, ever-active fluids which penetrate or are incessantly developed in the bodies which they animate." These subtile fluids we should in these days regard as the physico-chemical agents, such as heat, light, electricity.

What he says in the next two chapters as to the " orgasme " and irritability excited by the before-mentioned exciting cause may be regarded as a crude foreshadowing of the primary properties of proto-plasm, now regarded as the physical basis of life—*i.e.*, contractility, irritability, and metabolism. In Chapter VI. Lamarck discusses direct or spontaneous genera-tion in the same way as in 1802. In the following paragraph we have foreshadowed the characteristic

qualities of the primeval protoplasmic matter fitted
to receive the first traces of organization and life:

" Every mass of substance homogeneous in appearance, of a gelatinous or mucilaginous consistence,
whose parts, coherent among themselves, will be in
the state nearest fluidity, but will have only a consistence sufficient to constitute containing parts, will
be the body most fitted to receive the first traces of
organization and life."

In the third part of the *Philosophie zoologique*
Lamarck considers the physical causes of feeling—*i.e.*,
those which form the productive force of actions, and
those giving rise to intelligent acts. After describing
the nervous system and its functions, he discusses the
nervous fluid. His physiological views are based on
those of Richerand's *Physiologie*, which he at times
quotes.

Lamarck's thoughts on the nature of the nervous
fluid (*Recherches sur le fluide nerveux*) are curious
and illustrative of the gropings after the truth of his
age.

He claims that the supposed nervous fluid has
much analogy to the electric, that it is the *feu éthéré*
"animalized by the circumstances under which it
occurs." In his *Recherches sur l'organisation des
corps vivans* (1802) he states that, as the result of
changes continually undergone by the principal fluids
of an animal, there is continually set free in a state of
feu fixé a special fluid, which at the instant of its
disengagement occurs in the expansive state of the
caloric, then becomes gradually rarefied, and insensibly arrives at the state of an extremely subtile fluid

which then passes along the smallest nervous ramifications in the substance of the nerve, which is a very
good conductor for it.   On its side the brain sends
back the subtile fluid in question along the nerves to
the different organs.

In the same work (1802) Lamarck defines thought
as a physical act taking place in the brain.   "This
act of thinking gives rise to different displacements
of the subtile nervous fluid and to different accumulations of this fluid in the parts of the brain where the
ideas have been traced."   There result from the flow of
the fluid on the conserved impressions of ideas, special
movements which portions of this fluid acquire with
each impression, which give rise to compounds by
their union producing new impressions on the delicate
organ which receives them, and which constitute
abstract ideas of all kinds, also the different acts of
thought.

All the acts which constitute thought are the comparisons of ideas, both simple and complex, and the
results of these comparisons are judgments.

He then discusses the influence of the nervous fluid
on the muscles, and also its influence considered as
the cause of feeling (*sentiment*). Finally he concludes
that *feu fixé*, caloric, the nervous fluid, and the
electric fluid "are only one and the same substance
occurring in different states."

CHAPTER XI

DURING the century preceding the time of Lamarck, botany had not flourished in France with the
vigor shown in other countries. Lamarck himself
frankly stated in his address to the Committee of
Public Instruction of the National Convention that
the study of plants had been for a century neglected
by Frenchmen, and that the great progress which it
had made during this time was almost entirely due to
foreigners.

" I am free to say that since the distinguished
Tournefort the French have remained to some extent inactive in this direction; they have produced
almost nothing, unless we except some fragmentary
mediocre or unimportant works. On the other hand,
Linné in Sweden, Dilwillen in England, Haller in
Switzerland, Jacquin in Austria, etc., have immortal-
ized themselves by their own works, vastly extending
the limit of our knowledge in this interesting part of
natural history."

What led young Lamarck to take up botanical
studies, his botanical rambles about Paris, and his
longer journeys in different parts of France and
in other countries, his six years of unremitting labor
on his *Flore Française*, and the immediate fame it
brought him, culminating in his election as a mem-

ber of the French Academy, have been already recounted.

Lamarck was thirty-four when his *Flore Française* appeared. It was not preceded, as in the case of most botanical works, by any preliminary papers containing descriptions of new or unknown species, and the three stout octavo volumes appeared together at the same date.

The first volume opens with a report on the work made by MM. Duhamel and Guettard. Then follows the *Discours Préliminaire*, comprising over a hundred pages, while the main body of the work opens with the *Principes Élémentaires de Botanique*, occupying 223 pages. The work was a general elementary botany and written in French. Before this time botanists had departed from the artificial system of Linné, though it was convenient for amateurs in naming their plants. Jussieu had proposed his system of natural families, founded on a scientific basis, but naturally more difficult for the use of beginners. To obviate the matter Lamarck conceived and proposed the dichotomic method for the easy determination of species. No new species were described, and the work, written in the vernacular, was simply a guide to the indigenous plants of France, beginning with the cryptogams and ending with the flowering plants. A second edition appeared in 1780, and a third, edited and remodelled by A. P. De Candolle, and forming six volumes, appeared in 1805–1815. This was until within a comparatively few years the standard French botany.

Soon after the publication of his *Flore Française* he

projected two other works which gave him a still higher position among botanists. His *Dictionnaire de Botanique* was published in 1783–1817, forming eight volumes and five supplementary ones. The first two and part of the third volume were written by Lamarck, the remainder by other botanists, who completed it after Lamarck had abandoned botanical studies and taken up his zoölogical work. His second great undertaking was *L'Illustration des Genres* (1791–1800), with a supplement by Poiret (1823).

Cuvier speaks thus of these works:

"*L'Illustration des Genres* is a work especially fitted to enable one to acquire readily an almost complete idea of this beautiful science. The precision of the descriptions and of the definitions of Linnæus is maintained, as in the institutions of Tournefort, with figures adapted to give body to these abstractions, and to appeal both to the eye and to the mind, and not only are the flowers and fruits represented, but often the entire plant. More than two thousand genera are thus made available for study in a thousand plates in quarto, and at the same time the abridged characters of a vast number of species are given.

"The *Dictionnaire* contains more details of the history with careful descriptions, critical researches on their synonymy, and many interesting observations on their uses or on special points of their organizations. The matter is not all original in either of the works, far from it, but the choice of figures is skilfully made, the descriptions are drawn from the best authors, and there are a large number which relate to species and also some genera previously unknown."

Lamarck himself says that after the publication of his *Flore Française*, his zeal for work increasing, and after travelling by order of the government in different parts of Europe, he undertook on a vast scale a general work on botany.

"This work comprised two distinct features. In the first (*Le Dictionnaire*), which made a part of the new encyclopedia, the citizen Lamarck treats of philosophical botany, also giving the complete description of all the genera and species known. An immense work from the labor it cost, and truly original in its execution. . . . The second treatise, entitled *Illustration des Genres,* presents in the order of the sexual system the figures and the details of all the genera known in botany, and with a concise exposition of the generic characters and of the species known. This work, unique of its kind, already contains six hundred plates executed by the best artists, and will comprise nine hundred. Also for more than ten years the citizen Lamarck has employed in Paris a great number of artists. Moreover, he has kept running three separate presses for different works, all relating to natural history."

Cuvier in his *Éloge* also adds:

"It is astonishing that M. de Lamarck, who hitherto had been studying botany as an amateur, was able so rapidly to qualify himself to produce so extensive a work, in which the rarest plants were described. It is because, from the moment he undertook it, with all the enthusiasm of his nature, he collected them from the gardens and examined them in all the available herbaria; passing the days at the houses of the botanists he knew, but chiefly at the home of M. de Jussieu, in that home where for more than a century a scientific hospitality welcomed with equal kindness every one who was interested in the delightful study of botany.

When any one reached Paris with plants he might be sure that the first one who should visit him would be M. de Lamarck; this eager interest was the means of his receiving one of the most valuable presents he could have desired. The celebrated traveller Sonnerat, having returned in 1781 for the second time from the Indies, with very rich collections of natural history, imagined that every one who cultivated this science would flock to him; it was not at Pondichéry or in the Moluccas that he had conceived an idea of the vortex which too often in this capital draws the savants as well as men of the world; no one came but M. de Lamarck, and Sonnerat, in his chagrin, gave him the magnificent collection of plants which he had brought. He profited also by that of Commerson, and by those which had been accumulated by M. de Jussieu, and which were generously opened to him."

These works were evidently planned and carried out on a broad and comprehensive scale, with originality of treatment, and they were most useful and widely used. Lamarck's original special botanical papers were numerous. They were mostly descriptive of new species and genera, but some were much broader in scope and were published over a period of ten years, from 1784 to 1794, and appeared in the *Journal-d'Histoire naturelle*, which he founded, and in the *Mémoires* of the Academy of Sciences.

He discussed the shape or aspect of the plants characteristic of certain countries, while his last botanical effort was on the sensibility of plants (1798).

Although not in the front rank of botanists, compared with Linné, Jussieu, De Candolle, and others, yet during the twenty-six years of his botanical career it may safely be said that Lamarck gave an immense impetus to botany in France, and fully earned the title of "the French Linné."

Lamarck not only described a number of genera and species of plants, but he attempted a general classification, as Cleland states :

"In 1785 (*Hist. de l'Acad.*) he evinced his appreciation of the necessity of natural orders in botany by an attempt at the classification of plants, interesting though crude, and falling immeasurably short of the system which grew in the hands of his intimate friend Jussieu."—*Encycl. Brit.*, Art. LAMARCK.

A genus of tropical plants of the group *Solanaceæ* was named *Markea* by Richard, in honor of Lamarck, but changed by Persoon and Poiret to *Lamarckea*. The name *Lamarckia* of Moench and Koeler was proposed for a genus of grasses ; it is now *Chrysurus*.

Lamarck's success as a botanist led to more or less intimate relations with Buffon. But it appears that the good-will of this great naturalist and courtier for the rising botanist was not wholly disinterested. Lamarck owed the humble and poorly paid position of keeper of the herbarium to Buffon. Bourguin adds, however :

"*Mais il les dut moins à ses mérites qu'aux petits passions de la science officielle.* The illustrious Buffon, who was at the same time a very great lord at court, was jealous of Linné. He could not endure having any one compare his brilliant and eloquent word-pictures of animals with the cold and methodical descriptions of the celebrated Swedish naturalist. So he attempted to combat him in another field—botany. For this reason he encouraged and pushed Lamarck into notice, who, as the popularizer of the system of classification into natural families, seemed to him to oppose the development of the arrangement of Linné."

Lamarck's style was never a highly finished one, and his incipient essays seemed faulty to Buffon, who took so much pains to write all his works in elegant and pure French. So he begged the Abbé Haüy to review the literary form of Lamarck's works.

Here it might be said that Lamarck's is the philosophic style; often animated, clear, and pure, it at times, however, becomes prolix and tedious, owing to occasional repetition.

But after all it can easily be understood that the discipline of his botanical studies, the friendship manifested for him by Buffon, then so influential and popular, the relations Lamarck had with Jussieu, Haüy, and the zoölogists of the Jardin du Roi, were all important factors in Lamarck's success in life, a success not without terrible drawbacks, and to the full fruition of which he did not in his own life attain.

CHAPTER XII

LAMARCK THE ZOÖLOGIST

ALTHOUGH there has been and still may be a difference of opinion as to the value and permanency of Lamarck's theoretical views, there has never been any lack of appreciation of his labors as a systematic zoölogist. He was undoubtedly the greatest zoölogist of his time. Lamarck is the one dominant personage who in the domain of zoölogy filled the interval between Linné and Cuvier, and in acuteness and sound judgment he at times surpassed Cuvier. His was the master mind of the period of systematic zoölogy, which began with Linné—the period which, in the history of zoölogy, preceded that of comparative anatomy and morphology.

After Aristotle, no epoch-making zoölogist arose until Linné was born. In England Linné was preceded by Ray, but binomial nomenclature and the first genuine attempt at the classification of animals dates back to the *Systema Naturæ* of Linné, the tenth edition of which appeared in 1758.

The contemporaries of Lamarck in biological science, in the eighteenth century, were Camper (1722–89), Spallanzani (1729–99), Wolff (1733–94), Hunter (1728–93), Bichat (1771–1802), and Vicq d'Azyr (1748–94). These were all anatomists and

Ambroise Tardieu direxit.

PORTRAIT OF LAMARCK

physiologists, the last-named being the first to propose and use the term "comparative anatomy," while Bichat was the founder of histology and pathological anatomy. There was in fact no prominent systematic zoölogist in the interval between Linné and Lamarck. In France there were only two zoölogists of prominence when Lamarck assumed his duties at the Museum. These were Bruguière the conchologist and Olivier the entomologist. In Germany Hermann was the leading systematic zoölogist. We would not forget the labors of the great German anatomist and physiologist Blumenbach, who was also the founder of anthropology ; nor the German anatomists Tiedemann, Bojanus, and Carus; nor the embryologist Döllinger. But Lamarck's method and point of view were of a new order—he was much more than a mere systematist. His work in systematic zoölogy, unlike that of Linné, and especially of Cuvier, was that of a far higher grade. Lamarck, besides his rigid, analytical, thorough, and comprehensive work on the invertebrates, whereby he evolved order and system out of the chaotic mass of forms comprised in the Insects and Vermes of Linné, was animated with conceptions and theories to which his forerunners and contemporaries, Geoffroy St. Hilaire excepted, were entire strangers. His tabular view of the classes of the animal kingdom was to his mind a genealogical tree ; his idea of the animal kingdom anticipated and was akin to that of our day. He compares the animal series to a tree with its numerous branches, rather than to a single chain of being. This series, as he expressly states, began with the monad and ended with man; it began with the simple and ended with the complex, or, as we should now say, it proceeded from the generalized or undifferentiated to the specialized and differentiated. He perceived that many forms had been subjected to what he calls degeneration, or, as we say, modification, and that the progress from the simple to the complex was by no means direct. Moreover, fossil animals were, according to his views, practically extinct species, and stood in the light of being the ancestors of the members of our existing fauna. In fact, his views, notwithstanding shortcomings and errors in classification naturally due to the limited knowledge of anatomy and development of his time, have been at the end of a century entirely confirmed—a striking testimony to his profound insight, sound judgment, and philosophic breadth.

The reforms that he brought about in the classification of the invertebrate animals were direct and positive improvements, were adopted by Cuvier in his *Règne animal*, and have never been set aside. We owe to him the foundation and definition of the classes of Infusoria, Annelida, Arachnida, and Crustacea, the two latter groups being separated from the insects. He also showed the distinctness of echinoderms from polyps, thus anticipating Leuckart, who established the phylum of Cœlenterata nearly half a century later. His special work was the classification of the great group of Mollusca, which he regarded as a class. When in our boyhood days we attempted to arrange our shells, we were taught to use the Lamarckian system, that of Linné having

been discarded many years previous. The great
reforms in the classification of shells are evidenced
by the numerous manuals of conchology based on
the works of Lamarck.

We used to hear much of the Lamarckian genera
of shells, and Lamarck was the first to perceive the
necessity of breaking up into smaller categories the
few genera of Linné, which now are regarded as
families. He may be said to have had a wonderfully
good eye for genera. All his generic divisions were
at once accepted, since they were based on valid
characters.

Though not a comparative anatomist, he at once
perceived the value of a knowledge of the internal
structure of animals, and made effective use of the
discoveries of Cuvier and of his predecessors—in
fact, basing his system of classification on the
organs of respiration, circulation, and the nervous
system.

He intimated that specific characters vary most,
and that the peripheral parts of the body, as the
shell, outer protective structures, the limbs, mouth-
parts, antennæ, etc., are first affected by the causes
which produce variation, while he distinctly states
that it requires a longer time for variations to take
place in the internal organs. On the latter he relied
in defining his classes.

One is curious to know how Lamarck viewed the
question of species. This is discussed at length by
him in his general essays, which are reproduced
farther on in this biography, but his definition of
what a species is far surpasses in breadth and terse-

ness, and better satisfies the views now prevailing, than that of any other author.

His definition of a species is as follows:

" Every collection of similar individuals, perpetuated by generation in the same condition, so long as the circumstances of their situation do not change enough to produce variations in their habits, character, and form."

Lamarck's rare skill, thoroughness, and acuteness as an observer, combined with great breadth of view, were also supplemented by the advantages arising from residence in Paris, and his connection with the Museum of Natural History. Paris was in the opening years of the nineteenth century the chief centre of biological science. France having convalesced from the intestinal disorders of the Revolution, and, as the result of her foreign wars, adding to her territory and power, had begun with the strength of a young giant to send out those splendid exploring expeditions which gathered in collections in natural history from all parts of the known or accessible world, and poured them, as it were, into the laps of the professors of the Jardin des Plantes. The shelves and cases of the galleries fairly groaned with the weight of the zoölogical riches which crowded them. From the year 1800 to 1832 the French government showed the greatest activity in sending out exploring expeditions to Egypt, Africa, and the tropics.*

---

* During the same period (1803–1829) Russia sent out expeditions to the North and Northeast, accompanied by the zoölogists Tilesius, Langsdorff, Chamisso, Esschscholtz, and Brandt, all of them of Ger-

The zoölogists who explored Egypt were Geoffroy St. Hilaire and Savigny. Those who visited the East, the South Seas, the East Indian archipelago, and other regions were Bruguière, Olivier, Bory de St. Vincent, Péron, Lesueur, Quoy, Gaimard, Le Vaillant, Edoux, and Souleyet. The natural result was the enormous collections of the Jardin des Plantes, and consequently enlarged views regarding the number and distribution of species, and their relation to their environment.

In Paris, about the time of Lamarck's death, flourished also Savigny, who published his immortal works on the morphology of arthropods and of ascidians; and Straus-Durckheim, whose splendidly illustrated volumes on the anatomy of the cockchafer and of the cat will never cease to be of value ; and É. Geoffroy St. Hilaire, whose elaborate and classical works on vertebrate morphology, embryology, and comparative anatomy added so much to the prestige of French science.

We may be sure that Lamarck did his own work without help from others, and gave full credit to those who, like Defrance or Bruguière, aided or immediately preceded him. He probably was lacking in executive force, or in the art which Cuvier knew so well to practise, of enlisting young men to do the

---

man birth and education. From 1823 to 1850 England fitted up and sent out exploring expeditions commanded by Beechey, Fitzroy, Belcher, Ross, Franklin, and Stanley, the naturalists of which were Bennett, Owen, Darwin, Adams, and Huxley. From Germany, less of a maritime country, at a later date, Humboldt, Spix, Prince Wied-Nieuwied, Natterer, Perty, and others made memorable exploring expeditions and journeys.

drudgery or render material aid, and then, in some cases, neglecting to give them proper credit.

The first memoir or paper published on a zoölogical subject by Lamarck was a modest one on shells, which appeared in 1792 in the *Journal d'Histoire naturelle*, the editors of which were Lamarck, Bruguière, Olivier, Haüy, and Pelletier. This paper was a review of an excellent memoir by Bruguière, who preceded Lamarck in the work of dismemberment of the Linnæan genera. His next paper was on four new species of Helix. To this *Journal*, of which only two volumes were published, Cuvier contributed his first paper—namely, on some new species of "Cloportes" (Oniscus, a genus of terrestrial crustacea or "pill-bugs"); this was followed by his second memoir on the anatomy of the limpet, his next article being descriptions of two species of flies from his collection of insects.* Seven years later Lamarck

---

* These papers have been mercilessly criticised by Blainville in his "Cuvier et Geoffroy St. Hilaire." In the second article—*i.e.*, on the anatomy of the limpet—Cuvier, in considering the organs, follows no definite plan ; he gives a description " *tout-a-fait fantastique* " of the muscular fibres of the foot, and among other errors in this first essay on comparative anatomy he mistakes the tongue for the intromittent organ ; the salivary glands, and what is probably part of the brain, being regarded as the testes, with other "*erreurs matérielles inconcevables, même à l'époque ou elle fut rédigée.*" In his first article he mistakes a species of the myriapod genus Glomeris for the isopod genus Armadillo. In this he is corrected by the editor (possibly Lamarck himself), who remarks in a footnote that the forms to which M. Cuvier refers under the name of Armadillo are veritable species of Julus. We have verified these criticisms of Cuvier by reference to his papers in the " Journal." It is of interest to note, as Blainville does, that Cuvier at this period admits that there is a passage from the Isopoda to the armadilloes and Julus. Cuvier, then twenty-three years old, wrote : " *Nous sommes donc descendus par degrès, des Écrevisses aux Squilles, de celles-ci aux Aselles, puis aux Cloportes, aux Armadilles et aux Iules* " (*Journal d'Hist. nat.*, tom. ii., p. 29,

gave some account of the genera of cuttlefishes. His first general memoir was a prodromus of a new classification of shells (1799).

Meanwhile Lamarck's knowledge of shells and corals was utilized by Cuvier in his *Tableau élémentaire*, published in 1798, who acknowledges in the preface that in the exposition of the genera of shells he has been powerfully seconded, while he indicated to him (Cuvier) a part of the subgenera of corals and alcyonarians, and adds, " I have received great aid from the examination of his collection." Also he acknowledges that he had been greatly aided (*puissamment secondé*) by Lamarck, who had even indicated the most of the subdivisions established in his *Tableau élémentaire* for the insects (Blainville, *l. c.*, p. 129), and he also accepted his genera of cuttlefishes.

After this Lamarck judiciously refrained from publishing descriptions of new species, and other fragmentary labors, and for some ten years from the date of publication of his first zoölogical article reserved his strength and elaborated his first general zoölogical work, a thick octavo volume of 452 pages, entitled *Système des Animaux sans Vertèbres*, which appeared in 1801.

Linné had divided all the animals below the vertebrates into two classes only, the Insecta and Vermes, the insects comprising the present classes of insects, Myriapoda, Arachnida, and Crustacea; the Vermes embracing all the other invertebrate animals, from the molluscs to the monads.

1792). These errors, as regards the limpet, were afterwards corrected by Cuvier (though he does not refer to his original papers) in his *Mémoires pour servir à l'Histoire et à l'Anatomie des Mollusques* (1817).

Lamarck perceived the need of reform, of bringing order out of the chaotic mass of animal forms, and he says (p. 33) that he has been continually occupied since his attachment to the museum with this reform.

He relies for his characters, the fundamental ones, on the organs of respiration, circulation, and on the form of the nervous system. The reasons he gives for his classification are sound and philosophical, and presented with the ease and aplomb of a master of taxonomy.

He divided the invertebrates, which Cuvier had called animals with white blood, into the seven following classes.

We place in a parallel column the classification of Cuvier in 1798.

Classification of Lamarck.	*Classification of Cuvier.*
1. Mollusca.	I. *Mollusca.*
2. Crustacea.	II. *Insectes et Vers.*
3. Arachnides (comprising the Myriapoda).	1. Insectes.
	2. Vers.
4. Insectes.	III. *Zoophytes.*
5. Vers.	1. Echinodermes.
6. Radiaires.	2. Meduses, Animaux infusorines, Rotifer, Vibrio, Volvox.
7. Polypes.	3. Zoophytes proprement dits.

Of these, four were for the first time defined, and the others restricted. It will be noticed that he separates the Radiata (*Radiaires*) from the Polypes. His

"Radiaires" included the Echinoderms (the *Vers echinoderms* of Bruguière) and the Medusæ (his *Radiaires molasses*"), the latter forming the Discophora and Siphonophora of present zoölogists. This is an anticipation of the division by Leuckart in 1839 of the Radiata of Cuvier into Cœlenterata and Echinodermata.

The "Polypes" of Lamarck included not only the forms now known as such, but also the Rotifera and Protozoa, though, as we shall see, he afterwards in his course of 1807 eliminated from this heterogeneous assemblage the Infusoria.

Comparing this classification with that of Cuvier *
published in 1798, we find that in the most important respects, *i.e.*, the foundation of the classes of Crustacea, Arachnida, and Radiata, there is a great advance over Cuvier's system. In Cuvier's work the molluscs are separated from the worms, and they are divided into three groups, Cephalopodes, Gasteropodes, and Acephales—an arrangement which still holds, that of Lamarck into Mollusques céphalés and Mollusques acéphalés being much less natural. With the elimination of the Mollusca, Cuvier allowed the Vers or Vermes of Linné to remain undisturbed, except that the Zoöphytes, the equivalent of Lamarck's Polypes, are separately treated.

He agrees with Cuvier in placing the molluscs at the head of the invertebrates, a course still pursued by some zoölogists at the present day. He states in the *Philosophie Zoologique* † that in his course of lec-

---

* *Tableau élémentaire de l'Histoire naturelle des Animaux.* Paris, An VI. (1798). 8vo, pp. 710. With 14 plates.

† Tome i., p. 123.

tures of the year 1799 he established the class of
Crustacea, and adds that " although this class is essentially distinct, it was not until six or seven years
after that some naturalists consented to adopt it."
The year following, or in his course of 1800, he separated from the insects the class of Arachnida, as " easy
and necessary to be distinguished." But in 1809 he
says that this class " is not yet admitted into any other
work than my own." * As to the class of Annelides,
he remarks: " Cuvier having discovered the existence
of arterial and venous vessels in different animals
which have been confounded under the name of
worms (*Vers*) with other animals very differently
organized, I immediately employed the consideration
of this new fact in rendering my classification more
perfect, and in my course of the year 10 (1802) I established the class of Annelides, a class which I have
placed after the molluscs and before the crustaceans,
as their known organization requires." He first established this class in his *Recherches sur les corps
vivans* (1802), but it was several years before it was
adopted by naturalists.

The next work in which Lamarck deals with the
classification of the invertebrates is his *Discours
d'ouverture du Cours des Animaux sans Vertèbres*,
published in 1806.

---

* In his *Histoire des Progrès des Sciences naturelles* Cuvier takes
to himself part of the credit of founding the class Crustàcea, stating that Aristotle had already placed them in a class by themselves,
and adding, " *MM. Cuvier et de Lamarck les en ont distingués par des
caractères de premier ordre tirés de leur circulation.*" Undoubtedly
Cuvier described the circulation, but it was Lamarck who actually
realized the taxonomic importance of this feature and placed them
in a distinct class.

On page 70 he speaks of the animal chain or series, from the monad to man; ascending from the most simple to the most complex. The monad is one of his *Polypes amorphs*, and he says that it is the most simple animal form, the most like the original germ (*ébauche*) from which living bodies have descended. From the monad nature passes to the Volvox, Proteus (Amœba), and Vibrio. From them are derived the *Polypes rotifères* and other " Radiaires," and then the Vers, Arachnides, and Crustacea. On page 77 a tabular view is presented, as follows:

1. *Les Mollusques.*
2. *Les Cirrhipèdes.*
3. *Les Annelides.*
4. *Les Crustacés.*
5. *Les Arachnides.*
6. *Les Insectes.*
7. *Les Vers.*
8. *Les Radiaires.*
9. *Les Polypes.*

It will be seen that at this date two additional classes are proposed and defined—*i.e.*, the Annelides and the Cirrhipedes, though the class of Annelida was first privately characterized in his lectures for 1802.

The elimination of the barnacles or Cirrhipedes from the molluscs was a decided step in advance, and was a proof of the acute observation and sound judgment of Lamarck. He says that this class is still very imperfectly known and its position doubtful, and adds : " The Cirrhipedes have up to the present time been placed among the molluscs, but although

certain of them closely approach them in some respects, they have a special character which compels
us to separate them. In short, in the genera best
known the feet of these animals are distinctly articulated and even crustaceous (*crustacés*)." He does not
refer to the nervous system, but this is done in his
next work. It will be remembered that Cuvier overlooked this feature of the jointed limbs, and also the
crustaceous-like nervous system of the barnacles, and
allowed them to remain among the molluscs, notwithstanding the decisive step taken by Lamarck. It was
not until many years after (1830) that Thompson
proved by their life-history that barnacles are true
crustacea.

In the *Philosophie zoologique* the ten classes of the
invertebrates are arranged in the following order:

> *Les Mollusques.*
> *Les Cirrhipèdes.*
> *Les Annelides.*
> *Les Crustacés.*
> *Les Arachnides.*
> *Les Insectes.*
> *Les Vers.*
> *Les Radiaires.*
> *Les Polypes.*
> *Les Infusoires.*

At the end of the second volume Lamarck gives
a tabular view on a page by itself (p. 463), showing his
conception of the origin of the different groups of
animals. This is the first phylogeny or genealogical
tree ever published.

TABLEAU

*Servant à montrer l'origine des differens
animaux.*

Vers.

Infusoires.
Polypes.
Radiaires.

Insectes.
Arachnides.
Crustacés.

Annelides.
Cirrhipèdes.
Mollusques.

Poissons.
Reptiles.

Oiseaux.

Monotrèmes.

M. Amphibies.

M. Cétacés.

M. Ongulés.

M. Onguiculés.

13

The next innovation made by Lamarck in the *Extrait du Cours de Zoologie*, in 1812, was not a happy one. In this work he distributed the fourteen classes of the animal kingdom into three groups, which he named *Animaux Apathiques, Sensibles*, and *Intelligens*. In this physiologico-psychological base for a classification he unwisely departed from his usual more solid foundation of anatomical structure, and the results were worthless. He, however, repeats it in his great work, *Histoire naturelle des Animaux sans Vertèbres* (1815–1822).

The sponges were by Cuvier, and also by Lamarck, accorded a position among the Polypes, near Alcyonium, which represents the latter's *Polypiers empâtés;* and it is interesting to notice that, for many years remaining among the Protozoa, meanwhile even by Agassiz regarded as vegetables, they were by Haeckel restored to a position among the Cœlenterates, though for over twenty years they have by some American zoölogists been more correctly regarded as a separate phylum.* Lamarck also separated the seals and morses from the cetacea. Adopting his idea, Cuvier referred the seals to an order of carnivora.

Another interesting matter, to which Professor Lacaze-Duthiers has called attention in his interesting letter on p. 77, is the position assigned *Lucernaria* among his *Radiaires molasses* near what are now Ctenophora and Medusæ, though one would have

---

* See A. Hyatt's *Revision of North American Poriferæ*, Part II. (Boston, 1877, p. 11); also the present writer in his *Text-book of Zoölogy* (1878).

supposed he would, from its superficial resemblance
to polyps, have placed it among the polyps. To
Lamarck we are also indebted for the establishment
in 1818 of the molluscan group of Heteropoda.

Lamarck's acuteness is also shown in the fact that,
whereas Cuvier placed them among the acephalous
molluscs, he did not regard the ascidians as molluscs
at all, but places them in a class by themselves
under the name of *Tunicata*, following the Sipunculus
worms. Yet he allowed them to remain near the
Holothurians (then including Sipunculus) in his
group of *Radiaires echinodermes*, between the latter
and the Vers. He differs from Cuvier in regarding the tunic as the homologue of the shell of Lamelli-
branches, remarking that it differs in being muscular
and contractile.

Lamarck's fame as a zoölogist rests chiefly on this
great work. It elicited the highest praise from his
contemporaries. Besides containing the innovations
made in the classification of the animal kingdom,
which he had published in previous works, it was a
summary of all which was then known of the invertebrate classes, thus forming a most convenient
hand-book, since it mentioned all the known genera
and all the known species except those of the insects,
of which only the types are mentioned. It passed
through two editions, and still is not without value
to the working systematist.

In his *Histoire des Progrès des Sciences naturelles*
Cuvier does it justice. Referring to the earlier volume,
he states that " it has extended immensely the knowledge, especially by a new distribution, of the shelled

molluscs. . . . M. de Lamarck has established with as much care as sagacity the genera of shells." Again he says, in noticing the three first volumes: "The great detail into which M. de Lamarck has entered, the new species he has described, renders his work very valuable to naturalists, and renders most desirable its prompt continuation, especially from the knowledge we have of means which this experienced professor possesses to carry to a high degree of perfection the enumeration which he will give us of the shells" (*Œuvres complètes de Buffon*, 1828, t. 31, p. 354).

"His excellences," says Cleland, speaking of Lamarck as a scientific observer, "were width of scope, fertility of ideas, and a preëminent faculty of precise description, arising not only from a singularly terse style, but from a clear insight into both the distinctive features and the resemblance of forms" (*Encyc. Britannica*, Art. LAMARCK).

The work, moreover, is remarkable for being the first one to begin with the simplest and to end with the most highly developed forms.

Lamarck's special line of study was the Mollusca. How his work is still regarded by malacologists is shown by the following letter from our leading student of molluscs, Dr. W. H. Dall:

"SMITHSONIAN INSTITUTION,
"UNITED STATES NATIONAL MUSEUM,
WASHINGTON, D. C.,
"*November* 4, 1899.

"Lamarck was one of the best naturalists of his time, when geniuses abounded. His work was the first well-marked step toward a natural system as opposed to the formalities of Linné. He owed something to Cuvier, yet he knew how to utilize the work in anatomy offered by Cuvier in making a natural classification. His failing eyesight, which obliged him latterly to trust to the eyes of others; his poverty and trials of various kinds, more than excuse the occasional slips which we find in some of the later volumes of the *Animaux sans Vertèbres.* These are rather of the character of typographical errors than faults of scheme or principle.

"The work of Lamarck is really the foundation of rational natural malacological classification; practically all that came before his time was artificial in comparison. Work that came later was in the line of expansion and elaboration of Lamarck's, without any change of principle. Only with the application of embryology and microscopical work of the most modern type has there come any essential change of method, and this is rather a new method of getting at the facts than any fundamental change in the way of using them when found. I shall await your work on Lamarck's biography with great interest.

"I remain,

"Yours sincerely,

"WILLIAM H. DALL."

CHAPTER XIII

THE EVOLUTIONARY VIEWS OF BUFFON AND OF GEOFFROY ST. HILAIRE

OF the French precursors of Lamarck there were four—Duret (1609), De Maillet (1748), Robinet (1768), and Buffon. The opinions of the first three could hardly be taken seriously, as they were crude and fantastic, though involving the idea of descent. The suggestions and hypotheses of Buffon and of Erasmus Darwin were of quite a different order, and deserve careful consideration.

George Louis Leclerc, Comte de Buffon, was born in 1707 at Montbard, Burgundy, in the same year as Linné. He died at Paris in 1788, at the age of eighty-one years. He inherited a large property from his father, who was a councillor of the parliament of Burgundy. He studied at Dijon, and travelled abroad. Buffon was rich, but, greatly to his credit, devoted all his life to the care of the Royal Garden and to writing his works, being a most prolific author. He was not an observer, not even a closet naturalist. " I have passed," he is reported to have said, " fifty years at my desk." Appointed in 1739, when he was thirty-two years old, Intendant of the Royal Garden, he divided his time between his retreat at Montbard and Paris, spending four months in Paris and the re-

Drawn by A. Deroy, 1886

MAISON DE BUFFON, IN WHICH LAMARCK LIVED, 1793–1829

mainder of the year at Montbard, away from the distractions and dissipations of the capital. It is significant that he wrote his great *Histoire naturelle* at Montbard and not at Paris, where were the collections of natural history.

His biographer, Flourens, says : " What dominates in the character of Buffon is elevation, force, the love of greatness and glory ; he loved magnificence in everything. His fine figure, his majestic air, seemed to have some relation with the greatness of his genius ; and nature had refused him none of those qualities which could attract the attention of mankind.

" Nothing is better known than the *naïveté* of his self-esteem ; he admired himself with perfect honesty, frankly, but good-naturedly."

He was once asked how many great men he could really mention ; he answered : " Five—Newton, Bacon, Leibnitz, Montesquieu, and myself." His admirable style gained him immediate reputation and glory throughout the world of letters. His famous epigram, " *Le style est l'homme même,*" is familiar to every one. That his moral courage was scarcely of a high order is proved by his little affair with the theologians of the Sorbonne. Buffon was not of the stuff of which martyrs are made.

His forte was that of a brilliant writer and most industrious compiler, a popularizer of science. He was at times a bold thinker ; but his prudence, not to say timidity, in presenting in his ironical way his thoughts on the origin of things, is annoying, for we do not always understand what Buffon did really believe about the mutability or the fixity of species, as too plain speaking in the days he wrote often led to persecution and personal hazard.*

His cosmological ideas were based on those of Burnet and Leibnitz. His geological notions were founded on the labors of Palissy, Steno, Woodward, and Whiston. He depended upon his friend Daubenton for anatomical facts, and on Gueneau de Montbéliard and the Abbé Bexon for his zoölogical data. As Flourens says, " Buffon was not exactly an observer : others observed and discovered for him. He discovered, himself, the observations of others ; he sought for ideas, others sought facts for him." How fulsome his eulogists were is seen in the case of Flourens, who capped the climax in exclaiming, " Buffon is Leibnitz with the eloquence of Plato ; " and he adds, " He did not write for savants : he wrote for all mankind." No one now reads Buffon, while the works of Réaumur, who preceded him, are nearly as valuable as ever, since they are packed with careful observations.

The experiments of Redi, of Swammerdam, and of Vallisneri, and the observations of Réaumur, had no

---

* Mr. Morley, in his *Rousseau*, gives a startling picture of the hostility of the parliament at the period (1762) when Buffon's works appeared. Not only was Rousseau hunted out of France, and his books burnt by the public executioner, but there was "hardly a single man of letters of that time who escaped arbitrary imprisonment" (p. 270) ; among others thus imprisoned was Diderot. At this time (1750–1765) Malesherbes (born 1721, guillotined 1794), one of the " best instructed and most enlightened men of the century," was Directeur de la Libraire. " The process was this : a book was submitted to him ; he named a censor for it ; on the censor's report the director gave or refused permission to print or required alterations. Even after these formalities were complied with, the book was liable to a decree of the royal council, a decree of the parliament, or else a lettre-de-cachet might send the author to the Bastille " (Morley's *Rousseau*, p. 266).

effect on Buffon, who maintained that, of the different forms of genesis, " spontaneous generation " is not only the most frequent and the most general, but the most ancient—namely, the primitive and the most universal.*

Buffon by nature was unsystematic, and he possessed little of the spirit or aim of the true investigator. He left no technical papers or memoirs, or what we would call contributions to science. In his history of animals he began with the domestic breeds, and then described those of most general, popular interest, those most known. He knew, as Male-'sherbes claimed, little about the works even of Linné and other systematists, neither grasping their principles nor apparently caring to know their methods. His single positive addition to zoölogical science was generalizations on the geographical distribution of animals. He recognized that the animals of the tropical and southern portions of the old and new worlds were entirely unlike, while those of North America and northern Eurasia were in many cases the same.

We will first bring together, as Flourens and also Butler have done, his scattered fragmentary views, or rather suggestions, on the fixity of species, and then present his thoughts on the mutability of species.

---

* *Histoire naturelle, générale et particulière.* 1st edition. Imprimerie royale. Paris : 1749–1804, 44 vols. 4to. Tome iv., p. 357. This is the best of all the editions of Buffon, says Flourens, from whose *Histoire des Travaux et des Idées de Buffon,* 1st edition (Paris, 1844), we take some of the quotations and references, which, however, we have verified. We have also quoted some passages from Buffon translated by Butler in his " Evolution, Old and New " (London, 1879).

"The species" is then "an abstract and general term." *   "There only exist individuals and *suites* of individuals, that is to say, species."† He also says that Nature "imprints on each species its unalterable characters;" that "each species has an equal right to creation;"‡ that species, even those nearest allied, "are separated by an interval over which nature cannot pass;"§ and that "each species having been independently created, the first individuals have served as a model for their descendants."‖

Buffon, however, shows the true scientific spirit in speaking of final causes.

"The pig," he says, "is not formed as an original, special, and perfect type; its type is compounded of that of many other animals. It has parts which are evidently useless, or which, at any rate, it cannot use." . . . "But we, ever on the lookout to refer all parts to a certain end—when we can see no apparent use for them, suppose them to have hidden uses, and imagine connections which are without foundation, and serve only to obscure our perception of Nature as she really is: we fail to see that we thus rob philosophy of her true character, which is to inquire into the 'how' of these things — into the manner in which Nature acts—and that we substitute for this true object a vain idea, seeking to divine the 'why'—the ends which she has proposed in acting" (tome v., p. 104, 1755, *ex* Butler).

The volumes of the *Histoire naturelle* on animals,

---

* *L. c.*, tome iv., p. 384 (1753). This is the first volume on the animals below man.
† Tome xi., p. 369 (1764).
‡ Tome xii., p. 3 (1764).
§ Tome v., p. 59 (1755).
‖ Tome xiii., p. vii. (1765).

beginning with tome iv., appeared in the years 1753 to 1767, or over a period of fourteen years. Butler, in his *Evolution, Old and New*, effectually disposes of Isidore Geoffroy St. Hilaire's statement that at the beginning of his work (tome iv., 1753) he affirms the fixity of species, while from 1761 to 1766 he declares for variability. But Butler asserts from his reading of the first edition that " from the very first chapter onward he leant strongly to mutability, even if he did not openly avow his belief in it. . . . The reader who turns to Buffon himself will find that the idea that Buffon took a less advanced position in his old age than he had taken in middle life is also without foundation " * (p. 104).

But he had more to say on the other side, that of the mutability of species, and it is these tentative views that his commentators have assumed to have been his real sentiments or belief, and for this reason place Buffon among the evolutionists, though he had little or no idea of evolution in the enlarged and thoroughgoing sense of Lamarck.

He states, however, that the presence of callosities on the legs of the camel and llama " are the unmistakable results of rubbing or friction ; so also with the callosities of baboons and the pouched monkeys, and the double soles of man's feet." † In this point he anticipates Erasmus Darwin and Lamarck. As we shall see, however, his notions were much less firmly

---

* Osborn adopts, without warrant we think, Isidore Geoffroy St. Hilaire's notion, stating that he " shows clearly that his opinions marked three periods." The writings of Isidore, the son of Étienne Geoffroy, have not the vigor, exactness, or depth of those of his father.

† Tome xiv., p. 326 (1766).

grounded than those of Erasmus Darwin, who was a close observer as well as a profound thinker.

In his chapter on the *Dégénération des Animaux*, or, as it is translated, "modification of animals," Buffon insists that the three causes are climate, food, and domestication. The examples he gives are the sheep, which having originated, as he thought, from the mufflon, shows marked changes. The ox varies under the influence of food; reared where the pasturage is rich it is twice the size of those living in a dry country. The races of the torrid zones bear a hump on their shoulders; "the zebu, the buffalo, is, in short, only a variety, only a race of our domestic ox." He attributed the camel's hump to domesticity. He refers the changes of color in the northern hare to the simple change of seasons.

He is most explicit in referring to the agency of climate, and also to time and to the uniformity of nature's processes in causing variation. Writing in 1756 he says:

" If we consider each species in the different climates which it inhabits we shall find perceptible varieties as regards size and form; they all derive an impress to a greater or less extent from the climate in which they live. These changes are only made slowly and imperceptibly. Nature's great workman is time. He marches ever with an even pace and does nothing by leaps and bounds, but by degrees, gradations, and succession he does all things; and the changes which he works—at first imperceptible—become little by little perceptible, and show themselves eventually in results about which there can be no mistake. Nevertheless, animals in a free, wild state are perhaps less subject than any other living beings, man not excepted, to alterations, changes, and variations of all kinds. Being free to choose their own food and climate, they vary less than domestic animals vary." *

The Buffonian factor of the direct influence of climate is not in general of so thoroughgoing a character as usually supposed by the commentators of Buffon. He generally applies it to the superficial changes, such as the increase or decrease in the amount of hair, or similar modifications not usually regarded as specific characters. The modifications due to the direct influence of climate may be effected, he says, within even a few generations.

Under the head of geographical distribution (in tome ix., 1761), in which subject Buffon made his most original contribution to exact biology, he claims to have been the first " even to have suspected " that not a single tropical species is common to both eastern and western continents, but that the animals common to both continents are those adapted to a temperate or cold climate. He even anticipates the subject of migration in past geological times by supposing that those forms travelled from the Old World either over some land still unknown, or "more probably " over territory which has long since been submerged.†

The mammoth "was certainly the greatest and strongest of all quadrupeds, but it has disappeared; and if so, how many smaller, feebler, and less remarkable species must have perished without leaving us any traces or even hints of their having existed? How many other species have changed their nature,

---

* Tome vi., pp. 59–60 (1756).   † Butler, *l. c.*, pp. 145–146.

that is to say, become perfected or degraded, through great changes in the distribution of land and ocean ; through the cultivation or neglect of the country which they inhabit ; through the long-continued effects of climatic changes, so that they are no longer the same animals that they once were.   Yet of all living beings after man the quadrupeds are the ones whose nature is most fixed and form most constant ; birds and fishes vary much more easily ; insects still more again than these ; and if we descend to plants, which certainly cannot be excluded from animated nature, we shall be surprised at the readiness with which species are seen to vary, and at the ease with which they change their forms and adopt new natures." *

The following passages, debarring the error of deriving all the American from the Old World forms, and the mistake in supposing that the American forms grew smaller than their ancestors in the Old World, certainly smack of the principle of isolation and segregation, and this is Buffon's most important contribution to the theory of descent.

"It is probable, then, that all the animals of the New World are derived from congeners in the Old, without any deviation from the ordinary course of nature.   We may believe that, having become separated in the lapse of ages by vast oceans and countries which they could not traverse, they have gradually been affected by, and derived impressions from, a climate which has itself been modified so as to become a new one through the operations of those same causes which dissociated the individuals of the Old and the New World from one another ; thus in the course of time they have grown smaller and changed their

---

* Tome ix., p. 127, 1761 (*ex*. Butler).

characters. This, however, should not prevent our classifying them as different species now, for the difference is no less real though it dates from the creation. *Nature, I maintain, is in a state of continual flux and movement. It is enough for man if he can grasp her as she is in his own time, and throw but a glance or two upon the past and future, so as to try and perceive what she may have been in former times and what one day she may attain to.*" *

Buffon thus suggests the principle of the struggle for existence to prevent overcrowding, resulting in the maintenance of the balance of nature :

" It may be said that the movement of Nature turns upon two immovable pivots—one, the illimitable fecundity which she has given to all species; the other, the innumerable difficulties which reduce the results of that fecundity, and leave throughout time nearly the same quantity of individuals in every species ; . . . destruction and sterility follow closely upon excessive fecundity, and, independently of the contagion which follows inevitably upon overcrowding, each species has its own special sources of death and destruction, which are of themselves sufficient to compensate for excess in any past generation." †

He also adds, " The species the least perfect, the most delicate, the most unwieldy, the least active, the most unarmed, etc., have already disappeared or will disappear." ‡

On one occasion, in writing on the dog, he anticipates Erasmus Darwin and Lamarck in ascribing to the direct cause of modification the inner feelings of

---

* Tome ix., p. 127, 1761 (*ex* Butler).
† Tome vi., p. 252, 1756 (quoted from Butler, *l. c.*, pp. 123–126).
‡ Quoted from Osborn, who takes it from De Lanessan.

the animal modified, change of condition being the indirect cause. * He, however, did not suggest the idea of the transmission of acquired characters by heredity, and does not mention the word heredity.

These are all the facts he stated; but though not an observer, Buffon was a broad thinker, and was led from these few data to generalize, as he could well do, from the breadth of his knowledge of geology gained from the works of his predecessors, from Leibnitz to Woodward and Whiston.

"After the rapid glance," he says, "at these variations, which indicate to us the special changes undergone by each species, there arises a more important consideration, and the view of which is broader; it is that of the transformation (*changement*) of the species themselves; it is that more ancient modification which has gone on from time immemorial, which seems to have been made in each family or, if we prefer, in each of the genera in which were comprised more or less allied species." †

In the beginning of his first volume he states "that we can descend by almost imperceptible degrees from the most perfect creature to the most formless matter —from the most highly organized animal to the most entirely inorganic substance. We will recognize this gradation as the great work of nature; and we will observe it not only as regards size and form, but also in respect of movements and in the successive generations of every species."

"Hence," he continues, "arises the difficulty of

---

* Butler, *l. c.*, p. 122 (from Buffon, tome v., 1755).
† Tome xiv., p. 335 (1766).

arriving at any perfect system or method in dealing either with nature as a whole or even with any single one of her subdivisions. The gradations are so subtle that we are often obliged to make arbitrary divisions. Nature knows nothing about our classifications, and does not choose to lend herself to them without reasons. We therefore see a number of intermediate species and objects which it is very hard to classify, and which of necessity derange our system, whatever it may be."*

This is all true, and was probably felt by Buffon's predecessors, but it does not imply that he thought these forms had descended from one another.

" In thus comparing," he adds, " all the animals, and placing them each in its proper genus, we shall find that the two hundred species whose history we have given may be reduced to a quite small number of families or principal sources from which it is not impossible that all the others may have issued." †

He then establishes, on the one hand, nine species which he regarded as isolated, and, on the other, fifteen principal genera, primitive sources or, as we would say, ancestral forms, from which he derived all the animals (mammals) known to him.

Hence he believed that he could derive the dog, the jackal, the wolf, and the fox from a single one of these four species; yet he remarks, *per contra*, in 1753:

" Although we cannot demonstrate that the pro-duction of a species by modification is a thing impos-

---

* Tome i., p. 13.   † Tome xiv., p. 358.

14

sible to nature, the number of contrary probabilities is so enormous that, even philosophically, we can scarcely doubt it; for if any species has been produced by the modification of another, if the species of ass has been derived from that of the horse, this could have been done only successively and by gradual steps : there would have been between the horse and ass a great number of intermediate animals, the first of which would gradually differ from the nature of the horse, and the last would gradually approach that of the ass; and why do we not see to-day the representatives, the descendants of those intermediate species? Why are only the two extremes living?" (tome iv., p. 390). " If we once admit that the ass belongs to the horse family, and that it only differs from it because it has been modified (*dégénéré*), we may likewise say that the monkey is of the same family as man, that it is a modified man, that man and the monkey have had a common origin like the horse and ass, that each family has had but a single source, and even that all the animals have come from a single animal, which in the succession of ages has produced, while perfecting and modifying itself, all the races of other animals " (tome iv., p. 382). " If it were known that in the animals there had been, I do not say several species, but a single one which had been produced by modification from another species; if it were true that the ass is only a modified horse, there would be no limit to the power of nature, and we would not be wrong in supposing that from a single being she has known how to derive, with time, all the other organized beings " (*ibid.*, p. 382).

The next sentence, however, translated, reads as follows :

" But no. It is certain from revelation that all animals have alike been favored with the grace of an act of direct creation, and that the first pair of every species issued fully formed from the hands of the Creator " (tome iv., p. 383).

In which of these views did Buffon really believe ? Yet they appear in the same volume, and not at different periods of his life.

He actually does say in the same volume (iv., p. 358): " It is not impossible that all species may be derivations (*issues*)." In the same volume also (p. 215) he remarks :

" There is in nature a general prototype in each species on which each individual is modelled, but which seems, in being realized, to change or become perfected by circumstances ; so that, relatively to certain qualities, there is a singular (*bizarre*) variation in appearance in the succession of individuals, and at the same time a constancy in the entire species which appears to be admirable."

And yet we find him saying at the same period of his life, in the previous volume, that species " are the only beings in nature, beings perpetual, as ancient, as permanent as she." *   A few pages farther on in the same volume of the same work, apparently written at the same time, he is strongly and stoutly anti-evolutional, affirming : " The imprint of each species is a type whose principal features are graven in characters forever ineffaceable and permanent."†

In this volume (iv., p. 55) he remarks that the senses, whether in man or in animals, may be greatly developed by exercise.

---

* Tome xiii., p. i.   † Tome xiii., p. ix.

The impression left on the mind, after reading Buffon, is that even if he threw out these suggestions and then retracted them, from fear of annoyance or even persecution from the bigots of his time, he did not himself always take them seriously, but rather jotted them down as passing thoughts. Certainly he did not present them in the formal, forcible, and scientific way that Erasmus Darwin did. The result is that the tentative views of Buffon, which have to be with much research extracted from the forty-four volumes of his works, would now be regarded as in a degree superficial and valueless. But they appeared thirty-four years before Lamarck's theory, and though not epoch-making, they are such as will render the name of Buffon memorable for all time.

ÉTIENNE GEOFFROY ST. HILAIRE.

Étienne Geoffroy St. Hilaire was born at Étampes, April 15, 1772. He died in Paris in 1844. He was destined for the church, but his tastes were for a scientific career. His acquaintance with the Abbé Haüy and Daubenton led him to study mineralogy. He was the means of liberating Haüy from a political prison; the Abbé, as the result of the events of August, 1792, being promptly set free at the request of the Academy of Sciences. The young Geoffroy was in his turn aided by the illustrious Haüy, who obtained for him the position of sub-guardian and demonstrator of mineralogy in the Cabinet of Natural History. At the early age of twenty-one years, as we have seen, he was elected professor of zoölogy in

É. GEOFFROY ST. HILAIRE

the museum, in charge of the department of mammals and birds. He was the means of securing for Cuvier, then of his own age, a position in the museum as professor-adjunct of comparative anatomy. For two years (1795 and 1796) the two youthful savants were inseparable, sharing the same apartments, the same table, the same amusements, the same studies, and their scientific papers were prepared in company and signed in common.

Geoffroy became a member of the great scientific commission sent to Egypt by Napoleon (1789–1802). By his boldness and presence of mind he, with Savigny and the botanist Delille, saved the treasures which at Alexandria had fallen into the hands of the English general in command. In 1808 he was charged by Napoleon with the duty of organizing public instruction in Portugal. Here again, by his address and firmness, he saved the collections and exchanges made there from the hands of the English. When thirty-six years old he was elected a member of the Institute.

In 1818 he began to discuss philosophical anatomy, the doctrine of homologies; he also studied the embryology of the mammals, and was the founder of teratology. It was he who discovered the vestigial teeth of the baleen whale and those of embryo birds, and the bearing of this on the doctrine of descent must have been obvious to him.

As early as 1795, before Lamarck had changed his views as to the stability of species, the young Geoffroy, then twenty-three years old, dared to claim that species may be only " *les diverses dégénérations d'un même type.*" These views he did not abandon, nor, on the other hand, did he actively promulgate them. It was not until thirty years later, in his memoir on the anatomy of the gavials, that he began the series of his works bearing on the question of species. In 1831 was held the famous debates between himself and Cuvier in the Academy of Sciences. But the contest was not so much on the causes of the variation of species as on the doctrine of homologies and the unity of organization in the animal kingdom.

In fact, Geoffroy did not adopt the views peculiar to his old friend Lamarck, but was rather a follower of Buffon. His views were preceded by two premises.

The species is only "*fixé sous la raison du maintien de l'état conditionnel de son milieu ambiant.*"

It is modified, it changes, if the environment (*milieu ambiant*) varies, and according to the extent (*selon la portée*) of the variations of the latter.[*]

As the result, among recent or living beings there are no essential differences as regards them—"*c'est le même cours d'événements,*" or "*la même marche d'excitation.*" [†]

On the other hand, the *monde ambiant* having undergone more or less considerable change from one geological epoch to another, the atmosphere having even varied in its chemical composition, and the conditions of respiration having been thus modified, [‡] the beings then living would differ in structure from their ancestors of ancient times, and would

---

[*] *Études progressives d'un Naturaliste*, etc., 1835, p. 107.
[†] *Ibid.*
[‡] *Sur l'Influence du Monde ambiant pour modifier les Formes animaux* (*Mémoires Acad. Sciences*, xii., 1833, pp. 63, 75).

differ from them according "to the degree of the modifying power." *   Again, he says, "The animals living to-day have been derived by a series of uninterrupted generations from the extinct animals of the antediluvian world." †   He gave as an example the crocodiles of the present day, which he believed to have descended from the fossil forms. While he admitted the possibility of one type passing into another, separated by characters of more than generic value, he always, according to his son Isidore, rejected the view which made all the living species descend "*d'une espèce antediluvienne primitive.*" ‡ It will be seen that Geoffroy St. Hilaire's views were chiefly based on palæontological evidence. He was throughout broad and philosophical, and his eloquent demonstration in his *Philosophie anatomique* of the doctrine of homologies served to prepare the way for modern morphology, and affords one of the foundation stones on which rests the theory of descent. Though temporarily vanquished in the debate with Cuvier, who was a forceful debater and represented the views then prevalent, a later generation acknowledges that he was in the right, and remembers him as one of the founders of evolution.

---

* *Recherches sur l'Organisation des Gavials* (*Mémoires du Muséum d'Histoire naturelle*, xii., p. 97 (1825).

† *Sur l'Influence du Monde ambiant*, p. 74.

‡ *Dictionnaire de la Conversation*, xxxi., p. 487, 1836 (quoted by I. Geoffroy St. Hilaire); *Histoire nat. gén. des Règnes organiques*, ii., 2e partie ; also *Résumé*, p. 30 (1859).

CHAPTER XIV

THE VIEWS OF ERASMUS DARWIN

ERASMUS DARWIN, the grandfather of Charles Darwin, was born in 1731, or twenty-four years after Buffon. He was an English country physician with a large practice, and not only interested in philosophy, mechanics, and natural science, but given to didactic rhyming, as evinced by *The Botanical Garden* and *The Loves of the Plants*, the latter of which was translated into French in 1800, and into Italian in 1805. His "shrewd and homely mind," his powers of keen observation and strong common sense were revealed in his celebrated work *Zoonomia*, which was published in two volumes in 1794, and translated into German in 1795–99. He was not a zoölogist, published no separate scientific articles, and his striking and original views on evolution, which were so far in advance of his time, appear mostly in the section on "Generation," comprising 173 pages of his *Zoonomia*,* which was mainly a medical work. The book was widely read, excited much discussion, and his views decided opposition. Samuel Butler in his *Evolution, Old and New* (1879) remarks: "Paley's *Natural Theology* is written throughout at the *Zoo-*

---

* Vol. ii., 3d edition. Our references are to this edition.

nomia, though he is careful, *moro suo*, never to mention this work by name. Paley's success was probably one of the chief causes of the neglect into which the Buffonian and Darwinian systems fell in this country." Dr. Darwin died in the same year (1802) as that in which the *Natural Theology* was published.

Krause also writes of the reception given by his contemporaries to his "physio-philosophical ideas." "They spoke of his wild and eccentric fancies, and the expression 'Darwinising' (as employed, for example, by the poet Coleridge when writing on Stillingfleet) was accepted in England nearly as the antithesis of sober biological investigation." *

The grandson of Erasmus Darwin had little appreciation of the views of him of whom, through atavic heredity, he was the intellectual and scientific child. "It is curious," he says in the 'Historical Sketch' of the *Origin of Species*—"it is curious how largely my grandfather, Dr. Erasmus Darwin, anticipated the views and erroneous grounds of opinion of Lamarck in his *Zoonomia* (vol. i., pp. 500–510), published in 1794." It seems a little strange that Charles Darwin did not devote a few lines to stating just what his ancestor's views were, for certain of them, as we shall see, are anticipations of his own.

The views of Erasmus Darwin may thus be summarily stated :

1. All animals have originated "from a single living filament" (p. 230), or, stated in other words, re-

* Krause, *The Scientific Works of Erasmus Darwin*, footnote on p. 134: "See 'Athenæum,' March, 1875, p. 423."

ferring to the warm-blooded animals alone, " one is
led to conclude that they have alike been produced
from a similar living filament " (p. 236) ; and again he
expresses the conjecture that one and the same kind
of living filament is and has been the cause of all
organic life (p. 244). It does not follow that he was
a " spermist," since he strongly argued against the
incasement or " evolution " theory of Bonnet.

2. Changes produced by differences of climate and
even seasons. Thus " the sheep of warm climates are
covered with hair instead of wool, and the hares and
partridges of the latitudes which are long buried in
snow become white during the winter months " (p.
234). Only a passing reference is made to this factor,
and the effects of domestication are but cursorily referred to. In this respect Darwin's views differed
much from Buffon's, with whom they were the primary causes in the modification of animals.

The other factors or agencies are not referred to by
Buffon, showing that Darwin was not indebted to
Buffon, but thought out the matter in his own inde-
pendent way.

3. " Fifthly, from their first rudiment or primor-
dium to the termination of their lives, all animals
undergo perpetual transformations, which are in part
produced by their own exertions in consequence of
their desires and aversions, of their pleasures and their
pains, or of irritations or of associations ; and many
of these acquired forms or propensities are transmitted
to their posterity " (p. 237). The three great objects
of desire are, he says, " lust, hunger, and security "
(p. 237).

4. Contests of the males for the possession of the females, or law of battle. Under the head of desire he dwells on the desire of the male for the exclusive possession of the female; and "these have acquired weapons to combat each other for this purpose," as the very thick, shield-like horny skin on the shoulders of the boar, and his tusks, the horns of the stag, the spurs of cocks and quails. "The final cause," he says, " of this contest among the males seems to be that the strongest and most active animal should propagate the species, which should thence become improved " (p. 238). This savors so strongly of sexual selection that we wonder very much that Charles Darwin repudiated it as " erroneous." It is not mentioned by Lamarck, nor is Dr. Darwin's statement of the exertions and desires of animals at all similar to Lamarck's, who could not have borrowed his ideas on appetency from Darwin or any other predecessor.

5. The transmission of characters acquired during the lifetime of the parent. This is suggested in the following crude way:

" Thirdly, when we enumerate the great changes produced in the species of animals before their maturity, as, for example, when the offspring reproduces the effects produced upon the parent by accident or cultivation; or the changes produced by the mixture of species, as in mules; or the changes produced probably by the exuberance of nourishment supplied to the fetus, as in monstrous births with additional limbs, many of these enormities of shape are propagated and continued as a variety, at least, if not as a new species of animal. I have seen a breed of cats with an additional claw on every foot; of poultry also with an additional claw, and with wings to their feet, and of others without rumps. Mr. Buffon mentions a breed of dogs without tails, which are common at Rome and Naples, which he supposes to have been produced by a custom, long established, of cutting their tails close off. There are many kinds of pigeons admired for their peculiarities which are more or less thus produced and propagated." *

6. The means of procuring food has, he says, " diversified the forms of all species of animals. Thus the nose of the swine has become hard for the purpose of turning up the soil in search of insects and of roots. The trunk of the elephant is an elongation of the nose for the purpose of pulling down the branches of trees for his food, and for taking up water without bending his knees. Beasts of prey have acquired strong jaws or talons. Cattle have acquired a rough tongue and a rough palate to pull off the blades of grass, as cows and sheep. Some birds have acquired harder beaks to crack nuts, as the parrot. Others have acquired beaks to break the harder seeds, as sparrows. Others for the softer kinds of flowers, or the buds of trees, as the finches. Other birds have acquired long beaks to penetrate the moister soils in search of insects or roots, as woodcocks, and others broad ones to filtrate the water of lakes and to retain aquatic insects. All which seem to have been gradually produced during many generations by the perpetual endeavors of the creature to supply the want of food, and to have been delivered to their posterity with constant improvement of them for the purpose required " (p. 238).

7. The third great want among animals is that of security, which seems to have diversified the forms of their bodies and the color of them ; these consist in

---

* *Zoonomia*, i., p. 505 (3d edition, p. 335).

the means of escaping other animals more powerful than themselves.* Hence some animals have acquired wings instead of legs, as the smaller birds, for purposes of escape. Others, great length of fin or of membrane, as the flying-fish and the bat. Others have acquired hard or armed shells, as the tortoise and the Echinus marinus (p. 239).

" The colors of insects," he says, " and many smaller animals contribute to conceal them from the dangers which prey upon them. Caterpillars which feed on leaves are generally green; earthworms the color of the earth which they inhabit; butterflies, which frequent flowers, are colored like them; small birds which frequent hedges have greenish backs like the leaves, and light-colored bellies like the sky, and are hence less visible to the hawk, who passes under them or over them. Those birds which are much amongst flowers, as the goldfinch (*Fringilla carduelis*), are furnished with vivid colors. The lark, partridge, hare, are the color of dry vegetables or earth on which they rest. And frogs vary their color with the mud of the streams which they frequent; and those which live on trees are green. Fish, which are generally suspended in water, and swallows, which are generally suspended in air, have their backs the color of the distant ground, and their bellies of the sky. In the colder climates many of these become white during the existence of the snows. Hence there is apparent design in the colors of animals, whilst those of vege-

---

* The subject of protective mimicry is more explicitly stated by Dr. Darwin in his earlier book, *The Loves of the Plants*, and, as Krause states, though Rösel von Rosenhof in his *Insekten-Belustigungen* (Nurnberg, 1746) describes the resemblance which geometric caterpillars, and also certain moths when in repose, present to dry twigs, and thus conceal themselves, " this group of phenomena seems to have been first regarded from a more general point of view by Dr. Darwin."

tables seem consequent to the other properties of the materials which possess them " (*The Loves of the Plants*, p. 38, note).

In his *Zoonomia* (§ xxxix., vi.) Darwin also speaks of the efficient cause of the various colors of the eggs of birds and of the hair and feathers of animals which are adapted to the purpose of concealment. "Thus the snake, and wild cat, and leopard are so colored as to resemble dark leaves and their light interstices " (p. 248). The eggs of hedge-birds are greenish, with dark spots ; those of crows and magpies, which are seen from beneath through wicker nests, are white, with dark spots ; and those of larks and partridges are russet or brown, like their nests or situations. He adds : " The final cause of their colors is easily understood, as they serve some purpose of the animal, but the efficient cause would seem almost beyond conjecture." Of all this subject of protective mimicry thus sketched out by the older Darwin, we find no hint or trace in any of Lamarck's writings.

8. Great length of time. He speaks of the "great length of time since the earth began to exist, perhaps millions of ages before the commencement of the history of mankind " (p. 240).

In this connection it may be observed that Dr. Darwin emphatically opposes the preformation views of Haller and Bonnet in these words :

" Many ingenious philosophers have found so great difficulty in conceiving the manner of the reproduction of animals that they have supposed all the numerous progeny to have existed in miniature in

the animal originally created, and that these infinitely minute forms are only evolved or distended
as the embryon increases in the womb. This idea,
besides being unsupported by any analogy we are
acquainted with, ascribes a greater tenuity to organized matter than we can readily admit " (p. 317); and
in another place he claims that " we cannot but be
convinced that the fetus or embryon is formed by
apposition of new parts, and not by the distention
of a primordial nest of germs included one within
another like the cups of a conjurer" (p. 235).

9. To explain instinct he suggests that the young
simply imitate the acts or example of their parents.
He says that wild birds choose spring as their building
time " from the acquired knowledge that the mild
temperature of the air is more convenient for hatch-
ing their eggs;" and further on, referring to the fact
that seed-eating animals generally produce their
young in spring, he suggests that it is " part of the
traditional knowledge which they learn from the
example of their parents." *

10. Hybridity. He refers in a cursory way to the
changes produced by the mixture of species, as in
mules.

Of these ten factors or principles, and other views
of Dr. Darwin, some are similar to those of Lamarck,
while others are directly opposed. There are therefore no good grounds for supposing that Lamarck
was indebted to Darwin for his views. Thus Erasmus
Darwin supposes that the formation of organs precedes their use. As he says, " The lungs must be

---

* *Zoonomia*, vol. i., p. 170.

previously formed before their exertions to obtain
fresh air can exist ; the throat or œsophagus must be
formed previous to the sensation or appetites of hunger
and thirst " (*Zoonomia*, p. 222). Again (*Zoonomia*, i., p.
498), " From hence I conclude that with the acquisition
of new parts, new sensations and new desires, as well as
new powers, are produced " (p. 226). Lamarck does
not carry his doctrine of use-inheritance so far as
Erasmus Darwin, who claimed, what some still maintain at the present day, that the offspring reproduces
" the effects produced upon the parent by accident
or cultivation."

The idea that all animals have descended from a
similar living filament is expressed in a more modern
and scientific way by Lamarck, who derived them
from monads.

The Erasmus Darwin way of stating that the transformations of animals are in part produced by their
own exertions in consequence of their desires and
aversions, etc., is stated in a quite different way by
Lamarck.

Finally the principle of law of battle, or the combat between the males for the possession of the
females, with the result " that the strongest and most
active animal should propagate the species," is not
hinted at by Lamarck. This view, on the contrary,
is one of the fundamental principles of the doctrine
of natural selection, and was made use of by Charles
Darwin and others. So also Erasmus anticipated
Charles Darwin in the third great want of " security,"
in seeking which the forms and colors of animals
have been modified. This is an anticipation of the

principle of protective mimicry, so much discussed in these days by Darwin, Wallace, and others, and which was not even mentioned by Lamarck. From the internal evidence of Lamarck's writings we therefore infer that he was in no way indebted to Erasmus Darwin for any hints or ideas.*

---

* Mr. Samuel Butler, in his *Evolution, Old and New*, taking it for granted that Lamarck was "a partisan of immutability till 1801," intimates that "the secret of this sudden conversion must be found in a French translation by M. Deleuze of Dr. Darwin's poem, *The Loves of the Plants*, which appeared in 1800. Lamarck—the most eminent botanist of his time—was sure to have heard of and seen this, and would probably know the translator, who would be able to give him a fair idea of the *Zoonomia*" (p. 258).

But this notion seems disproved by the fact that Lamarck delivered his famous lecture, published in 1801, during the last of April or in the first half of May, 1800. The views then presented must have been formed in his mind at least for some time—perhaps a year or more—previous, and were the result of no sudden inspiration, least of all from any information given him by Deleuze, whom he probably never met. If Lamarck had actually seen and read the *Zoonomia* he would have been manly enough to have given him credit for any novel ideas. Besides that, as we have already seen, the internal evidence shows that Lamarck's views were in some important points entirely different from those of Erasmus Darwin, and were conceptions original with the French zoölogist.

Krause in his excellent essay on the scientific works of Erasmus Darwin (1879) refers to Lamarck as "evidently a disciple of Darwin," stating that Lamarck worked out "in all directions" Erasmus Darwin's principles of "will and active efforts" (p. 212).

15

CHAPTER XV

WHEN DID LAMARCK CHANGE HIS VIEWS REGARD-
ING THE MUTABILITY OF SPECIES?

LAMARCK'S mind was essentially philosophical. He was given to inquiring into the causes and origin of things. When thirty-two years old he wrote his "Researches on the Causes of the Principal Physical Facts," though this work did not appear from the press until 1794, when he was fifty years of age. In this treatise he inquires into the origin of compounds and of minerals ; also he conceived that all the rocks as well as all chemical compounds and minerals originated from organic life. These inquiries were re-iterated in his "Memoirs on Physics and Natural History," which appeared in 1797, when he was fifty-three years old.

The atmosphere of philosophic France, as well as of England and Germany in the eighteenth century, was charged with inquiries into the origin of things material, though more especially of things immaterial. It was a period of energetic thinking. Whether Lamarck had read the works of these philosophers or not we have no means of knowing. Buffon, we know, was influenced by Leibnitz.

Did Buffon's guarded suggestions have no influence on the young Lamarck? He enjoyed his friendship and patronage in early life, frequenting his house, and was for a time the travelling companion of Buffon's son. It should seem most natural that he would have been personally influenced by his great predecessor, but we see no indubitable trace of such influence in his writings. Lamarckism is not Buffonism. It comprises in the main quite a different, more varied and comprehensive set of factors.*

Was Lamarck influenced by the biological writings of Haller, Bonnet, or by the philosophic views of Condillac, whose *Essai sur l'Origine des Connaissances humaines* appeared in 1786; or of Condorcet, whom he must personally have known, and whose *Esquisse d'un Tableau historique des Progrès de l'Esprit humain* was published in 1794?† In one case only in Lamarck's works do we find reference to these thinkers.

Was Lamarck, as the result of his botanical studies from 1768 to 1793, and being puzzled, as systematic botanists are, by the variations of the more plastic species of plants, led to deny the fixity of species?

We have been unable to find any indications of a change of views in his botanical writings, though his papers are prefaced by philosophical reflections.

It would indeed be interesting to know what led Lamarck to change his views. Without any explana-

---

* See the comparative summary of the views of the founders of evolution at the end of Chapter XVII.

† While Rousseau was living at Montmorency " his thoughts wandered confusedly round the notion of a treatise to be called ' Sensitive Morality or the Materialism of the Age,' the object of which was to examine the influence of external agencies, such as light, darkness, sound, seasons, food, noise, silence, motion, rest, on our corporeal machine, and thus, indirectly, upon the soul also."—*Rousseau*, by John Morley (p. 164).

tion as to the reason from his own pen, we are led to suppose that his studies on the invertebrates, his perception of the gradations in the animal scale from monad to man, together with his inherent propensity to inquire into the origin of things, also his studies on fossils, as well as the broadening nature of his zoölogical investigations and his meditations during the closing years of the eighteenth century, must gradually have led to a change of views.

It was said by Isidore Geoffroy St. Hilaire that Lamarck was "long a partisan of the immutability of species," * but the use of the word "partisan" appears to be quite incorrect, as he only in one instance expresses such views.

The only place where we have seen any statement of Lamarck's earlier opinions is in his *Recherches sur les Causes des principaux Faits physiques*, which was written, as the "advertisement" states, "about eighteen years" before its publication in 1794. The treatise was actually presented April 22, 1780, to the Académie des Sciences.† It will be seen by the following passages, which we translate, that, as Huxley states, this view presents a striking contrast to those to be found in the *Philosophie zoologique :*

"685. Although my sole object in this article [article premier, p. 188] has only been to treat of the

---

* Butler's *Evolution, Old and New* (p. 244), and Isidore Geoffroy St. Hilaire's *Histoire naturelle générale*, tome ii., p. 404 (1859).

† After looking in vain through both volumes of the *Recherches* for some expression of Lamarck's earlier views, I found a mention of it in Osborn's *From the Greeks to Darwin*, p. 152, and reference to Huxley's *Evolution in Biology*, 1878 ("Darwiniana," p. 210), where the paragraphs translated above are quoted in the original.

physical cause of the maintenance of life of organic beings, still I have ventured to urge at the outset that the existence of these astonishing beings by no means depends on nature ; that all which is meant by the word nature cannot give life—namely, that all the faculties of matter, added to all possible circumstances, and even to the activity pervading the universe, cannot produce a being endowed with the power of organic movement, capable of reproducing its like, and subject to death.

"686. All the individuals of this nature which exist are derived from similar individuals, which, all taken together, constitute the entire species. However, I believe that it is as impossible for man to know the physical origin of the first individual of each species as to assign also physically the cause of the existence of matter or of the whole universe. This is at least what the result of my knowledge and reflection leads me to think. If there exist any varieties produced by the action of circumstances, these varieties do not change the nature of the species (*ces variétés ne dénaturent point les espèces*) ; but doubtless we are often deceived in indicating as a species what is only a variety ; and I perceive that this error may be of consequence in reasoning on this subject" (tome ii., pp. 213–214).

It must apparently remain a matter of uncertainty whether this opinion, so decisively stated, was that of Lamarck at thirty-two years of age, and which he allowed to remain, as then stated, for eighteen years, or whether he inserted it when reading the proofs in 1794. It would seem as if it were the expression of his views when a botanist and a young man.

In his *Mémoires de Physique et d'Histoire naturelle*, which was published in 1797, there is nothing said bearing on the stability of species, and though his work is largely a repetition of the *Recherches*, the author omits the passages quoted above. Was this period of six years, between 1794 and 1800, given to a reconsideration of the subject resulting in favor of the doctrine of descent?

Huxley quotes these passages, and then in a foot-note (p. 211), after stating that Lamarck's *Recherches* was not published before 1794, and stating that at that time it presumably expressed Lamarck's mature views, adds: "It would be interesting to know what brought about the change of opinion manifested in the *Recherches sur l'Organisation des Corps vivans*, published only seven years later."

In the appendix to this book (1802) he thus refers to his change of views: "I have for a long time thought that *species* were constant in nature, and that they were constituted by the individuals which belong to each of them. I am now convinced that I was in error in this respect, and that in reality only individuals exist in nature" (p. 141).

Some clew in answer to the question as to when Lamarck changed his views is afforded by an almost casual statement by Lamarck in the addition entitled *Sur les Fossiles* to his *Système des Animaux sans Vertèbres* (1801), where, after speaking of fossils as extremely valuable monuments for the study of the revolutions the earth has passed through at different regions on its surface, and of the changes living beings have there themselves successively undergone, he adds in parenthesis: "*Dans mes leçons j'ai toujours insiste sur ces considérations.*" Are we to infer from this that these evolutionary views were expressed in his first course, or in one of the earlier courses of zoölogical lectures—*i.e.*, soon after his appointment in 1793—and if not then, at least one or two, or perhaps several, years before the year 1800? For even if the change in his views were comparatively sudden, he must have meditated upon the subject for months and even, perhaps, years, before finally committing himself to these views in print. So strong and bold a thinker as Lamarck had already shown himself in these fields of thought, and one so inflexible and unyielding in holding to an opinion once formed as he, must have arrived at such views only after long reflection. There is also every reason to suppose that Lamarck's theory of descent was conceived by himself alone, from the evidence which lay before him in the plants and animals he had so well studied for the preceding thirty years, and that his inspiration came directly from nature and not from Buffon, and least of all from the writings of Erasmus Darwin.

CHAPTER XVI

THE STEPS IN THE DEVELOPMENT OF LAMARCK'S VIEWS ON EVOLUTION BEFORE THE PUBLICATION OF HIS *PHILOSOPHIE ZOOLOGIQUE*

I. *From the Système des Animaux sans Vertèbres* (1801).

THE first occasion on which, so far as his published writings show, Lamarck expressed his evolutional views was in the opening lecture * of his course on the invertebrate animals delivered in the spring of 1800, and published in 1801 as a preface to his *Système des Animaux sans Vertèbres*, this being the first sketch or prodromus of his later great work on the invertebrate animals. In the preface of this book, referring to the opening lecture, he says: " I have glanced at some important and philosophic views that the nature and limits of this work do not permit me to develop, but which I propose to take up elsewhere with the details necessary to show on what facts they are based, and with certain explana-

---

* *Discours d'ouverture du Cours de Zoologie donné dans le Muséum national d'Histoire naturelle, le 21 floréal, an 8 de la République* (1800). Floréal is the name adopted by the National Convention for the eighth month of the year. In the years of the Republic 1 to 7 it extended from April 20 to May 19 inclusive, and in the years 8 to 13 from April 21 to May 20 (*Century Cyclopedia of Names*). The lecture, then, in which Lamarck first presented his views was delivered on some day between April 21 and May 20, 1800.

tions which would prevent any one from misunderstanding them." It may be inferred from this that he had for some time previous meditated on this theme. It will now be interesting to see what factors of evolution Lamarck employed in this first sketch of his theory.

After stating the distinctions existing between the vertebrate and invertebrate animals, and referring to the great diversity of animal forms, he goes on to say that Nature began with the most simply organized, and having formed them, "then with the aid of much time and of favorable circumstances she formed all the others."

"It appears, as I have already said, that *time* and *favorable conditions* are the two principal means which nature has employed in giving existence to all her productions. We know that for her time has no limit, and that consequently she has it always at her disposal.

"As to the circumstances of which she has had need and of which she makes use every day in order to cause her productions to vary, we can say that they are in a manner inexhaustible.

"The essential ones arise from the influence and from all the environing media (*milieux*), from the diversity of local causes (*diversité des lieux*), of habits, of movements, of action, finally of means of living, of preserving their lives, of defending themselves, of multiplying themselves, etc. Moreover, as the result of these different influences the faculties, developed and strengthened by use (*usage*), became diversified by the new habits maintained for long ages, and by slow degrees the structure, the consistence, in a word the nature, the condition of the parts and of the organs consequently participating in all these influences, became preserved and were propagated by generation.*

"The bird which necessity (*besoin*) drives to the water to find there the prey needed for its subsistence separates the toes of its feet when it wishes to strike the water † and move on its surface. The skin, which unites these toes at their base, contracts in this way the habit of extending itself. Thus in time the broad membranes which connect the toes of ducks, geese, etc., are formed in the way indicated.

"But one accustomed to live perched on trees has necessarily the end of the toes lengthened and shaped in another way. Its claws are elongated, sharpened, and are curved and bent so as to seize the branches on which it so often rests.

"Likewise we perceive that the shore bird, which does not care to swim, but which, however, is obliged (*a besoin*) to approach the water to obtain its prey, will be continually in danger of sinking in the mud, but wishing to act so that its body shall not fall into the liquid, it will contract the habit of extending and lengthening its feet. Hence it will result in the generations of these birds which continue to live in this manner, that the individuals will find themselves raised as if on stilts, on long naked feet; namely, denuded of feathers up to and often above the thighs.

"I could here pass in review all the classes, all the orders, all the genera and species of animals which exist, and make it apparent that the conformation of individuals and of their parts, their organs, their

---

* Lamarck by the word *génération* implies heredity. He nowhere uses the word *hérédité*.

† "L'oiseau que le besoin attire sur l'eau pour y trouver la proie qui le fait vivre, écarte les doigts de ses pieds lorsqu'il veut frapper l'eau et se mouvoir à sa surface" (p. 13). If the word *veut* has suggested the doctrine of appetency its meaning has been pushed too far by the critics of Lamarck.

faculties, etc., is entirely the result of circumstances to which the race of each species has been subjected by nature.

"I could prove that it is not the form either of the body or of its parts which gives rise to habits, to the mode of life of animals, but, on the contrary, it is the habits, the mode of life, and all the influential circumstances which have, with time, made up the form of the body and of the parts of animals. With the new forms new faculties have been acquired, and gradually nature has reached the state in which we actually see her" (pp. 12–15).

He then points out the gradation which exists from the most simple animal up to the most composite, since from the monad, which, so to speak, is only an animated point, up to the mammals, and from them up to man, there is evidently a shaded gradation in the structure of all the animals. So also among the plants there is a graduated series from the simplest, such as *Mucor viridescens*, up to the most complicated plant. But he hastens to say that by this regular gradation in the complication of the organization he does not mean to infer the existence of a linear series, with regular intervals between the species and genera :

"Such a series does not exist ; but I speak of a series almost regularly graduated in the principal groups (*masses*) such as the great families ; series most assuredly existing, both among animals and among plants, but which, as regards genera and especially species, form in many places lateral ramifications, whose extremities offer truly isolated points."

This is the first time in the history of biological science that we have stated in so scientific, broad, and modern form the essential principles of evolution. Lamarck insists that time without limit and favorable conditions are the two principal means or factors in the production of plants and animals. Under the head of favorable conditions he enumerates variations in climate, temperature, the action of the environment, the diversity of local causes, change of habits, movement, action, variation in means of living, of preservation of life, of means of defence, and varying modes of reproduction. As the result of the action of these different factors, the faculties of animals, developed and strengthened by use, become diversified by the new habits, so that by slow degrees the new structures and organs thus arising become preserved and transmitted by heredity.

In this address it should be noticed that nothing is said of willing and of internal feeling, which have been so much misunderstood and ridiculed, or of the direct or indirect action of the environment. He does speak of the bird as wishing to strike the water, but this, liberally interpreted, is as much a physiological impulse as a mental desire. No reference also is made to geographical isolation, a factor which he afterwards briefly mentioned.

Although Lamarck does not mention the principle of selection, he refers in the following way to competition, or at least to the checks on the too rapid multiplication of the lower invertebrates:

" So were it not for the immense consumption as food which is made in nature of animals which compose the lower orders of the animal kingdom, these animals would soon overpower and perhaps destroy,

by their enormous numbers, the more highly organized and perfect animals which compose the first
classes and the first orders of this kingdom, so great
is the difference in the means and facility of multiplying between the two.

" But nature has anticipated the dangerous effects
of this vast power of reproduction and multiplication.
She has prevented it on the one hand by considerably limiting the duration of life of these beings so
simply organized which compose the lower classes,
and especially the lowest orders of the animal kingdom. On the other hand, both by making these
animals the prey of each other, thus incessantly re-
ducing their numbers, and also by determining
through the diversity of climates the localities where
they could exist, and by the variety of seasons—*i.e.*,
by the influences of different atmospheric conditions
—the time during which they could maintain their
existence.

" By means of these wise precautions of nature
everything is well balanced and in order. Individuals
multiply, propagate, and die in different ways. No
species predominates up to the point of effecting the
extinction of another, except, perhaps, in the highest
classes, where the multiplication of the individuals is
slow and difficult ; and as the result of this state of
things we conceive that in general species are preserved " (p. 22).

Here we have in anticipation the doctrine of Mal-
thus, which, as will be remembered, so much impressed Charles Darwin, and led him in part to work
out his principle of natural selection.

The author then taking up other subjects, first
asserts that among the changes that animals and
plants unceasingly bring about by their production
and *débris*, it is not the largest and most perfect ani-

mals which have caused the most considerable changes, but rather the coral polyps, etc.* He then, after dilating on the value of the study of the invertebrate animals, proceeds to define them, and closes his lecture by describing the seven classes into which he divides this group.

II. *Recherches sur l'Organisation des Corps vivans,* 1802 *(Opening Discourse).*

The following is an abstract with translations of the most important passages relating to evolution :

That the portion of the animal kingdom treated in these lectures comprises more species than all the other groups taken together is, however, the least of those considerations which should interest my hearers.

"It is the group containing the most curious forms, the richest in marvels of every kind, the most astonishing, especially from the singular facts of organization that they present, though it is that hitherto the least considered under these grand points of view.

"How much better than learning the names and characters of all the species is it to learn of the origin, relation, and mode of existence of all the natural productions with which we are surrounded.

"*First Part : Progress in structure of living beings in proportion as circumstances favor them.*

"When we give continued attention to the examination of the organization of different living beings, to that of different systems which this organization

---

* This he already touched upon in his *Mémoires de Physique et d'Histoire naturelle* (p. 342).

presents in each organic kingdom, finally to certain changes which are seen to be undergone in certain circumstances, we are convinced:

" 1. That the nature of organic movement is not only to develop the organization but also to multiply the organs and to fulfil the functions, and that at the outset this organic movement continually tends to restrict to functions special to certain parts the functions which were at first general—*i.e.*, common to all parts of the body;

" 2. That the result of *nutrition* is not only to supply to the developing organization what the organic movement tends to form, but besides, also by a forced inequality between the matters which are assimilated and those which are dissipated by losses, this function at a certain term of the duration of life causes a progressive deterioration of the organs, so that as a necessary consequence it inevitably causes death;

" 3. That the property of the movement of the fluids in the parts which contain them is to break out passages, places of deposit, and outlets; to there create canals and consequently different organs; to cause these canals, as well as the organs, to vary on account of the diversity both of the movements and of the nature of the fluids which give rise to them; finally to enlarge, elongate, to gradually divide and solidify [the walls of] these canals and these organs by the matters which form and incessantly separate the fluids which are there in movement, and one part of which is assimilated and added to the organs, while the other is rejected and cast out;

" 4. That the state of organization in each organism has been gradually acquired by the progress of the influences of the movement of fluids, and by those changes that these fluids have there continually undergone in their nature and their condition through the habitual succession of their losses and of their renewals;

" 5. That each organization and each form acquired by this course of things and by the circumstances which there have concurred, were preserved and transmitted successively by generation [heredity] until new modifications of these organizations and of these forms have been acquired by the same means and by new circumstances;

" 6. Finally, that from the uninterrupted concurrence of these causes or from these laws of nature, together with much time and with an almost inconceivable diversity of influential circumstances, organic beings of all the orders have been successively formed.

" Considerations so extraordinary, relatively to the ideas that the vulgar have generally formed on the nature and origin of living bodies, will be naturally regarded by you as stretches of the imagination unless I hasten to lay before you some observations and facts which supply the most complete evidence.

" From the point of view of knowledge based on observation the philosophic naturalist feels convinced that it is in that which is called the lowest classes of the two organic kingdoms—*i.e.*, in those which comprise the most simply organized beings—that we can collect facts the most luminous and observations the most decisive on the *production* and the reproduction of the living beings in question; on the causes of the formation of the organs of these wonderful beings; and on those of their developments, of their diversity and their multiplicity, which increase with the concourse of generations, of times, and of influential circumstances.

" Hence we may be assured that it is only among the singular beings of these lowest classes, and especially in the lowest orders of these classes, that it is possible to find on both sides the primitive germs of life, and consequently the germs of the most impor tant faculties of animality and vegetality."

*Modification of the organization from one end
to the other of the animal chain.*

" One is forced," he says, " to recognize that the
totality of existing animals constitute a *series of
groups* forming a true chain, and that there exists
from one end to the other of this chain a gradual
modification in the structure of the animals composing it, as also a proportionate diminution in the number of faculties of these animals from the highest to
the lowest (the first germs), these being without doubt
the form with which nature began, with the aid of
much time and favorable circumstances, to form all
the others.

He then begins with the mammals and descends to
molluscs, annelids, and insects, down to the polyps,
" as it is better to proceed from the known to the
unknown ;" but farther on (p. 38) he finally remarks :

" Ascend from the most simple to the most compound, depart from the most imperfect animalcule
and ascend along the scale up to the animal richest
in structure and faculties; constantly preserve the
order of relation in the group, then you will hold the
true thread which connects all the productions of
nature ; you will have a just idea of its progress, and
you will be convinced that the most simple of its living productions have successively given existence to
all the others.

" *The series which constitutes the animal scale resides in the distribution of the groups, and not in
that of the individuals and species.*

" I have already said * that by this shaded gradua-
tion in the complication of structure I do not mean

* *Système des Animaux sans Vertèbres*, pp. 16 and 17.

16

to speak of the existence of a linear and regular series of species or even genera : such a series does not exist. But I speak of a quite regularly graduated series in the principal groups, *i.e.*, in the principal system of organizations known, which give rise to classes and to great families, series most assuredly existing both among animals and plants, although in the consideration of genera, and especially in that of species, it offers many lateral ramifications whose extremities are truly isolated points.

" However, although there has been denied, in a very modern work, the existence in the animal kingdom of a single series, natural and at the same time graduated, in the composition of the organization of beings which it comprehends, series in truth necessarily formed of groups subordinated to each other as regards structure and not of isolated species or genera, I ask where is the well-informed naturalist who would now present a different order in the arrangement of the twelve classes of the animal kingdom of which I have just given an account ?

" I have already stated what I think of this view, which has seemed sublime to some moderns, and indorsed by *Professor Hermann*."

Each distinct group or mass of forms has, he says, its peculiar system of essential organs, but each organ considered by itself does not follow as regular a course in its degradations (modifications).

" Indeed, the least important organs, or those least essential to life, are not always in relation to each other in their improvement or their degradation ; and an organ which in one species is atrophied may be very perfect in another. These irregular variations in the perfecting and in the degradation of non-essential organs are due to the fact that these organs are oftener than the others submitted to the influences of external circumstances, and give rise to a diversity of species so considerable and so singularly ordered that instead of being able to arrange them, like the groups, in a single simple linear series under the form of a regular graduated scale, these very species often form around the groups of which they are part lateral ramifications, the extremities of which offer points truly isolated.

" There is needed, in order to change each internal system of organization, a combination of more influential circumstances, and of more prolonged duration than to alter and modify the external organs.

" I have observed, however, that, when circumstances demand, nature passes from one system to another without making a leap, provided they are allies. It is, indeed, by this faculty that she has come to form them all in succession, in proceeding from the simple to the more complex.

" It is so true that she has the power, that she passes from one system to the other, not only in two different families which are allied, but she also passes from one system to the other in the same individual.

" The systems of organization which admit as organs of respiration true lungs are nearer to systems which admit gills than those which require tracheæ. Thus not only does nature pass from gills to lungs in allied classes and families, as seen in fishes and reptiles, but in the latter she passes even during the life of the same individual, which successively possesses each system. We know that the frog in the tadpole state respires by gills, while in the more perfect state of frog it respires by lungs. We never see that nature passes from a system with tracheæ to a system with lungs.

" *It is not the organs, i.e., the nature and form of the parts of the body of an animal, which give rise to the special habits and faculties, but, on the contrary, its habits, its mode of life, and the circumstances in which individuals are placed, which have, with time, brought about the form of its body, the number and condition of its organs, finally the faculties which it possesses.*

. . . .

"Time and favorable circumstances are the two principal means which nature employs to give existence to all her productions. We know that time has for her no limit, and that consequently she has it always at her disposition.

"As to the circumstances of which she has need (*besoin*) and which she employs every day to bring about variations in all that she continues to produce, we can say that they are in her in some degree inexhaustible.

"The principal ones arise from the influence of climate, from that of different temperatures, of the atmosphere, and from all environing surroundings (*milieux*); from that of the diversity of places and their situations; from that of the most ordinary habitual movements, of actions the most frequent; finally from that of the means of preservation, of the mode of life, of defence, of reproduction, etc.

"Moreover, as the result of these different influences the faculties increase and strengthen themselves by use, diversify themselves by the new habits preserved through long periods, and insensibly the conformation, the consistence—in a word, the nature and state of the parts and also of the organs—consequently participate in all these influences, are preserved and propagate themselves by generation" (*Système des Animaux sans Vertèbres*, p. 12).

. . . .

"It is easy for any one to see that the habit of exercising an organ in every living being which has not reached the term of diminution of its faculties not only makes this organ more perfect, but even makes it acquire developments and dimensions which insensibly change it, with the result that with time it renders it very different from the same organ considered in another organism which has not, or has but slightly, exercised it. It is also very easy to prove that the constant lack of exercise of an organ gradually reduces it and ends by atrophying it."

Then follow the facts regarding the mole, spalax, ant-eater, and the lack of teeth in birds, the origin of shore birds, swimming birds and perching birds, which are stated farther on.

" Thus the efforts in any direction, maintained for a long time or made habitually by certain parts of a living body, to satisfy the needs called out (*exigés*) by nature or by circumstances, develop these parts and cause them to acquire dimensions and a form which they never would have obtained if these efforts had not become an habitual action of the animals which have exercised them. Observations made on all the animals known would furnish examples of this.

" When the will determines an animal to any kind of action, the organs whose function it is to execute this action are then immediately provoked by the flowing there of subtile fluids, which become the determining cause of movements which perform the action in question. A multitude of observations support this fact, which now no one would doubt.

" It results from this that multiplied repetitions of these acts of organization strengthen, extend, develop, and even create the organs which are there needed. It is only necessary to closely observe that which is everywhere happening in this respect to firmly convince ourselves of this cause of developments and organic changes.

" However, each change acquired in an organ by habitual use sufficient to have formed (*opéré*) it is preserved by generation, if it is common to the individuals which unite in the reproduction of their kind. Finally, this change propagates itself and is then handed down (*se passe*) to all the individuals which succeed and which are submitted to the same circumstances, without their having been obliged to acquire it by the means which have really created it.

"Besides, in the unions between the sexes the intermixtures between individuals which have different qualities or forms are necessarily opposed to the constant propagation of these qualities and forms. We see that which in man, who is exposed to such different circumstances which influence individuals, prevents the qualities of accidental defects which they have happened to acquire from being preserved and propagated by heredity (*génération*).

"You can now understand how, by such means and an inexhaustible diversity of circumstances, nature, with sufficient length of time, has been able to and should produce all these results.

"If I should choose here to pass in review all the classes, orders, genera, and species of animals in existence I could make you see that the structure of individuals and their organs, faculties, etc., is solely the result of circumstances to which each species and all its races have been subjected by nature, and of habits that the individuals of this species have been obliged to contract.

"The influences of localities and of temperatures are so striking that naturalists have not hesitated to recognize the effects on the structure, the developments, and the faculties of the living bodies subject to them.

"We have long known that the animals inhabiting the torrid zone are very different from those which live in the other zones. Buffon has remarked that even in latitudes almost the same the animals of the new continent are not the same as those of the old.

"Finally the Count Lacépède, wishing to give to this well-founded fact the precision which he believed it susceptible, has traced twenty-six zoölogical divisions on the dry parts of the globe, and eighteen over the ocean; but there are many other influences than those which depend on localities and temperatures.

"Everything tends, then, to prove my assertion—namely, that it is not the form either of the body or of its parts which has given rise to habits and to the mode of life of animals, but, on the contrary, it is the habits, the mode of life, and all the other influential circumstances which have with time produced the form of the bodies and organs of animals. With new forms new faculties have been acquired, and gradually nature has arrived at the state where we actually see it.

.   .   .   .

"Finally as it is only at that extremity of the animal kingdom where occur the most simply organized animals that we meet those which may be regarded as the true germs of animality, and it is the same at the same end of the vegetable series; is it not at this end of the scale, both animal and vegetable, that nature has commenced and recommenced without ceasing the first germ of her living production? Who is there, in a word, who does not see that the process of perfection of those of these first germs which circumstances have favored will gradually and after the lapse of time give rise to all the degrees of perfection and of the composition of the organization, from which will result this multiplicity and this diversity of living beings of all orders with which the exterior surface of our globe is almost everywhere filled or covered?

"Indeed, if the manner (*usage*) of life tends to develop the organization, and even to form and multiply the organs, as the state of an animal which has just been born proves it, compared to that where it finds itself when it has reached the term where its organs

(beginning to deteriorate) cease to make new developments; if, then, each particular organ undergoes remarkable changes, according as it is exercised and
according to the manner of which I have shown you
some examples, you will understand that in carrying
you to the end of the animal chain where are found
the most simple organizations, and that in considering among these organizations those whose simplicity
is so great that they lie at the very door of the
creative power of nature, then this same nature—that
is to say, the state of things which exist—has been to
form directly the first beginnings of organization;
she has been able, consequently, by the manner of
life and the aid of circumstances which favor its duration, to progressively render perfect its work, and to
carry it to the point where we now see it.

" Time is wanting to present to you the series of
results of my researches on this interesting subject,
and to develop—

" 1. What really is life.

" 2. How nature herself creates the first traces of
organization in appropriate groups where it had not
existed.

" 3. How the organic or vital movement is excited
by it and held together with the aid of a stimulating
and active cause which she has at her disposal in
abundance in certain climates and in certain seasons
of the year.

" 4. Finally, how this organic movement, by the influence of its duration and by that of the multitude
of circumstances which modify its effects, develops,
arranges, and gradually complicates the organs of the
living body which possesses them.

" Such has been without doubt the will of the infinite wisdom which reigns throughout nature; and
such is effectively the order of things clearly indicated
by the observation of all the facts which relate to
them." (End of the opening discourse.)

Appendix (p. 141).

On Species in Living Bodies.

" I have for a long time thought that *species* were constant in nature, and that they were constituted by the individuals which belong to each of them.

" I am now convinced that I was in error in this respect, and that in reality only individuals exist in nature.

" The origin of this error, which I have shared with many naturalists who still hold it, arises from *the long duration*, in relation to us, *of the same state of things* in each place which each organism inhabits ; but this duration of the same state of things for each place has its limits, and with much time it makes changes in each point of the surface of the globe, which produces changes in every kind of circumstances for the organisms which inhabit it.

" Indeed, we may now be assured that nothing on the surface of the terrestrial globe remains in the same state. Everything, after a while, undergoes different changes, more or less prompt, according to the nature of the objects and of circumstances. Elevated areas are constantly being lowered, and the loose material carried down to the lowlands. The beds of rivers, of streams, of even the sea, are gradually removed and changed, as also the climate ; * in a word, the whole surface of the earth gradually undergoes a change in situation, form, nature, and aspect. We see on every hand what ascertained facts prove ; it is only necessary to observe and to give one's attention to be convinced of it.

" However, if, relatively to living beings, the diver-

---

* I have cited the incontestable proofs in my *Hydrogéologie*, and I have the conviction that one day all will be compelled to accept these great truths.

sity of circumstances brings about for them a diversity
of habits, a different mode of existence, and, as the
result, modifications in their organs and in the shape
of their parts, one should believe that very gradually
every living body whatever would vary in its organization and its form.

"All the modifications that each living being will
have undergone as the result of change of circumstances which have influenced its nature will doubtless be propagated by heredity (*génération*). But as
new modifications will necessarily continue to operate,
however slowly, not only will there continually be
found new species, new genera, and even new orders,
but each species will vary in some part of its structure and its form.

"I very well know that to our eyes there seems in
this respect a *stability* which we believe to be constant, although it is not so truly; for a very great
number of centuries may form a period insufficient
for the changes of which I speak to be marked enough
for us to appreciate them. Thus we say that the
flamingo (*Phœnicopterus*) has always had as long legs
and as long a neck as have those with which we are
familiar; finally, it is said that all animals whose history has been transmitted for 2,000 or 3,000 years
are always the same, and have lost or acquired nothing in the process of perfection of their organs and
in the form of their different parts. We may be assured that this appearance of *stability* of things in
nature will always be taken for reality by the average
of mankind, because in general it judges everything
only relatively to itself.

"But, I repeat, this consideration which has given
rise to the admitted error owes its source to the very
great slowness of the changes which have gone on. A
little attention given to the facts which I am about
to cite will afford the strongest proof of my assertion.

"What nature does after a great length of time we

do every day by suddenly changing, as regards a living being, the circumstances in which it and all the individuals of its species are placed.

"All botanists know that the plants which they transplant from their natal spot into gardens for cultivation there gradually undergo changes which in the end render them unrecognizable. Many plants naturally very hairy, there become glabrous or nearly so; a quantity of those which were procumbent or trailing there have erect stems; others lose their spines or their thorns; finally, the dimensions of parts undergo changes which the circumstances of their new situation infallibly produce. This is so well known that botanists prefer not to describe them, at least unless they are newly cultivated. Is not wheat (*Triticum sativum*) a plant brought by man to the state wherein we actually see it, which otherwise I could not believe? Who can now say in what place its like lives in nature?

"To these known facts I will add others still more remarkable, and which confirm the view that change of circumstances operates to change the parts of living organisms.

"When *Ranunculus aquatilis* lives in deep water, all it can do while growing is to make the end of its stalks reach the surface of the water where they flourish. Then all the leaves of the plant are finely cut or pinked.* If the same plant grows in shallower water the growth of its stalks may give them sufficient extent for the upper leaves to develop out of the water; then its lower leaves only will be divided into hair-like joints, while the upper ones will be simple, rounded, and a little lobed.† This is not all: when the seeds of the same plant fall into some ditch where there is only water or moisture sufficient to make

---

* *Ranunculus aquaticus capillaceus* (Tournef., p. 291).
† *Ranunculus aquaticus* (folio rotundo et capillaceo, Tournef., p. 291).

them germinate, the plant develops all its leaves in the air, and then none of them is divided into capillary points, which gives rise to *Ranunculus hederaceus*, which botanists regard as a species.

"Another very striking proof of the effect of a change of circumstances on a plant submitted to it is the following :

"It is observed that when a tuft of *Juncus bufonius* grows very near the edge of the water in a ditch or marsh this rush then pushes out filiform stems which lie in the water, are there deformed, becoming disturbed (*traçantes*), proliferous, and very different from that of *Juncus bufonius* which grows out of water. This plant, modified by the circumstances I have just indicated, has been regarded as a distinct species; it is the *Juncus supinus* of Rotte.*

"I could also give citations to prove that the changes of circumstances relative to organisms necessarily change the influences which they undergo on the part of all that which environs them or which acts on them, and so necessarily bring about changes in their size, their shape, their different organs.

"Then among living beings nature seems to me to offer in an absolute manner only individuals which succeed one another by generation.

"However, in order to facilitate the study and recognition of these organisms, I give the name of *species* to every collection of individuals which during a long period resemble each other so much in all their parts that these individuals only present small accidental differences which, in plants, reproduction by seeds causes to disappear.

"But, besides that at the end of a long period the totality of individuals of such a species change as the circumstances which act on them, those of these individuals which from special causes are transported

---

* *Gramen junceum*, etc. (Moris. hist. 3, sec. 8, t. 9, f. 4).

into very different situations from those where the others occur, and then constantly submitted to other influences—the former, I say, assume new forms as the result of a long habit of this other mode of existence, and then they constitute a new *species*, which comprehends all the individuals which occur in the same condition of existence. We see, then, the faithful picture of that which happened in this respect in nature, and of that which the observation of its acts can alone discover to us."

III. *Lamarck's Views on Species, as published in* 1803.

In the opening lecture * of his course at the Museum of Natural History, delivered in prairial (May 20–June 18), 1803, we have a further statement of the theoretical views of Lamarck on species and their origin. He addresses his audience as "Citoyens," France still being under the *régime* of the Republic.

The brochure containing this address is exceedingly rare, the only copy existing, as far as we know, being in the library of the Museum of Natural History in Paris. The author's name is not even given, and there is no imprint. Lamarck's name, however, is written on the outside of the cover of the copy we have translated. At the end of the otherwise blank page succeeding the last page (p. 46) is printed the words : *Esquisse d'un Philosophie zoologique*, the preliminary sketch, however, never having been added.

He begins by telling his hearers that they should not desire to burden their memories with the infinite

---

* *Discours d'ouverture d'un Cours de Zoologie, prononcé en prairial, an XI, au Muséum d'Histoire naturelle, sur la question, Qu'est-ce que l'espèce parmi les corps vivans?* (1803).

details and immense nomenclature of the prodigious quantity of animals among which we distinguish an illimitable number of species, " but what is more worthy of you, and of more educational value, you should seek to know the course of nature." " You may enter upon the study of classes, orders, genera, and even of the most interesting species, because this would be useful to you; but you should never forget that all these subdivisions, which could not, however, be well spared, are artificial, and that nature does not recognize any of them."

" In the opening lecture of my last year's course I tried to convince you that it is only in the organization of animals that we find the foundation of the natural relations between the different groups, where they diverge and where they approach each other. Finally, I tried to show you that the enormous series of animals which nature has produced presents, from that of its extremities where are placed the most perfect animals, down to that which comprises the most imperfect, or the most simple, an evident modification, though irregularly defined (*nuancé*), in the structure of the organization.

" To-day, after having recalled some of the essential considerations which form the base of this great truth; after having shown you the principal means by which nature is enabled to create (*opérer*) her innumerable productions and to vary them infinitely; finally, after having made you see that in the use she has made of her power of generating and multiplying living beings she has necessarily proceeded from the more simple to the more complex, gradually complicating the organization of these bodies, as also the composition of their substance, while also in that which she has done on non-living bodies she has occupied herself unremittingly in the destruction of all preëxistent combinations, I shall undertake to examine under your eyes the great question in natural history—What is a *species* among organized beings?

"When we consider the series of animals, beginning at the end comprising the most perfect and complicated, and passing down through all the degrees of this series to the other end, we see a very evident modification in structure and faculties. On the contrary, if we begin with the end which comprises animals the most simple in organization, the poorest in faculties and in organs—in a word, the most imperfect in all respects—we necessarily remark, as we gradually ascend in the series, a truly progressive complication in the organization of these different animals, and we see the organs and faculties of these beings successively multiplying and diversifying in a most remarkable manner.

"These facts once known present truths which are, to some extent, eternal; for nothing here is the product of our imagination or of our arbitrary principles; that which I have just explained rests neither on systems nor on any hypothesis: it is only the very simple result of the observation of nature; hence I do not fear to advance the view that all that one can imagine, from any motives whatever, to contradict these great verities will always be destroyed by the evidence of the facts with which it deals.

"To these facts it is necessary to add these very important considerations, which observation has led me to perceive, and the basis of which will always be recognized by those who pay attention to them; they are as follows:

"Firstly, the exercise of life, and consequently of organic movement, constitutes its activity, tends, without ceasing, not only to develop and to extend the organization, but it tends besides to multiply the organs and to isolate them in special centres (*foyers*).

To make sure whether the exercise of life tends to extend and develop the organization, it suffices to consider the state of the organs of any animal which has just been born, and to compare them in this condition with what they are when the animal has attained the period when its organs cease to receive any new development. Then we will see on what this organic law is based, which I have published in my *Recherches sur les Corps vivans* (p. 8), *i.e.*, that—

" ' The special property of movement of fluids in the supple parts of the living body which contain them is to open (*frayer*) there routes, places of deposit and tissues; to create there canals, and consequently different organs; to cause these canals and these organs to vary there by reason of the diversity both of the movements as well as the nature of the fluids which occur there; finally to enlarge, to elongate, to divide and to gradually strengthen (*affermir*) these canals and their organs by the matters which are formed in the fluids in motion, which incessantly separate themselves, and a part of which is assimilated and united with organs while the rest is rejected.'

" Secondly, the continual employment of an organ, especially if it is strongly exercised, strengthens this organ, develops it, increases its dimensions, enlarges and extends its faculties.

" This second law of effects of exercise of life has been understood for a long time by those observers who have paid attention to the phenomena of organization.

" Indeed, we know that all the time that an organ, or a system of organs, is rigorously exercised throughout a long time, not only its power, and the parts which form it, grow and strengthen themselves, but there are proofs that this organ, or system of organs, at that time attracts to itself the principal active forces of the life of the individual, because it becomes the cause which, under these conditions, makes the functions of other organs to be diminished in power.

"Thus not only every organ or every part of the body, whether of man or of animals, being for a long period and more vigorously exercised than the others, has acquired a power and facility of action that the same organ could not have had before, and that it has never had in individuals which have exercised less, but also we consequently remark that the excessive employment of this organ diminishes the functions of the others and proportionately enfeebles them.

"The man who habitually and vigorously exercises the organ of his intelligence develops and acquires a great facility of attention, of aptitude for thought, etc., but he has a feeble stomach and strongly limited muscular powers. He, on the contrary, who thinks little does not easily, and then only momentarily fixes his attention, while habitually giving much exercise to his muscular organs, has much vigor, possesses an excellent digestion, and is not given to the abstemiousness of the savant and man of letters.

"Moreover, when one exercises long and vigorously an organ or system of organs, the active forces of life (in my opinion, the nervous fluid) have taken such a habit of acting (*porter*) towards this organ that they have formed in the individual an inclination to continue to exercise which it is difficult for it to overcome.

"Hence it happens that the more we exercise an organ, the more we use it with facility, the more does it result that we perceive the need (*besoin*) of continuing to use it at the times when it is placed in action. So we remark that the habit of study, of application, of work, or of any other exercise of our organs or of any one of our organs, becomes with time an indispensable need to the individual, and often a passion which it does not know how to overcome.

"Thirdly, finally, the effort made by necessity to

17

obtain new faculties is aided by the concurrence of favorable circumstances; they create (*créent*) with time the new organs which are adapted (*propres*) to their faculties, and which as the result develop after long use (*qu'en suite un long emploi développe*).

" How important is this consideration, and what light it spreads .on the state of organization of the different animals now living!

" Assuredly it will not be those who have long been in the habit of observing nature, and who have followed attentively that which happens to living individuals (to animals and to plants), who will deny that a great change in the circumstances of their situation and of their means of existence forces them and their race to adopt new habits; it will not be those, I say, who attempt to contest the foundation of the consideration which I have just exposed.

" They can readily convince themselves of the solidity of that which I have already published in this respect.*

" I have felt obliged to recall to you these great considerations, a sketch of which I traced for you last year, and which I have stated for the most part in my different works, because they serve, as you have seen, as a solution of the problem which interests so many naturalists, and which concerns the determination of *species* among living bodies.

" Indeed, if in ascending in the series of animals from the most simply organized animalcule, as from the monad, which seems to be only an animated point, up to the animals the most perfect, or whose structure is the most complicated—in a word, up to animals with mammæ—you observe in the different orders which comprise this great series a gradation, shaded (*nuancé*), although irregular, in the composition of the organization and in the increasing number

---

* *Recherches sur l'Organisation des Corps vivans*, p. 9.

of faculties, is it not evident that in the case where nature would exert some active power on the existence of these organized bodies she has been able to make them exist only by beginning with the most simple, and that she has been able to form directly among the animals only that which I call the rough sketches or germs (*ébauches*) of animality—that is to say, only these animalcules, almost invisible and to some extent without consistence, that we see develop spontaneously and in an astonishing abundance in certain places and under certain circumstances, while only in contrary circumstances are they totally destroyed?

"Do we not therefore perceive that by the action of the laws of organization, which I have just now indicated, and by that of different means of multiplication which are due to them (*qui en dérivent*), nature has in favorable times, places, and climates multiplied her first germs (*ébauches*) of animality, given place to developments of their organizations, rendered gradually greater the duration of those which have originally descended from them, and increased and diversified their organs? Then always preserving the progress acquired by the reproductions of individuals and the succession of generations, and aided by much time and by a slow but constant diversity of circumstances, she has gradually brought about in this respect the state of things which we now observe.

"How grand is this consideration, and especially how remote is it from all that is generally thought on this subject! Moreover, the astonishment which its novelty and its singularity may excite in you requires that at first you should suspend your judgment in regard to it. But the observation which establishes it is now on record (*consignée*), and the facts which support it exist and are incessantly renewed; however, as they open a vast field to your studies and to your own researches, it is to you yourselves that I appeal to pronounce on this great subject when you have sufficiently examined and followed all the facts which relate to it.

"If among living bodies there are any the consideration of whose organization and of the phenomena which they produce can enlighten us as to the power of nature and its course relatively to the existence of these bodies, also as to the variations which they undergo, we certainly have to seek for them in the lowest classes of the two organic kingdoms (the animals and the plants). It is in the classes which comprise the living bodies whose organization is the least complex that we can observe and bring together facts the most luminous, observations the most decisive on the origin of these bodies, on their reproduction and their admirable diversification, finally on the formation and the development of their different organs, the whole process being aided by the concurrence of generations, of time, and of circumstances.

"It is, indeed, among living bodies the most multiplied, the most numerous in nature, the most prompt and easy to regenerate themselves, that we should seek the most instructive facts bearing on the course of nature and on the means she has employed to create her innumerable productions. In this case we perceive that, relatively to the animal kingdom, we should chiefly give our attention to the invertebrate animals, because their enormous multiplicity in nature, the singular diversity of their systems of organization and of their means of multiplication, their increasing simplification, and the extreme fugacity of those which compose the lowest orders of these animals, show us much better than the others the true course of nature, and the means which she has used and which she is still incessantly employing to give existence to all the living bodies of which we have knowledge.

"Her course and her means are without doubt the same for the production of the different plants which exist. And, indeed, though it is not believed, as some naturalists have wrongly held, but without proof, that plants are bodies more simple in organization than the most simple animals, it is a veritable error which observation plainly denies.

" Truly, vegetable substance is less surcharged with constituent principles than any animal substance whatever, or at least most of them, but the substance of a living body and the organization of these bodies are two very different things. But there is in plants, as in animals, a true gradation in organization from the plant simplest in organization and parts up to plants the most complex in structure and with the most diversified organs.

" If there is some approach, or at least some comparison to make between vegetables and animals, this can only be by opposing plants the most simply organized, like fungi and algæ, to the most imperfect animals like the polyps, and especially the amorphous polyps, which occur in the lowest order.

" At present we clearly see that in order to bring about the existence of animals of all the classes, of all the orders, and of all the genera, nature has had to begin by giving existence to those which are the most simple in organization and lacking most in organs and faculties, the frailest in constituency, the most ephemeral, the quickest and easiest to multiply ; and we shall find in the *amorphous* or *microscopic polyps* the most striking examples of this simplification of organization, and the indication that it is solely among them that occur the astonishing germs of animality.

" At present we only know the principal law of the organization, the power of the exercise of the functions of life, the influence of the movement of fluids in the supple parts of organic bodies, and the power which the regenerations have of conserving the progress acquired in the composition of organs.

" At present, finally, relying on numerous observations, seeing that with the aid of much time, of changes in local circumstances, in climates, and consequently in the habits of animals, the progression in the complication of their organization and in the diversity of their parts has gradually operated (*a dû s'opérer*) in a way that all the animals now known have been successively formed such as we now see them, it becomes possible to find the solution of the following question :

" What is a *species* among living beings?

" All those who have much to do with the study of natural history know that naturalists at the present day are extremely embarrassed in defining what they mean by the word species.

" In truth, observation for a long time has shown us, and shows us still in a great number of cases, collections of individuals which resemble each other so much in their organization and by the *ensemble* of their parts that we do not hesitate to regard these collections of similar individuals as constituting so many species.

" From this consideration we call *species* every collection of individuals which are alike or almost so, and we remark that the regeneration of these individuals conserves the species and propagates it in continuing successively to reproduce similar individuals.

" Formerly it was supposed that each species was immutable, as old as nature, and that she had caused its special creation by the Supreme Author of all which exists.

" But we can impose on him laws in the execution of his will, and determine the mode which he has been pleased to follow in this respect, so it is only in this way that he permits us to recognize it by the aid of observation. Has not his infinite power created an order of things which successively gives existence to all that we see as well as to all that which exists and which we do not know?

" Assuredly, whatever has been his will, the omnipotence of his power is always the same ; and in whatever way this supreme will has been manifested, nothing can diminish its greatness. As regards, then, the decrees of this infinite wisdom, I confine myself to the limits of a simple observer of nature. Then, if I discover anything in the course that nature follows in her creations, I shall say, without fear of deceiving myself, that it has pleased its author that she possesses this power.

" The idea that was held as to species among living bodies was quite simple, easy to grasp, and seemed confirmed by the constancy in the similar form of the individuals which reproduction or generation perpetuated. There still occur among us a very great number of these pretended species which we see every day.

" However, the farther we advance in the knowledge of the different organized bodies with which almost every part of the surface of the globe is covered, the more does our embarrassment increase in determining what should be regarded as species, and the greater is the reason for limiting and distinguishing the genera.

" As we gradually gather the productions of nature, as our collections gradually grow richer, we see almost all the gaps filled up, and our lines of demarcation effaced. We find ourselves compelled to make an arbitrary determination, which sometimes leads us to seize upon the slightest differences between varieties to form of them the character of that which we call species, and sometimes one person designates as a variety of such a species individuals a little different, which others regard as constituting a particular species.

" I repeat, the richer our collections become, the more numerous are the proofs that all is more or less shaded (*nuancé*), that the remarkable differences be-

come obliterated, and that the more often nature
leaves it at our disposal to establish distinctions only
minute, and in some degree trivial peculiarities.

" But some genera among animals and plants are of
such an extent, from the number of species they contain, that the study and the determination of these
species are now almost impossible. The species of
these genera, arranged in series and placed together
according to their natural relations, present, with
those allied to them, differences so slight that they
shade into each other; and because these species are
in some degree confounded with one another they
leave almost no means of determining, by expression
in words, the small differences which distinguish them.

" There are also those who have been for a long time,
and strongly, occupied with the determination of the
species, and who have consulted rich collections, who
can understand up to what point species, among living bodies, merge one into another (*fondent les unes
dans les autres*), and who have been able to convince
themselves, in the regions (*parties*) where we see
isolated species, that this is only because there are
wanting other species which are more nearly related,
and which we have not yet collected.

" I do not mean to say by this that the existing
animals form a very simple series, one everywhere
equally graduated; but I say that they form a
branching series, irregularly graduated, and which
has no discontinuity in its parts, or which at best has
not always had, if it is true that it is to be found any-
where (*s'il est vrai qu'il s'en trouve quelque part*). It
results from this that the species which terminates
each branch of the general series holds a place at
least on one side apart from the other allied species
which intergrade with them. Behold this state of
things, so well known, which I am now compelled to
demonstrate.

" I have no need (*besoin*) of any hypothesis or any

supposition for this: I call to witness all observing naturalists.

"Not only many genera, but entire orders, and some classes even, already present us with portions almost complete of the state of things which I have just indicated.

"However, when in this case we have arranged the species in series, and they are all well placed according to their natural relations, if you select one of them, and it results in making a leap (*saut pardessus*) over to several others, you take another one of them a little less remote; these two species, placed in comparison, will then present the greatest differences from each other. It is thus that we had begun to regard most of the productions of nature which occur at our door. Then the generic and specific distinctions were very easy to establish. But now that our collections are very much richer, if you follow the series that I have cited above, from the species that you first chose up to that which you took in the second place, and which is very different from the first, you have passed from shade to shade without having remarked any differences worth noticing.

"I ask what experienced zoölogist or botanist is there who has not thoroughly realized that which I have just explained to you?

"Or how can one study, or how can one be able to determine in a thorough way the species, among the multitude of known polyps of all orders of radiates, worms, and especially of insects, where the simple genera of Papilio, Phalæna, Noctua, Tinea, Musca, Ichneumon, Curculio, Capricorn, Scarabæus, Cetonia, etc., etc., already contain so many closely allied species which shade into each other, are almost confounded one with another? What a host of molluscan shells exist in every country and in all seas which elude our means of distinction, and exhaust our resources in this respect! Ascend to the fishes, to the reptiles, to the birds, even to the mammals, and you will see, except the lacunæ which are still to be filled, everywhere shadings which take place between allied species, even the genera, and where after the most industrious study we fail to establish good distinctions. Does not botany, which considers the other series, comprising the plants, offer us, in its different parts, a state of things perfectly similar? In short, what difficulties do not arise in the study and in the determination of species in the genera Lichena, Fucus, Carex, Poa, Piper, Euphorbia, Erica, Hieracium, Solanum, Geranium, Mimosa, etc., etc.?

" When these genera were established but a small number of species were known, and then it was easy to distinguish them; but at present almost all the gaps between them are filled, and our specific differences are necessarily minute and very often insufficient.

" From this state of things well established we see what are the causes which have given rise to them ; we see whether nature possesses the means for this, and if observation has been able to give us our explanation of it.

" A great many facts teach us that gradually as the individuals of one of our species change their situation, climate, mode of life, or habits, they thus receive influences which gradually change the consistence and the proportions of their parts, their form, their faculties, even their organization ; so that all of them participate eventually in the changes which they have undergone.

" In the same climate, very different situations and exposures at first cause simple variations in the individuals which are found exposed there; but, as time goes on, the continual differences of situation of individuals of which I have spoken, which live and successively reproduce in the same circumstances, give rise among them to differences which are, in some degree, essential to their being, in such a way that at the end of many successive generations these individuals, which originally belonged to another species, are at the end transformed into a new species, distinct from the other.

" For example, if the seeds of a grass, or of every other plant natural to a humid field, should be transplanted, by an accident, at first to the slope of a neighboring hill, where the soil, although more elevated, would yet be quite cool (*frais*) so as to allow the plant to live, and then after having lived there, and passed through many generations there, it should gradually reach the poor and almost arid soil of a mountain side—if the plant should thrive and live there and perpetuate itself during a series of generations, it would then be so changed that the botanists who should find it there would describe it as a separate species.

" The same thing happens to animals which circumstances have forced to change their climate, manner of living, and habits; but for these the influences of the causes which I have just cited need still more time than in the case of plants to produce the notable changes in the individuals, though in the long run, however, they always succeed in bringing them about.

" The idea of defining under the word *species* a collection of similar individuals which perpetuate the same by generation, and which have existed thus as anciently as nature, implies the necessity that the individuals of one and the same species cannot mix, in their acts of generation, with the individuals of a different species. Unfortunately observation has proved, and still proves every day, that this consideration has no basis; for the hybrids, very common among plants, and the unions which are often observed between the individuals of very different species among animals, have made us perceive that the limits between these species, supposed to be constant, are not so rigid as is supposed.

" In truth, nothing often results from these singular unions, especially when they are very incongruous, as the individuals which result from them are usually sterile ; but also, when the disparities are less great, it is known that the drawbacks (*défauts*) with which it has to do no longer exist. However, this means alone suffices to gradually create the varieties which have afterwards arisen from races, and which, with time, constitute that which we call *species*.

" To judge whether the idea which is formed of species has any real foundation, let us return to the considerations which I have already stated ; they are, namely—

" 1. That all the organic bodies of our globe are veritable productions of nature, which she has created in succession at the end of much time.

" 2. That in her course nature has begun, and begins anew every day, by forming the simplest organic bodies, and that she directly forms only these —that is to say, only these first primitive germs (*ébauches*) of organization, which have been badly characterized by the expression of " spontaneous generations" (*qu'on a désignées mal-à-propos par l'expression de Générations spontanées*).

" 3. That the first germs (*ébauches*) of the animals and plants were formed in favorable places and circumstances. The functions of life beginning and an organic movement established, these have necessarily gradually developed the organs, so that after a time and under suitable circumstances they have been differentiated, as also the different parts (*elles les ont diversifiés ainsi qui les parties*).

" 4. That the power of increase in each portion of organic bodies being inherited at the first production (*effets*) of life, it has given rise to different modes of multiplication and of regeneration of individuals; and in that way the progress acquired in the composition of the organization and in the forms and the diversity of the parts has been preserved.

" 5. That with the aid of sufficient time, of circumstances which have been necessarily favorable, of changes that all parts of the surface of the globe have successively undergone in their condition—in a word, with the power that new situations and new habits have in modifying the organs of bodies endowed with life—all those which now exist have been imperceptibly formed such as we see them.

" 6. Finally, that according to a similar order of things, living beings, having undergone each of the more or less great changes in the condition of their organization and of their parts, that which is designated as a species among them has been insensibly and successively so formed, can have only a relative constancy in its condition, and cannot be as ancient as nature.

" But, it will be said, when it is necessary to suppose that, with the aid of much time and of an infinite variation in circumstances, nature has gradually formed the different animals that we know, would we not be stopped in this supposition by the sole consideration of the admirable diversity which we observe in the instinct of different animals, and by that of the marvels of all sorts which their different kinds of industry present?

" Will one dare to carry the spirit of system (*porter l'esprit de système*) to the point of saying that it is nature, and she alone, which creates this astonishing diversity of means, of ruses, of skill, of precautions, of patience, of which the industry of animals offers us so many examples! What we observe in this respect in the class of insects alone, is it not a thousand times more than is necessary to compel us to perceive that the limits of the power of nature by no means permit her herself to produce so many marvels, and to force the most obstinate philosophy to recognize that here the will of the supreme author of all things has been necessary, and has alone sufficed to cause the existence of so many admirable things?

"Without doubt one would be rash, or rather wholly unreasonable, to pretend to assign limits to the power of the first author of all things; and by that alone no one can dare to say that this infinite power has not been able to will that which nature herself shows us she has willed.

"This being so, if I discover that nature herself brings about or causes all the wonders just cited; that she creates the organization, the life, even feeling; that she multiplies and diversifies, within limits which are not known to us, the organs and faculties of organic bodies the existence of which she sustains or propagates; that she has created in animals by the single way of *need*, which establishes and directs the habits, the source of all actions, from the most simple up to those which constitute *instinct*, industry, finally reason, should I not recognize in this power of nature—that is to say, of existing things—the execution of the will of its sublime author, who has been able to will that it should have this power? Shall I any the less wonder at the omnipotence of the power of the first cause of all things, if it has pleased itself that things should be thus, than if by so many (separate) acts of his omnipotent will he should be occupied and occupy himself still continually with details of all the special creations, all the variations, and all the developments and perfections, all the destructions and all the renewals—in a word, with all the changes which are in general produced in things which exist?

"But I intend to prove in my 'Biologie' that nature possesses in her *faculties* all that is necessary to have to be able herself to produce that which we admire in her works; and regarding this subject I

shall then enter into sufficient details which I am
here obliged to omit.*

" However, it is still objected that all we see stated
regarding the state of living bodies are unalterable
conditions in the preservation of their form, and it is
thought that all the animals whom history has transmitted to us for two or three thousand years have
always remained the same, and have lost nothing nor
acquired anything in the perfecting of their organs
and in the form of their parts.

" While this apparent stability has for a long time
been accepted as true, it has just been attempted to
establish special proofs in a report on the collections
of natural history brought from Egypt by the citizen
Geoffroy."

Quotes three paragraphs in which the reporters
(Cuvier and Geoffroy St. Hilaire) say that the mummied animals of Thebes and Memphis are perfectly
similar to those of to-day. Then he goes on to say :

" I have seen them, these animals, and I believe in
the conformity of their resemblance with the individuals of the same species which live to-day. Thus
the animals which the Egyptians worshipped and
embalmed two or three thousand years ago are still
in every respect similar to those which actually live
in that country.

" But it would be assuredly very singular that this
should be otherwise; for the position of Egypt and
its climate are still or very nearly the same as at
former times. Therefore the animals which live there
have not been compelled to change their habits.

" There is, then, nothing in the observation which
has just been reported which should be contrary to

---

* " See at the end of this discourse the sketch of a *Philosophie zoologique* relative to this subject." [This sketch was not added—only
the title at the end of the book.]

the considerations which I have expressed on this subject ; and which especially proves that the animals of which it treats have existed during the whole period of nature. It only proves that they have existed for two or three thousand years ; and every one who is accustomed to reflect, and at the same time to observe that which nature shows us of the monuments of its antiquity, readily appreciates the value of a duration of two or three thousand years in comparison with it.

"Hence, as I have elsewhere said, it is sure that this appearance of the stability of things in nature will always be mistaken by the average of mankind for the reality ; because in general people only judge of everything relatively to themselves.

"For the man who observes, and who in this respect only judges from the changes which he himself perceives, the intervals of these changes are *stationary conditions* (*états*) which should appear to be limitless, because of the brevity of life of the individuals of his species. Thus, as the records of his observations and the notes of facts which he has consigned to his registers only extend and mount up to several thousands of years (three to five thousand years), which is an infinitely small period of time relatively to those which have sufficed to bring about the great changes which the surface of the globe has undergone, everything seems *stable* to him in the planet which he inhabits, and he is inclined to reject the monuments heaped up around him or buried in the earth which he treads under his feet, and which surrounds him on all sides.*

. . . .

"It seems to me [as mistaken as] to expect some small creatures which only live a year, which inhabit

---

* See the *Annales du Muséum d'Hist. nat.*, IVᵉ cahier, I., 1802, pp. 302, 303 : *Mémoires sur les Fossiles des Environs de Paris*, etc. He repeats in his *Discours* what he wrote in 1802 in the *Annales*.

some corner of a building, and which we may suppose are occupied with consulting among themselves as to the tradition, to pronounce on the duration of the edifice where they occur : and that going back in their paltry history to the twenty-fifth generation, they should unanimously decide that the building which serves to shelter them is eternal, or at least that it has always existed ; because it has always appeared the same to them ; and since they have never heard it said that it had a beginning. Great things (*grandeurs*) in extent and in duration are relative.*

" When man wishes to clearly represent this truth he will be reserved in his decisions in regard to stability, which he attributes in nature to the state of things which he observes there. †

" To admit the insensible change of species, and the modifications which individuals undergo as they are gradually forced to vary their habits or to contract new ones, we are not reduced to the unique consideration of too small spaces of time which our observations can embrace to permit us to perceive these changes ; for, besides this induction, a quantity of facts collected for many years throws sufficient light on the question that I examine, so that does not remain undecided, and I can say now that our sciences of observation are too advanced not to have the solution sought for made evident.

" Indeed, besides what we know of the influences and the results of heteroclite fecundations, we know positively to-day that a forced and long-sustained change, both in the habits and mode of life of animals, and in the situation, soil, and climate of plants, brings about, after a sufficient time has elapsed, a very remarkable change in the individuals which are exposed to them.

---

* *Ibid.* This is repeated from the article in the *Annales*.
† *Ibid.* "See my *Recherches sur les Corps vivans*" (Appendix, p. 141).

" The animal which lives a free, wandering life on plains, where it habitually exercises itself in running swiftly ; the birds whose needs (*besoins*) require them unceasingly to traverse great spaces in the air, finding themselves enclosed, some in the compartments of our menageries or in our stables, and others in our cages or in our poultry yards, are submitted there in time to striking influences, especially after a series of re- generations under the conditions which have made them contract new habits. The first loses in large part its nimbleness, its agility ; its body becomes stouter, its limbs diminish in power and suppleness, and its faculties are no longer the same. The second become clumsy ; they are unable to fly, and grow more fleshy in all parts of their bodies.

" Behold in our stout and clumsy horses, habituated to draw heavy loads, and which constitute a special race by always being kept together—behold, I say, the difference in their form compared with those of English horses, which are all slender, with long necks, because for a long period they have been trained to run swiftly : behold in them the influence of a differ- ence of habit, and judge for yourselves. You find them, then, such as they are in some degree in nature. You find there our cock and our hen in the condition we have [made] them, as also the mixed races that we have formed by mixed breeding be- tween the varieties produced in different countries, or where they were so in the state of domesticity. You find there likewise our different races of domestic pigeons, our different dogs, etc. What are our cul- tivated fruits, our wheat, our cabbage, our lettuce, etc, etc., if they are not the result of changes which we ourselves have effected in these plants, in chang- ing by our culture the conditions of their situation ? Are they now found in this condition in nature ? To these incontestable facts add the considerations which I have discussed in my *Recherches sur les*

Corps vivans (p. 56 *et suiv.*), and decide for your-selves.

"Thus, among living bodies, nature, as I have al-ready said, offers only in an absolute way individuals which succeed each other genetically, and which descend one from the other. So the *species* among them are only relative, and only temporary.

"Nevertheless, to facilitate the study and the knowledge of so many different bodies it is useful to give the name of *species* to the entire collection of individuals which are alike, which reproduction per-petuates in the same condition as long as the con-ditions of their situation do not change enough to make their habits, their character, and their form vary.

"Such is, citizens, the exact sketch of that which goes on in nature since she has existed, and of that which the observation of her acts has alone enabled us to discover. I have fulfilled my object if, in pre-senting to you the results of my researches and of my experience, I have been able to disclose to you that which in your studies of this kind deserves your special attention.

"You now doubtless conceive how important are the considerations which I have just exposed to you, and how wrong you would be if, in devoting yourself to the study of animals or of plants, you should seek to see among them only the multiplied distinctions that we have been obliged to establish; in a word, if you should confine yourselves to fixing in your mem-ory the variable and indefinite nomenclature which is applied to so many different bodies, instead of studying Nature herself—her course, her means, and the constant results that she knows how to attain."

On the next fly page are the following words: *Esquisse d'une Philosophie zoologique.*

IV. *Lamarck's Views as published in* 1806.*

"Those who have observed much and have
consulted the great collections, have been able to
convince themselves that as gradually as the circumstances of their habitat, of exposure to their
surroundings, of climate, food, mode of living, etc.,
have changed, the characters of size, form, of proportion between the parts, of color, of consistence, of
duration, of agility, and of industry have proportionately changed.

"They have been able to see, as regards the
animals, that the more frequent and longer sustained
use of any organ gradually strengthens this organ,
develops it, enlarges it, and gives it a power propor-
tional to the length of time it has been used ; while
the constant lack of use of such an organ insensibly
weakens it, causes it to deteriorate, progressively
diminishes its faculties, and tends to make it waste
away.†

"Finally, it has been remarked that all that nature
has made individuals to acquire or lose by the sustained influence of circumstances where their race
has existed for a long time, she has preserved by
heredity in the new individuals which have originated
from them (*elle le conserve par la génération aux nouveaux individus qui en proviennent*). These verities
are firmly grounded, and can only be misunderstood

---

* *Discours d'Ouverture du Cours des Animaux sans Vertèbres,
prononcé dans le Muséum d'Histoire naturelle en mai* 1806. (No
imprint. 8°, pp. 108.) Only the most important passages are here
translated.

† "We know that all the forms of organs compared to the uses of
these same organs are always perfectly adapted. But there is a
common error in this connection, since it is thought that the forms
of organs have caused their functions (*en ont amené l'emploi*), whereas
it is easy to demonstrate by observation that it is the uses (*usages*)
which have given origin to the forms of organs."

by those who have never observed and followed nature in her operations.

"Thus we are assured that that which is taken for *species* among living bodies, and that all the specific differences which distinguish these natural productions, have no absolute *stability*, but that they enjoy only a relative *stability;* which it is very important to consider in order to fix the limits which we must establish in the determination of that which we must call *species*.

"It is known that different places change in nature and character by reason of their position, their 'composition' [we should say geological structure or features], and their climate; that which is easily perceived in passing over different places distinguished by special characteristics; behold already a cause of variation for the natural productious which inhabit these different places. But that which is not sufficiently known, and even that which people refuse to believe, is that each place itself changes after a time, in exposure, in climate, in nature, and in character, although with a slowness so great in relation to our period of time that we attribute to it a perfect *stability*.

"Now, in either case, these changed places proportionately change the circumstances relative to the living bodies which inhabit them, and these produce again other influences on those same bodies.

"We see from this that if there are extremes in these changes there are also gradations (*nuances*), that is to say, steps which are intermediate, and which fill up the interval; consequently there are also gradations in the differences which distinguish that which we call *species*.

"Indeed, as we constantly meet with such shades (or intermediate steps) between these so-called *species*, we find ourselves forced to descend to the minutest details to find any distinctions; the slightest pecu-

liarities of form, of color, of size, and often even of
differences only perceived in the aspect of the individual compared with other individuals which are
related to it the more by their relations, are seized
upon by naturalists to establish specific differences;
so that, the slightest varieties being reckoned as
species, our catalogues of species grow infinitely
great, and the name of the productions of nature of
the most interest to us are, so to speak, buried in
these enormous lists, become very difficult to find,
because now the objects are mostly only determined
by characters which our senses can scarcely enable us
to perceive.

" Meanwhile we should remember that nothing of
all this exists in nature ; that she knows neither classes,
orders, genera, nor species, in spite of all the foundation which the portion of the natural series which our
collection contains has seemed to afford them ; and
that of organic or living bodies there are, in reality,
only individuals, and among different races which
gradually pass (*nuancent*) into all degrees of organization" (p. 14).

On p. 70 he speaks of the animal chain from monad
to man, ascending from the most simple to the most
complex.   The monad is the most simple, the most
like a germ of living bodies, and from its nature passes
to the volvoces, proteus, vibrios ; from them nature
arrives at the production of " polypes rotifères "—and
then at " Radiaires," worms, Arachnida, Crustacea,
and Cirripedes.

CHAPTER XVII

THE "PHILOSOPHIE ZOOLOGIQUE"

Lamarck's mature views on the theory of descent comprise a portion of his celebrated *Philosophie zoologique*. We will let him tell the story of creation by natural causes so far as possible in his own words.

In the *avertissement*, or preface, he says that his experience has led him to realize that a body of precepts and of principles relating to the study of animals and even applicable to other parts of the natural sciences would now be useful, our knowledge of zoölogical facts having, for about thirty years, made considerable progress.

After referring to the differences in structure and faculties characterizing animals of different groups, he proceeds to outline his theory, and begins by asking:

" How, indeed, can I consider the singular modification in the structure of animals, as we glance over the series from the most perfect to the least perfect, without asking how we can account for a fact so positive and so remarkable—a fact attested to me by so many proofs? Should I not think that nature has successively produced the different living beings by proceeding from the most simple to the most compound; because in ascending the animal scale from the most imperfect up to the most perfect, the organi-

zation perfects itself and becomes gradually complicated in a most remarkable way?"

This leads him to consider what is life, and he remarks (p. xv.) that it does not exist without external
stimuli. The conditions necessary for the existence
of life are found completely developed in the simplest
organization. We are then led to inquire how this
organization, by reason of certain changes, can give
rise to other organisms less simple, and finally originate creatures becoming gradually more complicated,
as we see in ascending the animal scale. Then employing the two following considerations, he believes
he perceives the solution of the problem which has
occupied his thoughts.

He then cites as factors (1) use and disuse; (2)
the movement of internal fluids by which passages
are opened through the cellular tissue in which they
move, and finally create different organs. Hence the
movement of fluids in the interior of animals, and the
influence of new circumstances as animals gradually
expose themselves to them in spreading into every
inhabitable place, are the two general causes which
have produced the different animals in the condition
we now see them. Meanwhile he perceived the importance of the preservation by heredity, though he
nowhere uses that word, in the new individuals reproduced of everything which the results of the life
and influencing circumstances had caused to be acquired in the organization of those which have transmitted existence to them.

In the *Discours préliminaire*, referring to the *pro-*

gression in organization of animals from the simplest
to man, as also to the successive acquisition of different
special organs, and consequently of as many faculties
as new organs obtained, he remarks :

" Then we can perceive how needs (*besoins*), at the
outset reduced to nullity, and of which the number
gradually increases, have produced the inclination
(*penchant*) to actions fitted to satisfy it ; how the actions, becoming habitual and energetic, have caused
the development of the organs which execute them ;
how the force which excites the organic movements
may, in the simplest animals, be outside of them and
yet animate them ; how, then, this force has been
transported and fixed in the animal itself; finally,
how it then has become the source of sensibility,
and in the end that of acts of intelligence.

" I shall add that if this method had been followed,
then *sensation* would not have been regarded as
the general and immediate cause of organic movements, and it would not have been said that life is a
series of movements which are executed in virtue of
sensations received by different organs ; or, in other
words, that all the vital movements are the product
of impressions received by the sensitive parts. *

" This cause seems, up to a certain point, established
as regards the most perfect animals ; but had it been
so relatively to all living beings, they should all be
endowed with the power of sensation. But it cannot
be proved that this is the case with plants, and it
cannot likewise be proved that it is so with all the
animals known.

" But nature in creating her organisms has not begun by suddenly establishing a faculty so eminent

---

* [Cabanis.] *Rapp. du Phys. et du Moral de l'Homme*, pp. 38 à
39, et 85.

as that of sensation : she has had the means of producing this faculty in the imperfect animals of the first classes of the animal kingdom," referring to the Protozoa. But she has accomplished this gradually and successively. " Nature has progressively created the different special organs, also the faculties which animals enjoy."

He remarks that though it is indispensable to classify living forms, yet that our classifications are all artificial ; that species, genera, families, orders, and classes do not exist in nature—only the individuals really exist. In the third chapter he gives the old definition of species, that they are fixed and immutable, and then speaks of the animal series, saying :

" I do not mean by this to say that the existing animals form a very simple series, and especially evenly graduated ; but I claim that they form a branched series,* irregularly graduated, and which has no discontinuity in its parts, or which, at least, has not always had, if it is true that, owing to the extinction of some species, there are some breaks. It follows that the *species* which terminates each branch of the general series is connected at least on one side with other *species* which intergrade with it " (p. 59).

---

* Lamarck's idea of the animal series was that of a branched one, as shown by his genealogical tree on p. 193, and he explains that the series begins at least by two special branches, these ending in branchlets. He thus breaks entirely away from the old idea of a continuous ascending series of his predecessors Bonnet and others. Professor R. Hertwig therefore makes a decided mistake and does Lamarck a great injustice in his " Zoölogy," where he states : " Lamarck, in agreement with the then prevailing conceptions, regarded the animal kingdom as a series grading from the lowest primitive animal up to man " (p. 26) ; and again, on the next page, he speaks of " the theory of Geoffroy St.-Hilaire and Lamarck " as having in it " as a fundamental error the doctrine of the serial arrangement of the animal world " (English Trans.). Hertwig is in error, and could never have carefully read what Lamarck did say, or have known that he was the first to throw aside the serial arrangement, and to sketch out a genealogical tree.

He then points out the difficulty of determining what are species in certain large genera, such as Papilio, Ichneumon, etc. How new species arise is shown by observation.

"A number of facts teaches us that in proportion as the individuals of one of our species are subjected to changes in situation, climate, mode of life or habits, they thereby receive influences which gradually change the consistence and the proportions of their parts, their form, their faculties, even their structure; so that it follows that all of them after a time participate in the changes to which they have been subjected.

"In the same climate very different situations and exposures cause simple variations in the individuals occurring there; but, after the lapse of time, the continual differences of situation of the individuals of which I speak, which live and successively reproduce under the same circumstances, produce differences in them which become, in some degree, essential to their existence, so that at the end of many successive generations these individuals, which originally belonged to another species, became finally transformed into a new species distinct from the other.

"For example, should the seeds of a grass or of any other plant natural to a moist field be carried by any means at first to the slope of a neighboring hill, where the soil, although more elevated, will yet be sufficiently moist to allow the plant to live there, and if it results, after having lived there and having passed through several generations, that it gradually reaches the dry and almost arid soil of a mountain side; if the plant succeeds in living there, and perpetuates itself there during a series of generations, it will then be so changed that any botanists who should find it there would make a distinct species of it.

"The same thing happens in the case of animals

which circumstances have forced to change in climate, mode of life, and habits; but in their case the influences of the causes which I have just cited need still more time than the plants to bring about notable changes in the individuals.

" The idea of embracing, under the name of *species*, a collection of like individuals which are perpetuated by generation, and which have remained the same as long as nature has endured, implies the necessity that the individuals of one and the same species should not cross with individuals of a different species.

" Unfortunately observation has proved, and still proves every day, that this consideration is unfounded; for hybrids, very common among plants, and the pairings which we often observe between the individuals of very different *species* of animals, have led us to see that the limits between these supposed constant species are not so fixed as has been imagined.

" In truth, nothing often results from these singular unions, especially if they are very ill-assorted, and then the individuals which do result from them are usually infertile; but also, when the disparities are less great, we know that the default in question does not occur.

" But this cause only suffices to create, step by step, varieties which finally become races, and which, with time, constitute what we call *species*.

" To decide whether the idea which is formed of the *species* has any real foundation, let us return to the considerations which I have already explained; they lead us to see:

" 1. That all the organized bodies of our globe are true productions of Nature, which she has successively formed after the lapse of much time ;

" 2. That, in her course, Nature has begun, and begins over again every day, to form the simplest organisms, and that she directly creates only those, namely, which are the first germs (*ébauches*) of organization, which are designated by the expression of *spontaneous generations;*

" 3. That the first germs of the animal and plant having been formed in appropriate places and circumstances, the faculties of a beginning life and of an organic movement established, have necessarily gradually developed the organs, and that with time they have diversified them, as also the parts;

" 4. That the power of growth in each part of the organized body being inherent in the first created forms of life, it has given rise to different modes of multiplication and of regeneration of individuals; and that consequently the progress acquired in the composition of the organization and in the shape and diversity of the parts has been preserved;

" 5. That with the aid of sufficient time, of circumstances which have been necessarily favorable, of changes of condition that every part of the earth's surface has successively undergone—in a word, by the power which new situations and new habits have of modifying the organs of living beings, all those which now exist have been gradually formed such as we now see them;

" 6. Finally, that, according to a similar order of things, living beings having undergone each of the more or less great changes in the condition of their structure and parts, that which we call a *species* among them has been gradually and successively so formed, having only a relative constancy in its condition, and not being as old as Nature herself.

" But, it will be said, when it is supposed that by the aid of much time and of an infinite variation in circumstances, Nature has gradually formed the different animals known to us, shall we not be stopped in this supposition by the simple consideration of the admirable diversity which we observe in the *instincts* of different animals, and by that of the marvels of every kind presented by their different kinds of *industry?*

" Shall we dare to extend the spirit of system so far as to say that it is Nature who has herself alone created this astonishing diversity of means, of contrivances, of skill, of precautions, of patience, of which the *industry* of animals offers us so many examples? What we observe in this respect in the simple class of *insects*, is it not a thousand times more than sufficient to make us realize that the limit to the power of Nature in nowise permits her to herself produce so many marvels, but to force the most obstinate philosopher to recognize that here the will of the Supreme Author of all things has been necessary, and has alone sufficed to create so many admirable things?

" Without doubt, one would be rash or, rather, wholly insensate, to pretend to assign limits to the power of the first Author of all things; but, aside from that, no one could dare to say that this infinite power could not will that which Nature even shows us it has willed "* (p. 67).

Referring to the alleged proof of the fixity of species brought forward by Cuvier in the *Annales du Muséum d'Histoire naturelle* (i., pp. 235 and 236) that the mummied birds, crocodiles, and other animals of Egypt present no differences from those now living, Lamarck says:

" It would assuredly be very singular if it were otherwise, because the position of Egypt and its climate are still almost exactly what they were at that epoch.   Moreover, the birds which live there still exist under the same circumstances as they were then, not having been obliged to change their habits.

" Moreover, who does not perceive that birds, which can so easily change their situation and seek

---

* The foregoing pages (283–286) are reprinted by the author from the *Discours* of 1803.   See pp. 266–270.

places which suit them are less subject than many other animals to the variations of local circumstances, and hence less restricted in their habits."

He adds the fact that the animals in question have inhabited Egypt for two or three thousand years, and not necessarily from all time, and that this is not time enough for marked changes. He then gives the following definition of species, which is the best ever offered: "Species, then, have only a relative stability, and are invariable only temporarily."

"Yet, to facilitate the study and knowledge of so many different organisms it is useful to give the name of *species* to every similar collection of similar individuals which are perpetuated by heredity (*génération*) in the same condition, so long as the circumstances of their situation do not change enough to render variable their habits, character, and form."

He then discusses fossil species in the way already described in Chapter III. (p. 75).

The subject of the checks upon over-population by the smaller and weaker animals, or the struggle for existence, is thus discussed in Chapter IV.:

"Owing to the extreme multiplication of the small species, and especially of the most imperfect animals, the multiplicity of individuals might be prejudicial to the preservation of the species, to that of the progress acquired in the improvement of the organization—in a word, to the general order, if nature had not taken precautions to keep this multiplication within due limits over which she would never pass.

"Animals devour one another, except those which live only on plants; but the latter are exposed to being devoured by the carnivorous animals.

"We know that it is the strongest and the best

armed which devour the weaker, and that the larger kinds devour the smaller. Nevertheless, the individuals of a single species rarely devour each other: they war upon other races.*

" The multiplication of the small species of animals is so considerable, and the renewals of their generations are so prompt, that these small species would render the earth uninhabitable to the others if nature had not set a limit to their prodigious multiplication. But since they serve as prey for a multitude of other animals, as the length of their life is very limited, and as the lowering of the temperature kills them, their numbers are always maintained in proper proportions for the preservation of their races and that of others.

" As to the larger and stronger animals, they would be too dominant and injure the preservation of other races if they should multiply in too great proportions. But their races devouring each other, they would only multiply slowly and in a small number at a time; this would maintain in this respect the kind of equilibrium which should exist.

" Finally, only man, considered separately from all which is characteristic of him, seems capable of multiplying indefinitely, because his intelligence and his resources secure him from seeing his increase arrested by the voracity of any animals. He exercises over them such a supremacy that, instead of fearing the larger and stronger races of animals, he is thus rather capable of destroying them, and he continually checks their increase.

" But nature has given him numerous passions, which, unfortunately, developing with his intelligence,

---

* Perrier thus comments on this passage : *Ici nous sommes bien près, semble-t-il, non seulement de la lutte pour la vie telle que la concevra Darwin, mais même de la sélection naturelle. Malheureusement, au lieu de poursuivre l'idée, Lamarck aussitôt s'engage dans une autre voie,"* etc. (*La Philosophie zoologique avant Darwin*, p. 81).

thus place a great obstacle to the extreme multiplication of the individuals of his species.

"Indeed, it seems as if man had taken it upon himself unceasingly to reduce the number of his fellow-creatures; for never, I do not hesitate to say, will the earth be covered with the population that it could maintain. Several of its habitable parts would always be alternately very sparsely populated, although the time for these alternate changes would be to us measureless.

"Thus by these wise precautions everything is preserved in the established order; the changes and perpetual renewals which are observable in this order are maintained within limits' over which they cannot pass; the races of living beings all subsist in spite of their variations; the progress acquired in the improvement of the organization is not lost; everything which appears to be disordered, overturned, anomalous, reënters unceasingly into the general order, and even coöperates with it; and especially and always the will of the sublime Author of nature and of all existing things is invariably executed " (pp. 98–101).

In the sixth chapter the author treats of the degradation and simplification of the structure from one end to the other of the animal series, proceeding, as he says, inversely to the general order of nature, from the compound to the more simple. Why he thus works out this idea of a general degradation is not very apparent, since it is out of tune with his views, so often elsewhere expressed, of a progressive evolution from the simple to the complex, and to his own classification of the animal kingdom, beginning as it does with the simplest forms and ending with man. Perhaps, however, he temporarily adopts the prevailing method of beginning with the highest forms in order

19

to bring out clearly the successive steps in inferiority or degradation presented in descending the animal scale.

We will glean some passages of this chapter which bear on his theory of descent. Speaking of the different kinds of aquatic surroundings he remarks:

"In the first place it should be observed that in the waters themselves she [Nature] presents considerably diversified circumstances; the fresh waters, marine waters, calm or stagnant waters, running waters or streams, the waters of warm climates, those of cold regions, finally those which are shallow and those which are very deep, offer many special circumstances, each of which acts differently on the animals living in them. Now, in a degree equal to the makeup of the organization, the races of animals which are exposed to either of these circumstances have been submitted to special influences and have been diversified by them."

He then, after referring to the general degradation of the Batrachians, touches upon the atrophy of legs which has taken place in the snakes:

"If we should consider as a result of *degradation* the loss of legs seen in the snakes, the *Ophidia* should be regarded as constituting the lowest order of reptiles; but it would be an error to admit this consideration. Indeed, the serpents being animals which, in order to hide themselves, have adopted the habit of gliding directly along the ground, their body has lengthened very considerably and disproportionately to its thickness. Now, elongated legs proving disadvantageous to their necessity of gliding and hiding, very short legs, being only four in number, since they are vertebrate animals, would be incapable of moving their bodies. Thus the habits of these animals have been the cause of the disappearance of their legs, and yet the *batrachians*, which have them, offer a more degraded organization, and are nearer the fishes" (p. 155).

Referring on the next page to the fishes, he remarks :—

"Without doubt théir general form, their lack of a constriction between the head and the body to form a neck, and the different fins which support them in place of legs, are the results of the influence of the dense medium which they inhabit, and not that of the *dégradation* of their organization. But this modification *(dégradation)* is not less real and very great, as we can convince ourselves by examining their internal organs; it is such as to compel us to assign to the fishes a rank lower than that of the reptiles."

He then states that the series from the lamprey and fishes to the mammals is not a regularly gradated one, and accounts for this "because the work of nature has been often changed, hindered, and diverted in direction by the influences which singularly different, even contrasted, circumstances have exercised on the animals which are there found exposed in the course of a long series of their renewed generations."

Lamarck thus accounts for the production of the radial symmetry of the medusæ and echinoderms, his *Radiaires*. At the present day this symmetry is attributed perhaps more correctly to their more or less fixed mode of life.

"It is without doubt by the result of this means which nature employs, at first with a feeble energy with *polyps*, and then with greater developments in the *Radiata*, that the radial form has been acquired;

because the subtile ambient fluids, penetrating by the alimentary canal, and being expansive, have been able, by an incessantly renewed repulsion from the centre towards every point of the circumference, to give rise to this radiated arrangement of parts.

"It is by this cause that, in the Radiata, the intestinal canal, although still very imperfect, since more often it has only a single opening, is yet complicated with numerous radiating vasculiform, often ramified, appendages.

"It is, doubtless, also by this cause that in the soft Radiates, as the medusæ, etc., we observe a constant isochronic movement, movement very probably resulting from the successive intermissions between the masses of subtile fluids which penetrate into the interior of these animals and those of the same fluids which escape from it, often being spread throughout all their parts.

"We cannot say that the isochronic movements of the soft Radiates are the result of their respiration ; for below the vertebrate animals nature does not offer, in that of any animal, these alternate and measured movements of inspiration and expiration. Whatever may be the respiration of Radiates, it is extremely slow, and is executed without perceptible movements " (p. 200).

The Influence of Circumstances on the Actions and Habits of Animals.

It is in Chapter VII. that the views of Lamarck are more fully presented than elsewhere, and we therefore translate all of it as literally as possible, so as to preserve the exact sense of the author.

"We do not here have to do with a line of argument, but with the examination of a positive fact, which is more general than is supposed, and which has not received the attention it deserves, doubtless because, very often, it is quite difficult to discover. This fact consists in the influence which circumstances exert on the different organisms subjected to them.

" In truth, for a long time there has been noticed the influence of different states of our organization on our character, our propensities (*penchants*), our actions, and even our ideas ; but it seems to me that no one has yet recognized that of our actions and of our habits on our organization itself. Now, as these actions and these habits entirely depend on the circumstances in which we habitually find ourselves, I shall try to show how great is the influence which these circumstances exercise on the general form, on the condition of the parts, and even on the organization of living bodies. It is therefore this very positive fact which is to be the subject of this chapter.

" If we have not had numerous occasions to plainly recognize the effects of this influence on certain organisms which we have transported under entirely new and different circumstances, and if we had not seen these effects and the changes resulting from them produced, in a way, under our very eyes, the important fact in question would have always remained unknown.

" The influence of circumstances is really continuously and everywhere active on living beings, but what renders it difficult for us to appreciate this influence is that its effects only become sensible or recognizable (especially in the animals) at the end of a long period.

" Before stating and examining the proofs of this fact, which deserves our attention, and which is very important for a zoölogical philosophy, let us resume the thread of the considerations we had begun to discuss.

" In the preceding paragraph we have seen that it is now an incontrovertible fact that, in considering the animal scale in a sense the inverse of that of nature, we find that there exists in the groups composing this scale a continuous but irregular modification (*dégradation*) in the organization of animals which they comprise, an increasing simplification in the organization of these organisms; finally, a proportionate diminution in the number of faculties of these beings.

" This fact once recognized may throw the greatest light on the very order which nature has followed in the production of all the existing animals; but it does not show why the structure of animals in its increasing complexity from the more imperfect up to the most perfect offers only an irregular gradation, whose extent presents a number of anomalies or digressions which have no appearance of order in their diversity.

" Now, in seeking for the reason of this singular irregularity in the increasing complexity of organization of animals, if we should consider the outcome of the influences that the infinitely diversified circumstances in all parts of the globe exercise on the general form, the parts, and the very organization of these animals, everything will be clearly explained.

" It will, indeed, be evident that the condition in which we find all animals is, on one side, the result of the increasing complexity of the organization which tends to form a regular gradation, and, on the other, that it is that of the influences of a multitude of very different circumstances which continually tend to destroy the regularity in the gradations of the increasing complexity of the organization.

" Here it becomes necessary for me to explain the meaning I attach to the expression *circumstances influencing the form and structure of animals*—namely, that in becoming very different they change, with time, both their form and organization by proportionate modifications.

" Assuredly, if these expressions should be taken literally, I should be accused of an error; for whatever may be the circumstances, they do not directly cause any modification in the form and structure of animals.

" But the great changes in the circumstances bring about in animals great changes in their needs, and such changes in their needs necessarily cause changes in their actions. Now, if the new needs become constant or very permanent, the animals then assume new *habits*, which are as durable as the needs which gave origin to them. We see that this is easily demonstrated and even does not need any explanation to make it clearer.

" It is then evident that a great change in circumstances having become constant in a race of animals leads these animals into new habits.

" Now, if new circumstances, having become permanent in a race of animals, have given to these animals new *habits*—that is to say, have led them to perform new actions which have become habitual—there will from this result the use of such a part by preference to that of another, and in certain cases the total lack of use of any part which has become useless.

" Nothing of all this should be considered as a hypothesis or as a mere peculiar opinion; they are, on the contrary, truths which require, in order to be made evident, only attention to and the observation of facts.

" We shall see presently by the citation of known facts which prove it, on one side that the new wants, having rendered such a part necessary, have really by the result of efforts given origin to this part, and that as the result of its sustained use it has gradually strengthened it, developed, and has ended in considerably increasing its size; on the other side we shall see that, in certain cases, the new circumstances and new wants having rendered such a part wholly useless, the total lack of use of this part has led to the result that it has gradually ceased to receive the development which the other parts of the animal obtain ; that it gradually becomes emaciated and thin ; and that finally, when this lack of use has been total during a long time, the part in question ends in disappearing. All this is a positive fact ; I propose to give the most convincing proofs.

" In the plants, where there are no movements, and, consequently, no habits properly so called, great changes in circumstances do not bring about less great differences in the development of their parts ; so that these differences originate and develop certain of them, while they reduce and cause several others to disappear. But here everything operates by the changes occurring in the nutrition of the plant, in its absorptions and transpirations, in the amount of heat, light, air, and humidity which it habitually receives ; finally, in the superiority that certain of the different vital movements may assume over others.

" Between individuals of the same species, some of which are constantly well nourished, and in circumstances favorable to their entire development, while the others live under reversed circumstances, there is brought about a difference in the condition of these individuals which gradually becomes very remarkable. How many examples could I not cite regarding animals and plants, which would confirm the grounds for this view ! Now, if the circumstances remain the same, rendering habitual and constant the condition of individuals badly fed, diseased, or languishing, their internal organization becomes finally modified, and reproduction between the individuals in question preserves the acquired modifications, and ends in giving rise to a race very distinct from that of the individuals which unceasingly meet with circumstances favorable to their development.

" A very dry spring-time is the cause of the grass of a field growing very slowly, remaining scraggy and puny, flowering and fruiting without growing much.

"A spring interspersed with warm days and rainy days makes the same grass grow rapidly, and the harvest of hay is then excellent.

" But if any cause perpetuates the unfavorable circumstances surrounding these plants, they vary proportionally, at first in their appearance and general condition, and finally in several particulars of their characters.

" For example, if some seed of any of the grasses referred to should be carried into an elevated place, on a dry and stony greensward much exposed to the winds, and should germinate there, the plant which should be able to live in this place would always be badly nourished, and the individuals reproduced there continuing to exist under these depressing circumstances, there would result a race truly different from that living in the field, though originating from it. The individuals of this new race would be small, scraggy, and some of their organs, having developed more than others, would then offer special proportions.

"Those who have observed much, and who have consulted the great collections, have become convinced that in proportion as the circumstances of habitat, exposure, climate, food, mode of life, etc., come to change, the characters of size, form, proportion between the parts, color, consistence, agility, and industry in the animals change proportionally.

" What nature accomplishes after a long time, we bring about every day by suddenly changing, in the case of a living plant, the circumstances under which it and all the individuals of its species exist.

" All botanists know that the plants which they transplant from their birthplace into gardens for cultivation gradually undergo changes which at last render them unrecognizable. Many plants naturally very hairy then become glabrous, or almost so; many of those which were creeping and trailing, then become erect; others lose their spines or their prickles; others still, from the woody and perennial condition which their stem possesses in a warm climate, pass, in our climate, into an herbaceous condition, and among these several are nothing more than annual plants; finally, the dimensions of their parts themselves undergo very considerable changes. These effects of changes of circumstances are so well known that botanists prefer not to describe garden plants, at least only those which have been newly cultivated.

"Is not cultivated wheat (*Triticum sativum*) only a plant brought by man into the condition in which we actually see it? Who can tell me in what country such a plant lives in a state of nature—that is to say, without being there the result of its culture in some neighboring region?

"Where occur in nature our cabbage, lettuce, etc., in the condition in which we see them in our kitchen-gardens? Is it not the same as regards a number of animals which domestication has changed or considerably modified?

"What very different races among our fowls and domestic pigeons, which we have obtained by raising them in different circumstances and in different countries, and how vainly do we now endeavor to rediscover them in nature!

"Those which are the least changed, without doubt by a more recent process of domestication, and because they do not live in a climate which is foreign to them, do not the less possess, in the condition of some of their parts, great differences produced by the habits which we have made them contract. Thus our ducks and our domestic geese trace back their type to the wild ducks and geese; but ours have lost the power of rising into the high regions of the air, and of flying over extensive regions; finally, a decided change has been wrought in the state of their parts compared with that of animals of the race from which they have descended.

" Who does not know that such a native bird, which we raise in a cage and which lives there five or six years in succession, and after that replaced in nature— namely, set free—is then unable to fly like its fellows which have always been free? The slight change of circumstance operating on this individual has only diminished its power of flight, and doubtless has not produced any change in the shape of its parts. But if a numerous series of generations of individuals of the same race should have been kept in captivity for a considerable time, there is no doubt but that even the form of the parts of these individuals would gradually undergo notable changes. For a much stronger reason, if, instead of a simple captivity constantly maintained over them, this circumstance had been at the same time accompanied by a change to a very different climate, and if these individuals by degrees had been habituated to other kinds of food, and to other kinds of movements to obtain it; certainly these circumstances, united and becoming constant, would insensibly form a new and special race.

" Where do we find, in nature, this multitude of races of *dogs*, which, as the result of domesticity to which we have reduced these animals, have been brought into their present condition? Where do we find these bull-dogs, greyhounds, water spaniels, spaniels, pug-dogs, etc., etc., races which present among themselves much greater differences than those which we admit to be specific in wild animals of the same genus?

" Without doubt, a primitive single race, very near the wolf, if it is not itself the true type, has been submitted by man, at some period, to the process of domestication. This race, which then offered no difference between its individuals, has been gradually

dispersed by man into different countries, with different climates ; and after a time these same individuals,
having undergone the influences of their habitats, and
of the different habits they were obliged to contract
in each country, have undergone remarkable changes,
and have formed different special races. Now, the
man who, for commercial reasons or from interests of
any other kind, travels a very great distance, having
carried into a densely populated place, as for example
a great capital, different races of dogs originated in
some very distant country, then the increase of these
races by heredity (*génération*) has given rise successively to all those we now know.

"The following fact proves, as regards plants, how
a change in any important circumstance leads to a
change in the parts of their organisms.

"So long as *Ranunculus aquatilis* is submerged
in the water, its leaves are all finely incised and the
divisions hair-like ; but when the stalks of this plant
reach the surface of the water, the leaves which grow
out in the air are wider, rounded, and simply lobed.
If some feet from the same plant the roots succeed
in pushing into a soil only damp, without being submerged, their stalks then are short, none of their
leaves are divided into capillary divisions, which gives
rise to *Ranunculus hederaceus*, which the botanists
regard as a species whenever they meet with it.

"There is no doubt that as regards animals important changes in the circumstances under which
they are accustomed to live do not produce alteration in their organs ; for here the changes are much
slower in operating than in plants, and, consequently,
are to us less marked, and their cause less recognizable.

"As to the circumstances which have so much
power in modifying the organs of living beings, the
most influential are, doubtless, the diversity of the
surroundings in which they live ; but besides this

there are many others which, in addition, have a considerable influence in the production of the effects in question.

" It is known that different localities change in nature and quality owing to their position, their nature, and their climate, as is easily seen in passing over different places distinguished by special features; hence we see a cause of variation for the animals and plants which live in these different places. But what we do not sufficiently know, and even what we generally refuse to believe, is that each place itself changes with time in exposure, in climate, in nature, and quality, although with a slowness so great in relation to our own continuance that we attribute to it a perfect stability.

" Now, in either case, these changed localities proportionally change the circumstances relative to the organisms which inhabit them, and the latter then give rise to other influences bearing on these same beings.

" We perceive from this that, if there are extremes in these changes, there are also gradations—namely, degrees which are intermediate and which fill the interval. Consequently there are also gradations in the differences which distinguish what we call *species*.

" It is then evident that the whole surface of the earth offers, in the nature and situation of the matters which occupy its different points, a diversity of circumstances which is throughout in relation with that of the forms and parts of animals, independent of the special diversity which necessarily results from the progress of the composition of organization in each animal.

" In each locality where animals can live, the circumstances which establish there an order of things remain for a long time the same, and really change there only with a slowness so great that man cannot directly notice them. He is obliged to consult monuments to recognize that in each one of these places the order of things that he discovers there has not always been the same, and to perceive that it will change more.

" The races of animals which live in each of these places should, then, retain their customary habits there also for a long time ; hence to us seems an apparent constancy of races which we call *species*—constancy which has originated among us the idea that these races are as ancient as nature.

" But in the different points of the earth's surface which can be inhabited, nature and the situation of the places and climates constitute there, for the animals as for the plants, *different circumstances* of all sorts of degrees. The animals which inhabit these different places should then differ from each other, not only on account of the state of nature of the organization in each race, but, besides, by reason of the habits that the individuals of each race there are forced to have ; so, in proportion as he traverses the larger parts of the earth's surface the observing naturalist sees circumstances changing in a manner somewhat noticeable ; he constantly sees that the species change proportionately in their characters.

" Now, the true order of things necessary to consider in all this consists in recognizing :

" 1. That every slight change maintained under the circumstances where occur each race of animals, brings about in them a real change in their wants.

" 2. That every change in the wants of animals necessitates in them other movements (*actions*) to satisfy the new needs, and consequently other habits.

" 3. That every new want necessitating new actions to satisfy it, demands of the animal which feels it both the more frequent use of such of its parts of which before it made less use, which develops and considerably enlarges them, and the use of new parts which necessity has caused to insensibly develop in it by the effects of its inner feelings ; which I shall constantly prove by known facts.

" Thus, to arrive at a knowledge of the true causes of so many different forms and so many different habits of which the known animals offer us examples, it is necessary to consider that circumstances infinitely diversified, but all slowly changing, into which the animals of each race are successively thrown, have caused, for each of them, new wants and necessarily changes in their habits. Moreover, this truth, which cannot be denied, being once recognized, it will be easy to see how the new needs have been able to be satisfied, and the new habits formed, if any attention be given to the two following laws of nature, which observation always confirms :

" *First Law.*

" In every animal which has not exceeded the term of its development, the more frequent and sustained use of any organ gradually strengthens this organ, develops and enlarges it, and gives it a strength proportioned to the length of .time of such use ; while the constant lack of use of such an organ imperceptibly weakens it, causes it to become reduced, progressively diminishes its faculties, and ends in its disappearance.

" *Second Law.*

" Everything which nature has caused individuals to acquire or lose by the influence of the circumstances to which their race may be for a long time exposed, and consequently by the influence of the predominant use of such an organ, or by that of the constant lack of use of such part, it preserves by heredity (*génération*) and passes on to the new individuals which descend from it, provided that the changes thus acquired are common to both sexes, or to those which have given origin to these new individuals.

" These are the two fundamental truths which can be misunderstood only by those who have never observed or followed nature in its operations, or only by those who allow themselves to fall into the error which I have combated.

" Naturalists having observed that the forms of the parts of animals compared with the uses of these parts are always in perfect accord, have thought that the forms and conditions of parts have caused the function; but this is a mistake, for it is easy to demonstrate by observation that it is, on the contrary, the needs and uses of organs which have developed these same parts, which have even given origin to them where they did not exist, and which consequently have given rise to the condition in which we observe them in each animal.

" If this were not so, it would have been necessary for nature to have created for the parts of animals as many forms as the diversity of circumstances in which they have to live had required, and that these forms and also the circumstances had never varied.

" This is certainly not the existing order of things, and if it were really such, we should not have the race-horses of England; we should not have our great draft horses, so clumsy and so different from the first named, for nature herself has not produced their like; we should not, for the same reason, have terrier dogs with bow legs, greyhounds so swift in running, water-spaniels, etc. ; we should not have tailless fowls, fantail pigeons, etc.; finally, we could cultivate the wild plants as much as we pleased in the rich and fertile soil of our gardens without fearing to see them change by long culture.

" For a long time we have felt the force of the saying which has passed into the well-known proverb— *habits form a second nature.*

" Assuredly, if the habits and nature of each animal can never vary, the proverb is false, has no foundation, and does not apply to the instances which led to its being spoken.

" If we should seriously consider all that I have just stated, it might be thought that I had good reason when in my work entitled *Recherches sur les Corps vivans* (p. 50) I established the following proposition :

" ' It is not the organs—that is to say, the nature and form of the parts of the body of an animal—which have given rise to its habits and its special faculties ; but it is, on the contrary, its habits, its manner of life, and the circumstances in which are placed the individuals from which it originates, which have, with time, brought about the form of its body, the number and condition of its organs, finally, the faculties which it enjoys.'

" If we weigh this proposition, and if we recall all the observations which nature and the state of things continually lead us to do, then its importance and its solidity will become more evident.

" Time and favorable circumstances are, as I have already said, the two principal means which nature employs to give existence to all her productions : we know that time for her has no limits, and that consequently it is ever at her disposal.

" As to the circumstances of which she has need, and which she uses still daily to cause variations in all that she continues to produce, we can say that they are, in some degree, for her inexhaustible.

" The principal circumstances arise from the influence of climate ; from those of different temperatures of the atmosphere, and from all the environing media ; from that of the diversity of different localities and their situation ; from that of habits, the ordinary movements, the most frequent actions ; finally, from that of means of preservation, of mode of living, of defence, of reproduction, etc.

" Moreover, owing to these diverse influences, the faculties increase and become stronger by use, become differentiated by the new habits preserved for long ages, and insensibly the organization, the consistence —in a word, the nature and condition of parts, as also of the organs—participate in the results of all these influences, become preserved, and are propagated by generation.

" These truths, which are only the results of the two natural laws above stated, are in every case completely confirmed by facts ; they clearly indicate the course of nature in all the diversity of its products.

" But instead of contenting ourselves with generalities which might be considered as hypothetical, let us directly examine the facts, and consider, in the animals, the result of the use or disuse of their organs on the organs themselves, according to the habits that each race has been compelled to contract.

" I shall now attempt to prove that the constant lack of exercise of organs at first diminishes their faculties, gradually impoverishes them, and ends by making them disappear, or even causing them to be atrophied, if this lack of use is perpetuated for a very long time through successive generations of animals of the same race.

" I shall next prove that, on the contrary, the habit of exercising an organ, in every animal which has not attained the limit of the diminution of its faculties, not only perfects and increases the faculties of this organ, but, besides, enables it to acquire developments and dimensions which insensibly change it; so that with time it renders it very different from the same organ in another animal which exercises it much less.

" *The lack of use of an organ, become constant by the habits formed, gradually impoverishes this organ, and ends by causing it to disappear and even to destroy it.*

" As such a proposition can only be admitted on proof, and not by its simple announcement, let us prove it by the citation of the leading known facts on which it is based.

" The vertebrate animals, whose plan of organization is in all nearly the same, although they offer much diversity in their parts, have jaws armed with *teeth ;* moreover, those among them which circumstances have placed in the habit of swallowing their food without previous *mastication* are exposed to the result that their teeth become undeveloped. These teeth, then, either remain concealed between the bony edges of the jaws, without appearing above, or even their gums are found to have been atrophied.

" In the baleen whales, which have been supposed to be completely deprived of teeth, M. Geoffroy has found them concealed in the jaws of the *fœtus* of this animal. This professor has also found in the birds the groove where the teeth should be situated ; but they are no longer to be seen there.

" In the class even of mammals, which comprises the most perfect animals, and chiefly those in which the vertebrate plan of organization is most perfectly carried out, not only the baleen has no usable teeth, but the ant-eater (*Myrmecophaga*) is also in the same condition, whose habit of not masticating its food has been for a long time established and preserved in its race.

" The presence of eyes in the head is a characteristic of a great number of different animals, and becomes an essential part of the plan of organization of vertebrates.

" Nevertheless the mole, which owing to its habits makes very little use of vision, has only very small eyes, which are scarcely visible, since they exercise these organs to a very slight extent.

" The *Aspalax* of Olivier (*Voyage en Egypte et en Perse*, ii. pl. 28 f. 2), which lives under ground like the mole, and which probably exposes itself still less than that animal to the light of day, has totally lost the power of sight; also it possesses only vestiges of the organ of which it is the seat; and yet these vestiges are wholly concealed under the skin and other parts which cover them, and do not permit the least access to the light.

"The *Proteus*, an aquatic reptile allied to the salamander in its structure, and which lives in the dark subterranean waters of deep caves, has, like the *Aspalax*, only vestiges of the organs of sight—vestiges which are covered and concealed in the same manner.

"We turn to a decisive consideration relative to this question.

"Light does not penetrate everywhere; consequently animals which habitually live in situations where it does not penetrate lack the occasion of exercising the organs of sight, if nature has provided them with them. Moreover, the animals which make part of the plan of organization in which *eyes* are necessarily present, have originally had them. However, since we find them among those which are deprived of the use of this organ, and which have only vestiges concealed and covered over, it should be evident that the impoverishment and even the disappearance of these organs are the result of a constant lack of exercise.

"What proves it is that the organ of *hearing* is never in this condition, and that we always find it in the animals when the nature of their organization should require its existence; the reason is as follows.

"The *cause of sound*, that which, moved by the shock or the vibrations of bodies, transmits to the organ of hearing the impression which it receives, penetrates everywhere, traverses all the media, and even the mass of the densest bodies: from this it results that every animal which makes a part of a plan of organization to which *hearing* is essential, has always occasion to exercise this organ in whatever situation it lives. So, among the *vertebrate animals* we see none deprived of their organs of hearing; but in the groups below them, when the same organs are once wanting, we do not again find them.

" It is not so with the organ of sight, for we see this organ disappear, reappear, and again disappear, in proportion to the possibility or impossibility of the animal's exercising it.

" In the *acephalous molluscs*, the great development of the mantle of these molluscs has rendered their eyes and even their head entirely useless. These organs, also forming a part of a plan of organization which should comprise them, have disappeared and atrophied from constant lack of use.

" Finally, it is a part of the plan of organization of *reptiles*, as in other vertebrate animals, to have four legs appended to their skeleton. The serpents should consequently have four, though they do not form the lowest order of reptiles, and are not so near the fishes as the batrachians (the frogs, the salamanders, etc.).

" However, the serpents having taken up the habit of gliding along the ground, and of concealing themselves in the grass, their body, owing to continually repeated efforts to elongate itself so as to pass through narrow spaces, has acquired a considerable length disproportionate to its size. Moreover, limbs would have been very useless to these animals, and consequently would not have been employed: because long legs would have interfered with their need of gliding, and very short legs, not being more than four in number, would have been incapable of moving their body. Hence the lack of use of these parts having been constant in the races of these animals, has caused the total disappearance of these same parts, although really included in the plan of organization of the animals of their class.

" Many insects which by the natural character of their order, and even of their genus, should have wings, lack them more or less completely from disuse. A quantity of Coleoptera, Orthoptera, Hymenoptera, and of Hemiptera, etc., afford examples; the habits of these animals do not require them to make use of their wings.

"But it is not sufficient to give the explanation of the cause which has brought about the condition of the organs of different animals—a condition which we see to be always the same in those of the same species; we must besides observe the changes of condition produced in the organs of one and the same individual during its life, by the single result of a great change in the special habits in the individuals of its species. The following fact, which is one of the most remarkable, will serve to prove the influence of habits on the condition of organs, and show how changes wrought in the habits of an individual, produce the condition of the organs which are brought into action during the exercise of these habits.

"M. Tenon, member of the Institute, has given an account to the Class of Sciences, that having examined the intestinal canal of several men who had been hard drinkers all their lives, he had constantly found it to be shortened to an extraordinary extent, compared with the same organ in those not given to such a habit.

"We know that hard drinkers, or those who are addicted to drunkenness, take very little solid food, that they eat very lightly, and that the beverage which they take in excess frequently suffices to nourish them.

"Moreover, as fluid aliments, especially spirituous liquors, do not remain a long time either in the stomach or in the intestines, the stomach and the remainder of the intestinal canal lose the habit of being distended in intemperate persons, so also in sedentary persons and those engaged in mental labor, who are habituated to take but little food. Gradually and at length their stomach becomes contracted, and their intestines shortened.

" We are not concerned here with the shrinkage and shortening produced by a puckering of the parts, which permit ordinary extension, if instead of a continued emptiness these viscera should be filled ; the shrinkage and shortening in question are real, considerable, and such that these organs would burst open rather than yield suddenly to the causes which would require ordinary extension.

" In circumstances of persons of the same age, compare a man who, in order to devote himself to habitual study and mental work, which have rendered his digestion more difficult, has contracted the habit of eating lightly, with another who habitually takes a good deal of exercise, walks out often, and eats heartily ; the stomach of the first will be weakened, and a small quantity of food will fill it, while that of the second will be not only maintained in its ordinary health but even strengthened.

" We have here the case of an organ much modified in its dimensions and in its faculties by the single cause of a change in habits during the life of the individual.

" *The frequent use of an organ become constant by habit increases the faculties of this organ, even develops it, and enables it to acquire dimensions and a power of action which it does not possess in animals which exercise less.*

" We have just said that the lack of employment of an organ which necessarily exists modifies it, impoverishes it, and ends by its disappearing entirely.

" I shall now demonstrate that the continued employment of an organ, with the efforts made to draw out its powers under circumstances where it would be of service, strengthens, extends, and enlarges this organ, or creates a new one which can exercise the necessary functions.

" The bird which necessity drives to the water to find there prey fitted for its sustenance, opens the digits of its feet when it wishes to strike the water and propel itself along its surface. The skin which unites these digits at their base, by these acts of spreading apart being unceasingly repeated contracts the habit of extending; so that after a while the broad membranes which connect the digits of ducks, geese, etc., are formed as we see them. The same efforts made in swimming—*i.e.*, in pushing back the water, in order to advance and to move in this liquid—have likewise extended the membrane situated between the digits of the frogs, the sea-turtles, the otter, beaver, etc.

" On the contrary, the bird whose mode of life habituates it to perch on trees, and which is born of individuals who have all contracted this habit, has necessarily the digits of the feet longer and shaped in another way than those of the aquatic animals which I have just mentioned. Its claws, after a while, became elongated, pointed, and curved or hook-like in order to grasp the branches on which the animal often rests.

" Likewise we see that the shore bird, which is not inclined to swim, and which moreover has need of approaching the edge of the water to find there its prey, is in continual danger of sinking in the mud. Now, this bird, wishing to act so that its body shall not fall into the water, makes every effort to extend and elongate its legs. It results from this that the long-continued habit that this bird and the others of its race contract, of extending and continually elongating their legs, is the *cause* of the individuals of this race being raised as if on stilts, having gradually acquired long, naked legs, which are denuded of feathers up to the thighs and often above them (*Système des Animaux sans Vertèbres*, p. 16).

" We also perceive that the same bird, wishing to catch fish without wetting its body, is obliged to make continual efforts to lengthen its neck. Now, the results of these habitual efforts in this individual and in those of its race have enabled them, after a time, to singularly elongate them—as, indeed, is proved by the long neck of all shore birds.

" If any swimming birds, such as the swan and the goose, whose legs are short, nevertheless have a very long neck, it is because these birds in swimming on the surface of the water have the habit of plunging their head down as far as they can, to catch aquatic larvæ and different animalcules for food, and because they make no effort to lengthen their legs.

" When an animal to satisfy its wants makes repeated efforts to elongate its tongue, it will acquire a considerable length (the ant-eater, green woodpecker); when it is obliged to seize anything with this same organ, then its tongue will divide and become forked. That of the humming-birds, which seize with their tongue, and that of the lizard and serpents, which use it to feel and examine objects in front of them, are proofs of what I advocate.

" Wants, always occasioned by circumstances, and followed by sustained efforts to satisfy them, are not limited in results, in modifying—that is to say, in increasing or diminishing—the extent and the faculties of organs; but they also come to displace these same organs when certain of these wants become a necessity.

" The fishes which habitually swim in large bodies of water, having need of seeing laterally, have, in fact, their eyes placed on the sides of the head. Their bodies, more or less flattened according to the *species*, have their sides perpendicular to the plane of the water, and their eyes are placed in such a way that there is an eye on each flattened side. But those fishes whose habits place them under the necessity of constantly approaching the shores, and especially the shelving banks or where the slope is slight, have been forced to swim on their flattened faces, so as to be able to approach nearer the edge of the water. In this situation, receiving more light from above than from beneath, and having a special need of being always attentive to what is going on above them, this need has forced one of their eyes to undergo a kind of displacement, and to assume the very singular situation which is familiar to us in the *soles, turbots, dabs,* etc. (*Pleuronectes* and *Achirus*). The situation of these eyes is asymmetrical, because this results from an incomplete change. Now, this change is entirely completed in the rays, where the transverse flattening of the body is entirely horizontal, as also the head. Also the eyes of the rays, both situated on the upper side, have become symmetrical.

" The serpents which glide along the surface of the ground are obliged chiefly to see elevated objects, or what are above their eyes. This necessity has brought an influence to bear on the situation of the organs of vision in these animals; and, in fact, they have the eyes placed in the lateral and upper parts of the head, so as to easily perceive what is above or at their sides; but they only see for a short distance what is in front of them. Moreover, forced to supply the lack of ability to see and recognize what is in front of their head, and which might injure them, they need only to feel such objects with the aid of their tongue, which they are obliged to dart out with all their power. This habit has not only contributed to render the tongue slender, very long and retractile, but has also led in a great number of species to its division, so as to enable them to feel several objects at once; it has likewise allowed them to form an opening at the end of their head, to enable the tongue to dart out without their being obliged to open their jaws.

" Nothing is more remarkable than the result of habits in the herbivorous mammals.

" The quadruped to whom circumstances and the

wants which they have created have given for a long period, as also to others of its race, the habit of browsing on grass, only walks on the ground, and is obliged to rest there on its four feet the greater part of its life, moving about very little, or only to a moderate extent. The considerable time which this sort of creature is obliged to spend each day to fill itself with the only kind of food which it requires, leads it to move about very little, so that it uses its legs only to stand on the ground, to walk, or run, and they never serve to seize hold of or to climb trees.

" From this habit of daily consuming great amounts of food which distend the organs which receive it, and of only moving about to a limited extent, it has resulted that the bodies of these animals are thick, clumsy, and massive, and have acquired a very great volume, as we see in elephants, rhinoceroses, oxen, buffaloes, horses, etc.

" The habit of standing upright on their four feet during the greater part of the day to browse has given origin to a thick hoof which envelops the extremity of the digits of their feet; and as their toes are not trained to make any movement, and because they have served no other use than as supports, as also the rest of the leg, the most of them are short, are reduced in size, and even have ended by totally disappearing. Thus in the *pachyderms*, some have five toes enveloped in horn, and consequently their foot is divided into five parts; others have only four, and still others only three. But in the *ruminants*, which seem to be the most ancient of mammals, which are limited only to standing on the ground, there are only two digits on each foot, and only a single one is to be found in the *solipedes* (the horse, the ass).

" Moreover, among these herbivorous animals, and especially among the ruminants, it has been found that from the circumstances of the desert countries they inhabit they are incessantly exposed to be the prey of carnivorous animals, and find safety only in precipitous flight. Necessity has forced them to run swiftly; and from the habit they have thus acquired their body has become slenderer and their limbs much more delicate: we see examples in the antelopes, the gazelles, etc.

"Other dangers in our climate to which are continually exposed the deer, the roebuck, the fallow-deer, of perishing from the chase made by man, have reduced them to the same necessity, restrained them to similar habits, and have given rise to the same results.

"The ruminating animals only using their legs as supports, and not having strong jaws, which are only exercised in cutting and browsing on grass, can only fight by striking with the head, by directing against each other the *vertex* of this part.

"In their moments of anger, which are frequent, especially among the males, their internal feelings, by their efforts, more strongly urge the fluids toward this part of their head, and it there secretes the corneous matter in some, and osseous matter mixed with corneous matter in others, which gives origin to solid protuberances; hence the origin of horns and antlers, with which most of these animals have the head armed.

"As regards habits, it is curious to observe the results in the special form and height of the giraffe (*camelopardalis*); we know that this animal, the tallest of mammals, inhabits the interior of Africa, and that it lives in localities where the earth, almost always arid and destitute of herbage, obliges it to browse on the foliage of trees, and to make continual efforts to reach it. It has resulted from this habit, maintained for a long period in all the individuals of its race, that its forelegs have become longer than the hinder ones, and that its neck is so elongated that the giraffe, without standing on its hind legs, raises its head and reaches six meters in height (almost twenty feet).

" Among the birds, the ostriches, deprived of the power of flight, and raised on very long legs, probably owe their singular conformation to analogous circumstances.

" The result of habits is as remarkable in the carnivorous mammals as it is in the herbivorous, but it presents effects of another kind.

" Indeed, those of these mammals which are habituated, as their race, both to climb as well as to scratch or dig in the ground, or to tear open and kill other animals for food, have been obliged to use the digits of their feet; moreover, this habit has favored the separation of their digits, and has formed the claws with which they are armed.

" But among the carnivores there are some which are obliged to run in order to overtake their prey; moreover, since these need and consequently have the habit of daily tearing with their claws and burying them deeply in the body of another animal, to seize and then to tear the flesh, and have been enabled by their repeated efforts to procure for these claws a size and curvature which would greatly interfere in walking or running on stony soil, it has resulted in this case that the animal has been obliged to make other efforts to draw back these too salient and curved claws which would impede it, and hence there has resulted the gradual formation of those special sheaths in which the cats, tigers, lions, etc., withdraw their claws when not in action.

" Thus the efforts in any direction whatever, maintained for a long time or made habitually by certain parts of a living body to satisfy necessities called out by nature or by circumstances, develop these parts and make them acquire dimensions and a shape which they never would have attained if these efforts had not become the habitual action of the animals which have exercised them. The observations made on all the animals known will everywhere furnish examples.

" Can any of them be more striking than that which the *kangaroo* offers us? This animal, which carries its young in its abdominal pouch, has adopted the habit of holding itself erect, standing only on its hind feet and tail, and only changing its position by a series of leaps, in which it preserves its erect attitude so as not to injure its young.

" Let us see the result :

" 1. Its fore legs, of which it makes little use, and on which it rests only during the instant when it leaves its erect attitude, have never reached a development proportionate to that of the other parts, and have remained thin, very small, and weak;

" 2. The hind legs, almost continually in action, both for supporting the body and for leaping, have, on the contrary, obtained a considerable development, and have become very large and strong;

" 3. Finally, the tail, which we see is of much use in supporting the animal and in the performance of its principal movements, has acquired at its base a thickness and a strength extremely remarkable.

" These well-known facts are assuredly well calculated to prove what results from the habitual use in the animals of any organ or part ; and if, when there is observed in an animal an organ especially well developed, strong, and powerful, it is supposed that its habitual use has not produced it, that its continual disuse will make it lose nothing, and, finally, that this organ has always been such since the creation of the species to which this animal belongs, I will ask why our domestic ducks cannot fly like wild ducks—in a word, I might cite a multitude of examples which prove the differences in us resulting from the exercise or lack of use of such of our organs, although these differences might not be maintained in the individuals which follow them genetically, for then their products would be still more considerable.

"I shall prove, in the second part, that when the will urges an animal to any action, the organs which should execute this action are immediately provoked by the affluence of subtile fluids (the nervous fluid), which then become the determining cause which calls for the action in question. A multitude of observations prove this fact, which is now indisputable.

"It results that the multiplied repetitions of these acts of organization strengthen, extend, develop, and even create the organs which are necessary. It is only necessary attentively to observe that which is everywhere occurring to convince ourselves of the well-grounded basis of this cause of organic developments and changes.

"Moreover, every change acquired in an organ by a habit of use sufficient to have produced it is then preserved by heredity (*génération*) if it is common to the individuals which, in fecundation, unite in the reproduction of their species. Finally, this change is propagated, and thus is transmitted to all the individuals which succeed and which are submitted to the same circumstances, unless they have been obliged to acquire it by the means which have in reality created it.

"Besides, in reproductive unions the crossings between the individuals which have different qualities or forms are necessarily opposed to the continuous propagation of these qualities and these forms. We see that in man, who is exposed to so many diverse circumstances which exert an influence on him, the qualities or the accidental defects which he has been in the way of acquiring, are thus prevented from being preserved and propagated by generation. If, when some particular features of form or any defects are acquired, two individuals under this condition should always pair, they would reproduce the same features, and the successive generations being confined to such unions, a special and distinct race would then be formed. But perpetual unions between individuals which do not have the same peculiarities of form would cause all the characteristics acquired by special circumstances to disappear.

"From this we can feel sure that if distances of habitation did not separate men the intermixture by generation would cause the general characteristics which distinguish the different nations to disappear.

"If I should choose to pass in review all the classes, all the orders, all the genera, and all the species of animals which exist, I should show that the structure of individuals and their parts, their organs, their faculties, etc., etc., are in all cases the sole result of the circumstances in which each species is found to be subjected by nature and by the habits which the individuals which compose it have been obliged to contract, and whic. are only the product of a power primitively existing, which has forced the animals into their well-known habits.

"We know that the animal called the *ai*, or the sloth (*Bradypus tridactylus*), is throughout life in a condition so very feeble that it is very slow and limited in its movements, and that it walks on the ground with much difficulty. Its movements are so slow that it is thought that it cannot walk more than fifty steps in a day. It is also known that the structure of this animal is in direct relation with its feeble state or its inaptitude for walking; and that should it desire to make any other movements than those which it is seen to make, it could not do it.

"Therefore, supposing that this animal had received from nature its well-known organization, it is said that this organization has forced it to adopt the habits and the miserable condition it is in.

"I am far from thinking so; because I am convinced that the habits which the individuals of the race of the *ai* were originally compelled to contract have necessarily brought their organization into its actual state.

" Since continual exposure to dangers has at some time compelled the individuals of this species to take refuge in trees and to live in them permanently, and then feed on their leaves, it is evident that then they would give up making a multitude of movements that animals which live on the ground perform.

" All the needs of the *ai* would then be reduced to seizing hold of the branches, to creeping along them or to drawing them in so as to reach the leaves, and then to remain on the tree in a kind of inaction, so as to prevent falling. Besides, this kind of sluggishness would be steadily provoked by the heat of the climate ; for in warm-blooded animals the heat urges them rather to repose than to activity.

" Moreover, during a long period of time the individuals of the race of the *ai* having preserved the habit of clinging to trees and of making only slow and slightly varied movements, just sufficient for their needs, their organization has gradually become adapted to their new habits, and from this it will result :

" 1. That the arms of these animals making continual efforts readily to embrace the branches of trees, would become elongated;

" 2. That the nails of their digits would acquire much length and a hooked shape, by the continued efforts of the animal to retain its hold ;

" 3. That their digits never having been trained to make special movements, would lose all mobility among themselves, would become united, and would only preserve the power of bending or of straightening out all together;

" 4. That their thighs, continually embracing both the trunks and the larger branches of trees, would contract a condition of habitual separation which would tend to widen the pelvis and to cause the cotyloid cavities to be directed backward;

"5. Finally, that a great number of their bones would become fused, and hence several parts of their skeleton would assume an arrangement and a figure conformed to the habits of these animals, and contrary to what would be necessary for them to have for other habits.

"Indeed, this can never be denied, because, in fact, nature on a thousand other occasions shows us, in the power exercised by circumstances on habits, and in that of the influence of habits on forms, dispositions, and the proportion of the parts of animals, truly analogous facts.

"A great number of citations being unnecessary, we now see to what the case under discussion is reduced.

"The fact is that divers animals have each, according to their genus and their species, special habits, and in all cases an organization which is perfectly adapted to these habits.

"From th consideration of this fact, it appears that we should be free to admit either one or the other of the following conclusions, and that only one of them is susceptible of proof.

"*Conclusion admitted up to this day :* Nature (or its Author), in creating the animals, has foreseen all the possible kinds of circumstances in which they should live, and has given to each species an unchanging organization, as also a form determinate and invariable in its different parts, which compels each species to live in the places and in the climate where we find it, and has there preserved its known habits.

"*My own conclusion :* Nature, in producing in succession every species of animal, and beginning with the least perfect or the simplest to end her work with the most perfect, has gradually complicated their structure ; and these animals spreading generally throughout all the inhabitable regions of the globe, each species has received, through the influence of circumstances to which it has been exposed, the habits which we have observed, and the modifications in its organs which observation has shown us it possesses.

" The first of these two conclusions is that believed up to the present day—namely, that held by nearly every one; it implies, in each animal, an unchanging organization and parts which have never varied, and which will never vary; it implies also that the circumstances of the places which each species of animal inhabits will never vary in these localities; for should they vary, the same animals could not live there, and the possibility of discovering similar forms elsewhere, and of transporting them there, would be forbidden.

" The second conclusion is my own : it implies that, owing to the influence of circumstances on habits, and as the result of that of habits on the condition of the parts and even on that of the organization, each animal may receive in its parts and its organization, modifications susceptible of becoming very considerable, and of giving rise to the condition in which we find all animals.

" To maintain that this second conclusion is unfounded, it is necessary at first to prove that each point of the surface of the globe never varies in its nature, its aspect, its situation whether elevated or depressed, its climate, etc., etc.; and likewise to prove that any part of animals does not undergo, even at the end of a long period, any modification by changes of circumstances, and by the necessity which directs them to another kind of life and action than that which is habitual to them.

" Moreover, if a single fact shows that an animal for a long time under domestication differs from the wild form from which it has descended, and if in such a species in domesticity we find a great difference in conformation between the individuals submitted to such habits and those restricted to different habits, then it will be certain that the first conclusion does not conform to the laws of nature, and that, on the contrary, the second is perfectly in accord with them.

"Everything combines then to prove my assertion—namely, that it is not the form, either of the body or of its parts, which gives rise to habits, and to the mode of life among animals; but that it is on the contrary the habits, the manner of living, and all the other influencing circumstances which have, after a time, constituted the form of the body and of the parts of animals. With the new forms, new faculties have been acquired, and gradually nature has come to form the animals as we actually see them.

"Can there be in natural history a consideration more important, and to which we should give more attention, than that which I have just stated?

"We will end this first part with the principles and the exposition of the natural classification of animals."

In the fourth chapter of the third part (vol. ii. pp. 276–301) Lamarck treats of the internal feelings of certain animals, which provoke wants (*besoins*). This is the subject which has elicited so much adverse criticism and ridicule, and has in many cases led to the wholesale rejection of all of Lamarck's views. It is generally assumed or stated by Lamarck's critics, who evidently did not read his book carefully, that while he claimed that the plants were evolved by the direct action of the physical factors, that in the case of all the animals the process was indirect. But this is not correct. He evidently, as we shall see, places the lowest animals, those without (or what he supposed to be without) a nervous system, in the same category as the plants. He distinctly states at the outset that only certain animals and man are endowed with this singular faculty, " which consists in being able to experience *internal emotions* which provoke the wants and different external or internal causes, and which give birth to the power which enables them to perform different actions."

" The nervous fluid," he says, " can, then, undergo movements in certain parts of its mass, as well as in every part at once ; moreover, it is these latter movements which constitute the *general movements* (*ébranlements*) of this fluid, and which we now proceed to consider.

" The general movements of the nervous fluid are of two kinds ; namely,

" 1. Partial movements (*ébranlements*), which finally become general and end in a reaction. It is the movements of this sort which produce feeling. We have treated of them in the third chapter.

" 2. The movements which are general from the time they begin, and which form no reaction. It is these which constitute internal emotions, and it is of them alone of which we shall treat.

" But previously, it is necessary to say a word regarding the *feeling of existence*, because this feeling is the source from which the inner emotions originate.

" *On the Feeling of Existence.*

" The feeling of existence (*sentiment d'existence*), which I shall call *inner feeling*,* so as to separate from it the idea of a general condition (*généralité*) which it does not possess, since it is not common to

---

* The expression " *sentiment intérieur* " may be nearly equivalent to the " organic sense " of modern psychologists, but more probably corresponds to our word consciousness.

all living beings and not even to all animals, is a very obscure feeling, with which are endowed those animals provided with a nervous system sufficiently developed to give them the faculty of feeling.

" This sentiment, very obscure as it is, is nevertheless very powerful, for it is the source of inner emotions which test (*éprouvent*) the individuals possessing it, and, as the result, this singular force urges these individuals to themselves produce the movements and the actions which their wants require. Moreover this feeling, considered as a very active *motor*, only acts thus by sending to the muscles which necessarily cause these movements and actions the nervous fluid which excites them. . . .

" Indeed, as the result of organic or vital movements which are produced in every animal, that which possesses a nervous system sufficiently developed has physical sensibility and continually receives in every inner and sensitive part impressions which continually affect it, and which it feels in general without being able to distinguish any single one.

" The sentiment of existence [consciousness] is general, since almost every sensitive part of the body shares in it. ' It constitutes this *me* (*moi*) with which all animals, which are only sensitive, are penetrated, without perceiving it, but which those possessing a brain are able to notice, having the power of thought and of giving attention to it. Finally, it is in all the source of a power which is aroused by wants, which acts effectively only by emotion, and through which the movements and actions derive the force which produces them.' . . .

" Finally, the inner feeling only manifests its power, and causes movements, when there exists a system for muscular movement, which is always dependent on the nervous system, and cannot take place without it."

The author then states that these emotions of the organic sense may operate in the animals and in man either without or with an act of their will.

"From what has been said, we cannot doubt but that the inner and general feeling which urges the animals possessing a nervous system fitted for feeling should be susceptible of being aroused by the causes which affect it; moreover, these causes are always the need both of satisfying hunger, of escaping dangers, of avoiding pain, of seeking pleasure, or that which is agreeable to the individual, etc.

"The emotions of the inner feeling can only be recognized by man, who alone pays attention to them, but he only perceives those which are strong, which excite his whole being, such as a view from a precipice, a tragic scene, etc."

Lamarck then divides the emotions into physical and moral, the latter arising from our ideas, thoughts —in short, our intellectual acts—in the account of which we need not follow him.

In the succeeding chapter (V.) the author dilates on the force which causes actions in animals. "We know," he says "that plants can satisfy their needs without moving, since they find their food in the environing *milieux*. But it is not the same with animals, which are obliged to move about to procure their sustenance. Moreover, most of them have other wants to satisfy, which require other kinds of movements and acts." This matter is discussed in the author's often leisurely and prolix way, with more or less repetition, which we will condense.

The lowest animals—those destitute of a nervous system—move in response to a stimulus from without.

Nature has gradually created the different organs of animals, varying the structure and situation of these organs according to circumstances, and has progressively improved their powers. She has begun by borrowing from without, so to speak—from the environment—the *productive force*, both of organic movements and those of the external parts. "She has thus transported this force [the result of heat, electricity, and perhaps others (p. 307)] into the animal itself, and, finally, in the most perfect animals she has placed a great part of this force at their disposal, as I will soon show."

This force incessantly introduced into the lowest animals sets in motion the visible fluids of the body and excites the irritability of their contained parts, giving rise to different contractile movements which we observe; hence the appearance of an irresistible propensity (*penchant*) which constrains them to execute those movements which by their continuity or their repetition give rise to habits.

The most imperfect animals, such as the *Infusoria*, especially the monads, are nourished by absorption and by "an internal inhibition of absorbed matters." "They have," he says, "no power of seeking their food, they have not even the power of recognizing it, but they absorb it because it comes in contact with every side of them (*avec tous les points de leur individu*), and because the water in which they live furnishes it to them in sufficient abundance."

"These frail animals, in which the subtile fluids of the environing *milieux* constitute the stimulating cause of the orgasm, of irritability and of organic

movements, execute, as I have said, contractile movements which, provoked and varied without ceasing
by this stimulating cause, facilitate and hasten the
absorptions of which I have just spoken." . . .

*On the Transportation of the force-producing Move-
ments in the Interior of Animals.*

" If nature were confined to the employment of its
first means—namely, of a force entirely external and
foreign to the animal—its work would have remained
very important ; the animals would have remained
machines totally passive, and she would never have
given origin in any of these living beings to the admirable phenomena of sensibility, of inmost feelings
of existence which result therefrom, of the power of
action, finally, of ideas, by which she can create the
most wonderful of all, that of thought—in a word,
intelligence.

" But, wishing to attain these grand results, she has
by slow degrees prepared the means, in gradually
giving consistence to the internal parts of animals ;
in differentiating the organs, and in multiplying and
farther forming the fluids contained, etc., after which
she has transported into the interior of these animals
that force productive of movements and of actions
which in truth it would not dominate at first, but
which she has come to place, in great part, at their
disposition when their organization should become
very much more perfect.

" Indeed, from the time that the animal organization had sufficiently advanced in its structure to possess a nervous system—even slightly developed, as in
insects—the animals provided with this organization
were endowed with an intimate sense of their existence, and from that time the force productive of
movements was conveyed into the very interior of
the animal.

" I have already made it evident that this internal force which produces movements and actions should derive its origin in the intimate feeling of existence which animals with a nervous system possess, and that this feeling, solicited or aroused by needs, should then start into motion the subtile fluid contained in the nerves and carry it to the muscles which should act, this producing the actions which the needs require.

" Moreover, every want felt produces an emotion in the inner feeling of the individual which experiences it; and from this emotion of the feeling in question arises the force which gives origin to the movement of the parts which are placed in activity. . . .

" Thus, in the animals which possess the power of acting—namely, the force productive of movements and actions—the inner feeling, which on each occasion originates this force, being excited by some need, places in action the power or force in question; excites the movement of displacement in the subtile fluid of the nerves—which the ancients called *animal spirits;* directs this fluid towards that of its organs which any want impels to action; finally makes this same fluid flow back into its habitual reservoirs when the needs no longer require the organ to act.

" The inner feeling takes the place of the *will;* for it is now important to consider that every animal which does not possess the special organ in which or by which it executes thoughts, judgments, etc., has in reality no will, does not make a choice, and consequently cannot control the movements which its inner feeling excites. *Instinct* directs these actions, and we shall see that this direction always results from emotions of the inner feeling, in which intelligence has no part, and from the organization even which the habits have modified, in such a manner that the needs of animals which are in this category, being necessarily limited and always the same in the same species, the inner feeling and, consequently, the power of acting, always produces the same actions.

" It is not the same in animals which besides a nervous system have a brain [the author meaning the higher vertebrates], and which make comparisons, judgments, thoughts, etc. These same animals control more or less their power of action according to the degree of perfection of their brain ; and although they are still strongly subjected to the results of their habits, which have modified their structure, they enjoy more or less freedom of the will, can choose, and can vary their acts, or at least some of them."

Lamarck then treats of the consumption and exhaustion of the nervous fluid in the production of animal movements, resulting in fatigue.

He next occupies himself with the origin of the inclination to the same actions, and of instinct in animals.

" The cause of the well-known phenomenon which constrains almost all animals to always perform the same acts, and that which gives rise in man to a propensity (*penchant*) to repeat every action, becoming habitual, assuredly merits investigation.

" The animals which are only ' sensible ' *—namely, which possess no brain, cannot think, reason, or perform intelligent acts, and their perceptions being often very confused—do not reason and can scarcely vary their actions. They are, then, invariably bound by habits. Thus the insects, which of all animals endowed with feeling have the least perfect nervous

---

* Lamarck's division of *Animaux sensibles* comprises the insects, arachnids, crustacea, annelids, cirripedes, and molluscs.

system,* have perceptions of objects which affect them, and seem to have memory of them when they are repeated. Yet they can vary their actions and change their habits, though they do not possess the organ whose acts could give them the means.

" On the Instincts of Animals.

"We define *instinct* as the sum (*ensemble*) of the decisions (*déterminations*) of animals in their actions; and, indeed, some have thought that these determinations were the product of a rational choice, and consequently the fruit of experience. Others, says Cabanis, may think with the observers of all ages that several of these decisions should not be ascribed to any kind of reasoning, and that, without ceasing as for that to have their source in physical sensibility, they are most often formed without the will of the individuals able to have any other part than in better directing the execution. It should be added, without the will having any part in it ; for when it does not act, it does not, of course, direct the execution.

"If it had been considered that all the animals which enjoy the power of sensation have their inner feeling susceptible of being aroused by their needs, and that the movements of their nervous fluids, which result from these emotions, are constantly directed by this inner sentiment and by habits, then it has been felt that in all the animals deprived of intelligence all the decisions of action can never be the result of a rational choice, of judgment, of profitable experience—in a word, of will—but that they are subjected to needs which certain sensations excite, and which awaken the inclinations which urge them on.

"In the animals even which enjoy the power of

---

* Rather a strange view to take, as the brain of insects is now known to be nearly as complex as that of mammals.

performing certain intelligent acts, it is still more often the inner feeling ,and the inclinations originating from habits which decide, without choice, the acts which animals perform.

" Moreover, although the executing power of movements and of actions, as also the cause which directs them, should be entirely internal, it is not well, as has been done,* to limit to internal impressions the primary cause or provocation of these acts, with the intention to restrict to external impressions that which provokes intelligent acts ; for, from what few facts are known bearing on these considerations, we are convinced that, either way, the causes which arouse and provoke acts are sometimes internal and sometimes external, that these same causes give rise in reality to impressions all of which act internally.

" According to the idea generally attached to the word *instinct* the faculty which this word expresses is considered as a light which illuminates and guides animals in their actions, and which is with them what reason is to us.   No one has shown that instinct can be a force which calls into action; that this force acts effectively without any participation of the will, and that it is constantly directed by acquired inclinations."

There are, the author states, two kinds of causes which can arouse the inner feeling (organic sense)— namely, those which depend on intellectual acts, and those which, without arising from it, immediately excite it and force it to direct its power of acting in the direction of acquired inclinations.

" These are the only causes of this last kind, which

---

* Richerand, *Physiologie.* vol ii. p. 151.

constitute all the acts of *instinct ;* and. as these acts are not the result of deliberation, of choice, of judgment, the actions which arise from them always satisfy, surely and without error, the wants felt and the propensities arising from habits.

" Hence, *instinct* in animals is an inclination which necessitates that from sensations provoked while giving rise to wants the animal is impelled to act without the participation of any thought or any act of the will.

" This propensity owes to the organization what the habits have modified in its favor, and it is excited by impressions and wants which arouse the organic sense of the individual and put it in the way of sending the nervous fluid in the direction which the propensity in activity needs to the muscles to be placed in action.

" I have already said that the habit of exercising such an organ, or such a part of the body, to satisfy the needs which often spring up, should give to the subtile fluid which changes its place where is to be operated the power which causes action so great a facility in moving towards this organ, where it has been so often employed, that this habit should in a way become inherent in the nature of the individual, which is unable to change it.

" Moreover, the wants of animals possessing a nervous system being, in each case, dependent on the structure of these organisms, are :

" 1. Of obtaining any kind of food ;

" 2. Of yielding to sexual fecundation which excites in them certain sensations ;

" 3. Of avoiding pain ;

" 4. Of seeking pleasure or happiness.

" To satisfy these wants they contract different kinds of habits, which are transformed into so many propensities, which they can neither resist nor change. From this originate their habitual actions, and their special propensities to which we give the name of *instinct*.*

" This propensity of animals to preserve their habits and to renew the actions resulting from them being once acquired, is then propagated by means of reproduction or generation, which preserves the organization and the disposition of parts in the state thus attained, so that this same propensity already exists in the new individuals even before they have exercised it.

" It is thus that the same habits and the same *instinct* are perpetuated from generation to generation in the different species or races of animals, without offering any notable variation,† so long as it does not suffer change in the circumstances essential to the mode of life."

---

* " As all animals do not have the power of performing voluntary acts, so in like manner *instinct* is not common to all animals ; for those lacking the nervous system also want the organic sense, and can perform no instinctive acts.

" These imperfect animals are entirely passive, they do nothing of themselves, they have no wants, and nature as regards them treats them as she does plants. But as they are irritable in their parts, the means which nature employs to maintain their existence enables them to execute movements which we call actions."

It thus appears that Lamarck practically regards the lowest animals as automata, but we must remember that the line he draws between animals with and without a nervous system is an artificial one, as some of the forms which he supposed to be destitute of a nervous system are now known to possess one.

† It should be noticed that Lamarck does *not* absolutely state that there are *no* variations whatever in instinct. His words are much less positive : " *Sans offrer de variation notable.*" This does not exclude the fact, discovered since his time, that instincts are more or less variable, thus affording grounds for Darwin's theory of the origin of new kinds of instincts from the " accidental variation of instincts." Professor James' otherwise excellent version of Lamarck's view is inexact and misleading when he makes Lamarck say that instincts are " perpetuated *without variation* from one generation to another, so long as the outward conditions of existence remain the same " (*The Principles of Psychology*, vol. ii., p. 678, 1890). He leaves out the word notable. The italics are ours. Farther on (p. 337), it will be seen that Lamarck acknowledges that in birds and mammals instinct is variable.

"*On the Industry of Certain Animals.*

" In those animals which have no brain that which we call *industry* as ɛpplied to certain of their actions does not deserve such a name, for it is a mistake to attribute to them a faculty which they do not possess.

" Propensities transmitted and received by heredity (*génération*); habits of performing complicated actions, and which result from these acquired propensities; finally, different difficulties gradually and habitually overcome by as many emotions of the organic sense (*sentiment intérieur*), constitute the sum of actions which are always the same in the individuals of the same race, to which we inconsiderately give the name of *industry*.

" The instinct of animals being formed by the habit of satisfying the four kinds of wants mentioned above, and resulting from the ɛ ropensities acquired for a long time which urge them on in a way determined for each species, there comes to pass, in the case of some, only a complication in the actions which can satisfy these four kinds of wants, or certain of them, and, indeed, only the different difficulties necessary to be overcome have gradually compelled the animal to extend and make contrivances, and have led it, without choice or any intellectual act, but only by the emotions of the organic sense, to perform such and such acts.

" Hence the origin, in certain animals, of different complicated actions, which has been called *industry*, and which are so enthusiastically admired, because it has always been supposed, at least tacitly, that these actions were contrived and deliberately planned, which is plainly erroneous. They are evidently the fruit of a necessity which has expanded and directed the habits of the animals performing them, and which renders them such as we observe.

" What I have just said is especially applicable to the invertebrate animals, in which there enters no

act of intelligence. None of these can indeed freely
vary its actions; none of them has the power of
abandoning what we call its *industry* to adopt any
other kind.

" There is, then, nothing wonderful in the supposed
industry of the ant-lion (*Myrmeleon formica-leo*),
which, having thrown up a hillock of movable sand,
waits until its booty is thrown down to the bottom
of its funnel by the showers of sand to become its
victim; also there is none in the manœuvre of the
oyster, which, to satisfy all its wants, does nothing but
open and close its shell. So long as their organization is not changed they will always, both of them,
do what we see them do, and they will do it neither
voluntarily nor rationally.

" This is not the case with the vertebrate animals,
and it is among them, especially in the birds and
mammals, that we observe in their actions traces of a
true *industry;* because in difficult cases their intelligence, in spite of their propensity to habits, can aid
them in varying their actions. These acts, however,
are not common, and are only slightly manifested in
certain races which have exercised them more, as we
have had frequent occasion to remark."

Lamarck then (chapter vi.) examines into the nature
of the *will*, which he says is really the principle underlying all the actions of animals. The will, he says, is
one of the results of thought, the result of a reflux of
a portion of the nervous fluid towards the parts which
are to act.

He compares the brain to a register on which are
imprinted ideas of all kinds acquired by the individual,
so that this individual provokes at will an effusion of
the nervous fluid on this register, and directs it to any
particular page. The remainder of the second volume

22

(chapter vii.) is devoted to the understanding, its origin and that of ideas. The following additions relative to chapters vii. and viii. of the first part of this work are from vol. ii., pp. 451–466.

In the last of June, 1809, the menagerie of the Museum of Natural History having received a Phoca (*Phoca vitulina*), Lamarck, as he says, had the opportunity of observing its movements and habits. After describing its habits in swimming and moving on land and observing its relation to the clawed mammals, he says his main object is to remark that the seals do not have the hind legs arranged in the same direction as the axis of their body, because these animals are constrained to habitually use them to form a caudal fin, closing and widening, by spreading their digits, the paddle (*palette*) which results from their union.

" The morses, on the contrary, which are accustomed to feed on grass near the shore, never use their hind feet as a caudal fin; but their feet are united together with the tail, and cannot separate. Thus in animals of similar origin we see a new proof of the effect of habits on the form and structure of organs."

He then turns to the flying mammals, such as the flying squirrel (*Sciurus volans, ærobates, petaurista, sagitta,* and *volucella*), and then explains the origin of their adaptation for flying leaps.

" These animals, more modern than the seals, having the habit of extending their limbs while leaping to form a sort of *parachute*, can *only* make a very prolonged leap when they glide down from a tree or spring only a short distance from one tree to another. Now, by frequent repetitions of such leaps, in the individuals of these races the skin of their sides is expanded on each side into a loose membrane, which connects the hind and fore legs, and which, enclosing a volume of air, prevents their sudden falling. These animals are, moreover, without membranes between the fingers and toes.

" The Galeopithecus (*Lemur volans*), undoubtedly a more ancient form but with the same habits as the flying squirrel (*Pteromys* Geoff.), has the skin of the *flancs* more ample, still more developed, connecting not only the hinder with the fore legs, but in addition the fingers and the tail with the hind feet. Moreover, they leap much farther than the flying squirrels, and even make a sort of flight.*

" Finally, the different bats are probably mammals still older than the Galeopithecus, in the habit of extending their membrane and even their fingers to encompass a greater volume of air, so as to sustain their bodies when they fly out into the air.

" By these habits, for so long a period contracted and preserved, the bats have obtained not only lateral membranes, but also an extraordinary elongation of the fingers of their fore feet (with the exception of the thumb), between which are these very ample membranes uniting them; so that these membranes of the hands become continuous with those of the

---

* It is interesting to compare with this Darwin's theory of the origin of the same animals, the flying squirrels and Galeopithecus (*Origin of Species*, 5th edition, New York, pp. 173–174), and see how he invokes the Lamarckian factors of change of " climate and vegetation " and " changing conditions of life," to originate the variations before natural selection can act. His account is a mixture of Lamarckism with the added Darwinian factors of competition and natural selection. We agree with this view, that the change in environment and competition sets the ball in motion, the work being finished by the selective process. The act of springing and the first attempts at flying also involve strong emotions and mental efforts, and it can hardly be denied that these Lamarckian factors came into continual play during the process of evolution of these flying creatures.

flanks, and with those which connect the tail with the two hind feet, forming in these animals great membranous wings with which they fly perfectly, as everybody knows.

"Such is then the power of habits, which have a singular influence on the conformation of parts, and which give to the animals which have for a long time contracted certain of them, faculties not found in other animals.

"As regards the amphibious animals of which I have often spoken, it gives me pleasure to communicate to my readers the following reflections which have arisen from an examination of all the objects which I have taken into consideration in my studies, and seen more and more to be confirmed.

"I do not doubt but that the mammals have in reality originated from them, and that they are the veritable cradle (*berceau*) of the entire animal kingdom.

"Indeed, we see that the least perfect animals (and they are the most numerous) live only in the water; hence it is probable, as I have said (vol. ii., p. 85), that it is only in the water or in very humid places that nature causes and still forms, under favorable conditions, direct or spontaneous generations which have produced the simplest animalcules and those from which have successively been derived all the other animals.

"We know that the Infusoria, the polyps, and the Radiata only live in the water; that the worms even only live some in the water and others in very damp places.

"Moreover, regarding the worms, which seem to form an initial branch of the animal scale, since it is evident that the Infusoria form another branch, we may suppose that among those of them which are wholly aquatic—namely, which do not live in the bodies of other animals, such as the Gordius and many others still unknown—there are doubtless a great many different aquatic forms; and that among these aquatic worms, those which afterwards habitually expose themselves to the air have probably produced amphibious insects, such as the mosquitoes, the ephemeras, etc., etc., which have successively given origin to all the insects which live solely in the air. But several races of these having changed their habits by the force of circumstances, and having formed habits of a life solitary, retired, or hidden, have given rise to the arachnides, almost all of which also live in the air.

" Finally, those of the arachnides which have frequented the water, which have consequently become progressively habituated to live in it, and which finally cease to expose themselves to the air—this indicates the relations which, connecting the Scolopendræ to Julus, this to the Oniscus, and the last to Asellus, shrimps, etc., have caused the existence of all the Crustacea.

" The other aquatic worms which are never exposed to the air, multiplying and diversifying their races with time, and gradually making progress in the complication of their structure, have caused the formation of the Annelida, Cirripedia, and molluscs, which together form an uninterrupted portion of the animal scale.

" In spite of the considerable hiatus which we observe between the known molluscs and the fishes, the molluscs, whose origin I have just indicated, have, by the intermediation of those yet remaining unknown, given origin to the fishes, as it is evident that the latter have given rise to the reptiles.

" In continuing to consult the probabilities on the origin of different animals, we cannot doubt but that the reptiles, by two distinct branches which circumstances have brought about, have given rise on one side to the formation of birds, and on the other to that of amphibious mammals, which have given in their turn origin to all the other mammals.*

" Indeed, the fishes having caused the formation of Batrachia, and these of the Ophidian reptiles, both having only one auricle in the heart, nature has easily come to give a heart with a double auricle to other reptiles which constitute two special branches ; finally, she has easily arrived at the end of forming, in the animals which had originated from each of these branches, a heart with two ventricles.

" Thus, among the reptiles whose heart has a double auricle, on the one side, the Chelonians seem to have given origin to the birds ; if, independently of several relations which we cannot disregard, I should place the head of a tortoise on the neck of certain birds, I should perceive almost no disparity in the general physiognomy of the factitious animal ; and on the other side, the saurians, especially the ' planicaudes,' such as the crocodiles, seem to have given origin to the amphibious mammals.

" If the branch of the Chelonians has given rise to birds, we can yet presume that the palmipede aquatic birds, especially the *brevipennes,* such as the penguins and the *manchots,* have given origin to the mono-tremes.

" Finally, if the branch of saurians has given rise to the amphibious mammals, it will be most probable that this branch is the source whence all the mammals have taken their origin.

" I therefore believe myself authorized to think that the terrestrial mammals originally descended from those aquatic mammals that we call Amphibia. Because the latter being divided into three branches by the diversity of the habits which, with the lapse of time, they have adopted, some have caused the forma-

* This sagacious, though crude suggestion of the origin of birds and mammals from the reptiles is now, after the lapse of nearly a century, being confirmed by modern morphologists and palæontologists.

tion of the Cetacea, others that of the ungulated mammals, and still others that of the unguiculate mammals.

" For example, those of the Amphibia which have preserved the habit of frequenting the shores differ in the manner of taking their food. Some among them accustoming themselves to browse on herbage, such as the morses and lamatines, gradually gave origin to the ungulate mammals, such as the pachyderms, ruminants, etc.; the others, such as the Phocidæ, contracting the habit of feeding on fishes and marine animals, caused the existence of the unguiculate mammals, by means of races which, while becoming differentiated, became entirely terrestrial.

" But those ·aquatic mammals which would form the habit of never leaving the water, and only rising to breathe at the surface, would probably give origin to the different known cetaceans. Moreover, the ancient and complete habitation of the Cetacea in the ocean has so modified their structure that it is now very difficult to recognize the source whence they have derived their origin.

" Indeed, since the enormous length of time during which these animals have lived in the depths of the sea, never using their hind feet in seizing objects, their disused feet have wholly disappeared, as also their skeleton, and even the pelvis serving as their attachment.

" The alteration which the cetaceans have undergone in their limbs, owing to the influence of the medium in which they live and the habits which they have there contracted, manifests itself also in their fore limbs, which, entirely enveloped by the skin, no longer show externally the fingers in which they end ; so that they only offer on each side a fin which contains concealed within it the skeleton of a hand.

" Assuredly, the cetaceans being mammals, it entered into the plan of their structure to have four limbs like the others, and consequently a pelvis to sustain their hind legs. But here, as elsewhere, that which is lacking in them is the result of atrophy brought about, at the end of a long time, by the want of use of the parts which were useless.

" If we consider that in the Phocæ, where the pelvis still exists, this pelvis is impoverished, narrowed, and with no projections on the hips, we see that the lessened (*médiocre*) use of the hind feet of these animals must be the cause, and that if this use should entirely cease, the hind limbs and even the pelvis would in the end disappear.

" The considerations which I have just presented may doubtless appear as simple conjectures, because it is possible to establish them only on direct and positive proofs. But if we pay any attention to the observations which I have stated in this work, and if then we examine carefully the animals which I have mentioned, as also the result of their habits and their surroundings, we shall find that these conjectures will acquire, after this examination, an eminent probability.

" The following *tableau** will facilitate the comprehension of what I have just stated. It will be seen that, in my opinion, the animal scale begins at least by two special branches, and that in the course of its extent some branchlets (*rameaux*) would seem to terminate in certain places.

" This series of animals beginning with two branches where are situated the most imperfect, the first of these branches received their existence only by direct or spontaneous generation.

" A strong reason prevents our knowing the changes successively brought about which have produced the condition in which we observe them ; it is because we are never witnesses of these changes. Thus we see the work when done, but never watching them

* Reproduced on page 193.

during the process, we are naturally led to believe that things have always been as we see them, and not as they have progressively been brought about.

"Among the changes which nature everywhere incessantly produces in her *ensemble*, and her laws remain always the same, such of these changes as, to bring about, do not need much more time than the duration of human life, are easily understood by the man who observes them; but he cannot perceive those which are accomplished at the end of a considerable time.

"If the duration of human life only extended to the length of a *second*, and if there existed one of our actual clocks mounted and in movement, each individual of our species who should look at the hour-hand of this clock would never see it change its place in the course of his life, although this hand would really not be stationary. The observations of thirty generations would never learn anything very evident as to the displacement of this hand, because its movement, only being that made during half a minute, would be too slight to make an impression; and if observations much more ancient should show that this same hand had really moved, those who should see the statement would not believe it, and would suppose there was some error, each one having always seen the hand on the same point of the dial-plate.

"I leave to my readers all the applications to be made regarding this supposition.

"*Nature*, that immense totality of different beings and bodies, in every part of which exists an eternal circle of movements and changes regulated by law; totality alone unchangeable, so long as it pleases its SUBLIME AUTHOR to make it exist, should be regarded as a whole constituted by its parts, for a purpose which its Author alone knows, and not exclusively for any one of them.

" Each part necessarily is obliged to change, and to cease to be one in order to constitute another, with interests opposed to those of all ; and if it has the power of reasoning it finds this whole imperfect.   In reality, however, this whole is perfect, and completely fulfils the end for which it was designed."

The last work in which Lamarck discussed the theory of descent was in his introduction to the *Animaux sans Vertèbres*.   But here the only changes of importance are his four laws, which we translate, and a somewhat different phylogeny of the animal kingdom.

The four laws differ from the two given in the *Philosophie zoologique* in his theory (the second law) accounting for the origin of a new organ, the result of a new need.

" *First law :* Life, by its proper forces, continually tends to increase the volume of every body which possesses it, and to increase the size of its parts, up to a limit which it brings about.

" *Second law :* The production of a new organ in an animal body results from the supervention of a new want (*besoin*) which continues to make itself felt, and of a new movement which this want gives rise to and maintains.

" *Third law :* The development of organs and their power of action are constantly in ratio to the employment of these organs.

" *Fourth law :* Everything which has been acquired, impressed upon, or changed in the organization of individuals, during the course of their life is preserved by generation and transmitted to the new individuals which have descended from. those which have undergone those changes."

In explaining the second law he says:

" The foundation of this law derives its proof from the third, in which the facts known allow of no doubt; for, if the forces of action of an organ, by their increase, further develop this organ—namely, increase its size and power, as is constantly proved by facts—we may be assured that the forces by which it acts, just originated by a new want felt, would necessarily give birth to the organ adapted to satisfy this new want, if this organ had not before existed.

" In truth, in animals so low as not to be able to *feel*, it cannot be that we should attribute to a felt want the formation of a new organ, this formation being in such a case the product of a mechanical cause, as that of a new movement produced in a part of the fluids of the animal.

" It is not the same in animals with a more complicated structure, and which are able to *feel*. They feel wants, and each want felt, exciting their inner feeling, forthwith sets the fluids in motion and forces them towards the point of the body where an action may satisfy the want experienced. Now, if there exists at this point an organ suitable for this action, it is immediately cited to act; and if the organ does not exist, and only the felt want be for instance pressing and continuous, gradually the organ originates, and is developed on account of the continuity and energy of its employment.

" If I had not been convinced: 1, that the thought alone of an action which strongly interests it suffices to arouse the *inner feeling* of an individual; 2, that a felt want can itself arouse the feeling in question; 3, that every emotion of *inner feeling*, resulting from a want which is aroused, directs at the same instant a mass of nervous fluid to the points to be set in activity, that it also creates a flow thither of the fluids of the body, and especially nutrient ones; that, finally, it then places in activity the organs already existing, or makes efforts for the formation of those which would not have existed there, and which a continual want would therefore render necessary—I should have had doubts as to the reality of the law which I have just indicated.

" But, although it may be very difficult to verify this law by observation, I have no doubt as to the grounds on which I base it, the necessity of its existence being involved in that of the third law, which is now well established.

" I conceive, for example, that a *gasteropod mollusc*, which, as it crawls along, finds the need of feeling the bodies in front of it, makes efforts to touch those bodies with some of the foremost parts of its head, and sends to these every time supplies of nervous fluids, as well as other fluids—I conceive, I say, that it must result from this reiterated afflux towards the points in question that the nerves which abut at these points will, by slow degrees, be extended. Now, as in the same circumstances other fluids of the animal flow also to the same places, and especially nourishing fluids, it must follow that two or more tentacles will appear and develop insensibly under those circumstances on the points referred to.

" This is doubtless what has happened to all the races of *Gasteropods*, whose wants have compelled them to adopt the habit of feeling bodies with some part of their head.

" But if there occur, among the *Gasteropods*, any races which, by the circumstances which concern their mode of existence or life, do not experience such wants, then their head remains without tentacles; it has even no projection, no traces of tentacles, and this is what has happened in the case of *Bullæa, Bulla*, and *Chiton*."

In the *Supplément à la Distribution générale des Animaux* (Introduction, p. 342), concerning the real order of origin of the invertebrate classes, Lamarck proposes a new genealogical tree. He states that the order of the animal series " is far from simple, that it is branching, and seems even to be composed of several distinct series;" though farther on (p. 456) he adds:

" Je regarde *l'ordre de la production* des animaux comme formé de deux séries distinctes.

" Ainsi, je soumets à la méditation des zoologistes l'ordre présumé de la *formation* des animaux, tel que l'exprime le tableau suivant:"

In the matter of the origin of instinct, as in evolution in general, Lamarck appears to have laid the foundation on which Darwin's views, though he throws aside Lamarck's factors, must rest. The " inherited habit " theory is thus stated by Lamarck.

Instinct, he claims, is not common to all animals, since the lowest forms, like plants, are entirely passive under the influences of the surrounding medium; they have no wants, are automata.

" But animals with a nervous system have *wants*, *i.e.*, they feel hunger, sexual desires, they desire to avoid pain or to seek pleasure, etc. To satisfy these wants they contract habits, which are gradually transformed into so many *propensities* which they can neither resist nor change. Hence arise habitual actions and special propensities, to which we give the name of *instinct*.

" These propensities are inherited and become innate in the young, so that they act instinctively from the moment of birth. Thus the same habits and instincts are perpetuated from one generation to another, with no *notable* variations, so long as the species does not suffer change in the circumstances essential to its mode of life."

The same views are repeated in the introduction to the *Animaux sans Vertèbres* (1815), and again in 1820, in his last work, and do not need to be translated, as they are repetitions of his previously published views in the *Philosophie zoologique*.

Unfortunately, to illustrate his thoughts on instinct Lamarck does not give us any examples, nor did he apparently observe to any great extent the habits of animals. In these days one cannot follow him in drawing a line—as regards the possession of instincts—between the lowest organisms, or Protozoa, and the groups provided with a nervous system.

Lamarck's meaning of the word " besoins," or wants or needs.—Lamarck's use of the word wants or needs (*besoins*) has, we think, been greatly misunderstood and at times caricatured or pronounced as " absurd." The distinguished French naturalist, Quatrefages, although he was not himself an evolutionist, has protested against the way Lamarck's views have been caricatured. By nearly all authors he is represented as claiming that by simply " willing " or " desiring " the individual bird or other animal radically and with more or less rapidity changed its shape or that of some particular organ or part of the body. This is, as we have seen, by no means what he states. In no instance does he speak of an animal as simply " desiring " to modify an organ in any way. The doctrine of appetency attributed to Lamarck is without foundation. In all the examples given he intimates that owing to changes in environment, leading to isolation in a new area separating a large number of individuals from their accustomed habitat, they are driven by necessity (*besoin*) or new needs to adopt a new or different mode of life—new habits. These efforts, whatever they may be—such as attempts to fly, swim, wade, climb, burrow, etc., continued for a long time "in all the individuals of its species," or the great number forced by competition to migrate and become segregated from the others of the original species—finally, owing to the changed surroundings, affect the mass of individuals thus isolated, and their organs thus exercised in a special direction undergo a slow modification.

Even so careful a writer as Dr. Alfred R. Wallace does not quite fairly, or with exactness, state what Lamarck says, when in his classical essay of 1858 he represents Lamarck as stating that the giraffe acquired its long neck by *desiring* to reach the foliage of the more lofty shrubs, and constantly stretching its neck for the purpose. On the contrary, he does not use the word "desiring" at all. What Lamarck does say is that—

"The giraffe lives in dry, desert places, without herbage, so that it is obliged to browse on the leaves of trees, and is continually forced to reach up to them. It results from this habit, continued for a long time in all the individuals of its species, that its fore limbs have become so elongated that the giraffe, without raising itself erect on its hind legs, raises its head and reaches six meters high (almost twenty feet)." *

---

* This is taken from my article, "Lamarck and Neo-lamarckianism," in the *Open Court*, Chicago, February, 1897. Compare also "Darwin Wrong," etc., by R. F. Licorish, M.D., Barbadoes, 1898, reprinted in *Natural Science*, April, 1899.

We submit that this mode of evolution of the giraffe is quite as reasonable as the very hypothetical one advanced by Mr. Wallace; * *i.e.*, that a variety occurred with à longer neck than usual, and these " at once secured a fresh range of pasture over the same ground as their shorter-necked companions, and on the first scarcity of food were thereby enabled to outlive them." Mr. Wallace's account also of Lamarck's general theory appears to us to be one-sided, inadequate, and misleading. He states it thus: " The hypothesis of Lamarck—that progressive changes in species have been produced by the attempts of animals to increase the development of their own organs, and thus modify their structure and habits." This is a caricature of what Lamarck really taught. Wants, needs (*besoins*), volitions, desires, are not mentioned by Lamarck in his two fundamental laws (see p. 303), and when the word *besoins* is introduced it refers as much to the physiological needs as to the emotions of the animal resulting from some new environment which forces it to adopt new habits such as means of locomotion or of acquiring food.

It will be evident to one who has read the original or the foregoing translations of Lamarck's writings that he does not refer so much to mental desires or volitions as to those physiological wants or needs thrust upon the animal by change of circumstances or by competition ; and his *besoins* may include lust, hunger, as well as the necessity of making muscular exertions such as walking, running, leaping, climbing, swimming, or flying.

---

* *Natural Selection*, pp. 41–42.

As we understand Lamarck, when he speaks of the incipient giraffe or long-necked bird as making efforts to reach up or outwards, the efforts may have been as much physiological, reflex, or instinctive as mental. A recent writer, Dr. R. T. Jackson, curiously and yet naturally enough uses the same phraseology as Lamarck when he says that the long siphon of the common clam (Mya) " was brought about by the effort to reach the surface, induced by the habit of deep burial " in its hole.*

On the other hand, can we in the higher vertebrates entirely dissociate the emotional and mental activities from their physiological or instinctive acts? Mr. Darwin, in his *Expressions of the Emotions in Man and Animals*, discusses in an interesting and detailed way the effects of the feelings and passions on some of the higher animals.

It is curious, also, that Dr. Erasmus Darwin went at least as far as Lamarck in claiming that the transformations of animals " are in part produced by their own exertions in consequence of their desires and aversions, of their pleasures and their pains, or of irritations or of associations."

Cope, in the final chapter of his *Primary Factors of Organic Evolution*, entitled "The Functions of Consciousness," goes to much farther extremes than the French philosopher has been accused of doing, and unhesitatingly attributes consciousness to all animals. "Whatever be its nature," he says, "the preliminary to any animal movement which is not auto-

---

* *American Naturalist*, 1891, p. 17.

matic is an effort." Hence he regards effort as the immediate source of all movement, and considers that the control of muscular movements by consciousness is distinctly observable; in fact, he even goes to the length of affirming that reflex acts are the product of conscious acts, whereas it is plain enough that reflex acts are always the result of some stimulus.

Another case mentioned by Lamarck in his *Animaux sans Vertèbres,* which has been pronounced as absurd and ridiculous, and has aided in throwing his whole theory into disfavor, is his way of accounting for the development of the tentacles of the snail, which is quoted on p. 348.

This account is a very probable and, in fact, the only rational explanation. The initial cause of such structures is the intermittent stimulus of occasional contact with surrounding objects, the irritation thus set up causing a flow of the blood to the exposed parts receiving the stimuli. The general cause is the same as that concerned in the production of horns and other hard defensive projections on the heads of various animals.

In commenting on this case of the snail, Professor Cleland, in his just and discriminating article on Lamarck, says:

" However absurd this may seem, it must be admitted that, unlimited time having been once granted for organs to be developed in series of generations, the objections to their being formed in the way here imagined are only such as equally apply to the theory of their origin by natural selection. . . . In judging the reasonableness of the second law of

Lamarck [referring to new wants, see p. 346] as compared with more modern and now widely received theories, it must be observed that it is only an extension of his third law; and that third law is a fact. The strengthening of the blacksmith's arm by use is proverbially notorious. It is, therefore, only the sufficiency of the Lamarckian hypothesis to explain the first commencement of new organs which is in question, if evolution by the mere operation of forces acting in the organic world be granted; and surely the Darwinian theory is equally helpless to account for the beginning of a new organ, while it demands as imperatively that every stage in the assumed hereditary development of an organ must have been useful. . . . Lamarck gave great importance to the influence of new wants acting indirectly by stimulating growth and use. Darwin has given like importance to the effects of accidental variations acting indirectly by giving advantage in the struggle for existence. The speculative writings of Darwin have, however, been interwoven with a vast number of beautiful experiments and observations bearing on his speculations, though by no means proving his theory of evolution; while the speculations of Lamarck lie apart from his wonderful descriptive labors, unrelieved by intermixture with other matters capable of attracting the numerous class who, provided they have new facts set before them, are not careful to limit themselves to the conclusions strictly deducible therefrom. But those who read the *Philosophie Zoologique* will find how many truths often supposed to be far more modern are stated with abundant clearness in its pages." (*Encyc. Brit.*, art. " Lamarck.")

COMPARATIVE SUMMARY OF THE VIEWS OF THE FOUNDERS OF THE THEORY OF EVOLUTION, WITH DATES OF PUBLICATION.

Buffon (1761-1778).	Erasmus Darwin (1790-1794).	Lamarck (1801-1809-1815).	Geoffroy St. Hilaire (1795-1831).	Charles Darwin (1859).
All animals possibly derived from a single type.	All animals derived from a single filament.	All organisms arose from germs. First germ originated by spontaneous generation. Development from the simple to the complex. Animal series not continuous, but tree-like; graduated from monad to man; constructed the first phylogenetic tree.	Unity of organization in animal kingdom. Change of "milieu ambiant," direct.	Universal tendency to fortuitous variability assumed.
Time, its great length, stated.	Time, great length of, definitely demanded.	Time, great length of, definitely postulated; its duration practically unlimited.		
Immutability of species stated and then denied.		Uniformitarianism of Hutton and of Lyell anticipated.	Founded the doctrine of homologies.	Struggle for existence.
Nature advances by gradations, passing from one species to another by imperceptible degrees.		Effects of favorable circumstances, such as changes of environment, climate, soil, food, temperature; direct in case of plants and lowest animals, indirect in case of the higher animals and man.		
Changes in distribution of land and water as causing variation.	Effects of change of climate, direct (briefly stated).	Conditions of existence remaining constant, species do not vary and *vice-versa*.	Founder of teratology.	
Effects of changes of climate, direct.	Domestication, briefly referred to.	Struggle for existence; stronger devour the weaker. Competition stated in case of *ai* or sloth. Balance of nature.	His embryological studies influenced his philosophic views.	Competition strongly advocated.
Effects of changes of food.	Effects of use; characters produced by their own exertions in consequence of their desires, aversions, lust, hunger, and security.	Effects of use and disuse, discussed at length.		
Effects of domestication.	Sexual selection, law of battle.	Vestigial structures the remains of organs actively used by ancestors of present forms.		Natural selection. Sexual selection. Effects of use and disuse (in some cases).
Effects of use. (The only examples given are the callosities on legs of camel, of baboon, and the thickening by use of soles of man's feet.)	Protective mimicry.	New wants or necessities induced by change of climate, habitat, etc., result in production of new propensities, new habits, and functions.		
	Origin of organs before development of their functions.	Change of habits originate organs; change of functions create new organs; formation of new habits precede the origin of new or modification of organs already formed.		
	Inheritance of acquired characters (vaguely stated).	Geographical isolation suggested as a factor in case of man.		Isolation "an important element."
	Instinct result of imitation. Opposed preformation views of Haller and Bonnet.	Swamping effects of crossing. Lamarck's definition of species the most satisfactory yet stated. Inheritance of acquired characters. Instinct the result of inherited habits. Opposed preformation views; epigenesis definitely stated and adopted.	Species are "different modifications of one and the same type."	Inheritance of acquired characters.

CHAPTER XVIII

LAMARCK'S THEORY AS TO THE EVOLUTION OF MAN

LAMARCK'S views on the origin of man are contained in his *Recherches sur l'Organisation des Corps vivans* (1802) and his *Philosophie zoologique*, published in 1809. We give the following literal translation in full of the views he presented in 1802, and which were probably first advanced in lectures to his classes.

" As to man, his origin, his peculiar nature, I have already stated in this book that I have not kept these subjects in view in making these observations. His extreme superiority over the other living creatures indicates that he is a privileged being who has in common with the animals only that which concerns animal life.

" In truth, we observe a sort of gradation in the intelligence of animals, like what exists in the gradual improvement of their organization, and we remark that they have ideas, memory; that they think, choose, love, hate, that they are susceptible of jealousy, and that by different inflexions of their voice and by signs they communicate with and understand each other. It is not less evident that man alone is endowed with reason, and that on this account he is clearly distinguished from all the other productions of nature.

" However, were it not for the picture that so many celebrated men have drawn of the weakness and lack of human reason; were it not that, independently of all the freaks into which the passions of man almost constantly allure him, the *ignorance* which makes him the opinionated slave of custom and the continual dupe of those who wish to deceive him; were it not that his reason has led him into the most revolting errors, since we actually see him so debase himself as to worship animals, even the meanest, of addressing to them his prayers, and of imploring their aid; were it not, I say, for these considerations, should we feel authorized to raise any doubts as to the excellence of this special light which is the attribute of man ?

" An observation which has for a long time struck me is that, having remarked that the habitual use and exercise of an organ proportionally develops its size and functions, as the lack of employment weakens in the same proportion its power, and even more or less completely atrophies it, I am apprised that of all the organs of man's body which is the most strongly submitted to this influence, that is to say, in which the effects of exercise and of habitual use are the most considerable, is it not the organ of thought—in a word, is it not the brain of·man ?

" Compare the extraordinary difference existing in the degree of intelligence of a man who rarely exercises his powers of thought, who has always been accustomed to see but a small number of things, only those related to his ordinary wants and to his limited desires; who at no time thinks about these same objects, because he is obliged to occupy himself incessantly with providing for these same wants; finally, who has few ideas, because his attention, continually fixed on the same things, makes him notice nothing, that he makes no comparisons, that he is in the very heart of nature without knowing it, that he looks upon it almost in the same way as do the beasts, and that all that surrounds him is nothing to him: compare, I say, the intelligence of this individual with that of the man who, prepared at the outset by education, has contracted the useful practice of exercising the organ of his thought in devoting himself to the study of the principal branches of knowledge; who observes and compares everything he sees and which affects him; who forgets himself in examining everything he can see, who insensibly accustoms himself to judge of everything for himself, instead of giving a blind assent to the authority of others; finally, who, stimulated by reverses and especially by injustice, quietly rises by reflection to the causes which have produced all that we observe both in nature and in human society; then you will appreciate how enormous is the difference between the intelligence of the two men in question.

" If Newton, Bacon, Montesquieu, Voltaire, and so many other men have done honor to the human species by the extent of their intelligence and their genius, how nearly does the mass of brutish, ignorant men approach the animal, becoming a prey to the most absurd prejudices and constantly enslaved by their habits, this mass forming the majority of all nations ?

" Search deeply the facts in the comparison I have just made, you will see how in one part the organ which serves for acts of thought is perfected and acquires greater size and power, owing to sustained and varied exercise, especially if this exercise offers no more interruptions than are necessary to prevent the exhaustion of its powers; and, on the other hand, you will perceive how the circumstances which prevent an individual from exercising this organ, or from exercising it habitually only while considering a small number of objects which are always of the same nature, impede the development of his intellectual faculties.

" After what I have just stated as to the results in man of a slight exercise of the organ by which he thinks, we shall no longer be astonished to see that in the nations which have come to be the most distinguished, because there is among them a small number of men who have been able, by observation and reflection, to create or advance the higher sciences, the multitude in these same nations have not been for all that exempted from the most absurd errors, and have not the less always been the dupe of impostors and victims of their prejudices.

" Such is, in fact, the fatality attached to the destiny of man that, with the exception of a small number of individuals who live under favorable though special circumstances, the multitude, forced to continually busy itself with providing for its needs, remains permanently deprived of the knowledge which it should acquire; in general, exercises to a very slight extent the organ of its intelligence; preserves and propagates a multitude of prejudices which enslave it, and cannot be as happy as those who, guiding it, are themselves guided by reason and justice.

" As to the animals, besides the fact that they in descending order have the brain less developed, they are otherwise proportionally more limited in the means of exercising and of varying their intellectual processes. They each exercise them only on a single or on some special points, on which they become more or less expert according to their species. And while their degree of organization remains the same and the nature of their needs (*besoins*) does not vary, they can never extend the scope of their intelligence, nor apply it to other objects than to those which are related to their ordinary needs.

" Some among them, whose structure is a little

more perfect than in others, have also greater means of varying and extending their intellectual faculties; but it is always within limits circumscribed by their necessities and habits.

" The power of habit which is found to be still so great in man, especially in one who has but slightly exercised the organ of his thought, is among animals almost insurmountable while their physical state remains the same. Nothing compels them to vary their powers, because they suffice for their wants and these require no change. Hence it is constantly the same objects which exercise their degree of intelligence, and it results that these actions are always the same in each species.

" The sole acts of variation, *i.e.*, the only acts which rise above the limits of habits, and which we see performed in animals whose organization allows them to, are *acts of imitation*. I only speak of actions which they perform voluntarily or freely (*actions qu'ils font de leur plein gré*).

" Birds, very limited in this respect in the powers which their structure furnishes, can only perform acts of imitation with their vocal organ; this organ, by their habitual efforts to render the sounds, and to vary them, becomes in them very perfect. Thus we know that several birds (the parrot, starling, raven, jay, magpie, canary bird, etc.) imitate the sounds they hear.

" The monkeys, which are, next to man, the animals by their structure having the best means to this end, are most excellent imitators, and there is no limit to the things they can mimic.

" In man, infants which are still of the age when simple ideas are formed on various subjects, and who think but little, forming no complex ideas, are also very good imitators of everything which they see or hear.

" But if each order of things in animals is dependent on the state of organization occurring in each of them, which is not doubted, there is no occasion for thinking that in these same animals the order which is superior to all the others in organization is proportionally so also in extent of means, invariability of actions, and consequently in intellectual powers.

" For example, in the mammals which are the most highly organized, the *Quadrumana*, which form a part of them, have, besides the advantages over other mammals, a conformation in several of their organs which considerably increases their powers, which allows of a great variability in their actions, and which extends and even makes predominant their intelligence, enabling them to deal with a greater variety of objects with which to exercise their brain. It will doubtless be said: But although man may be a true mammal in his general structure, and although among the mammals the *Quadrumana* are most nearly allied to him, this will not be denied, not only that man is strongly distinguished from the *Quadrumana* by a great superiority of intelligence, but he is also very considerably so in several structural features which characterize him.

" First, the occipital foramen being situated entirely at the base of the cranium of man and not carried up behind, as in the other vertebrates, causes his head to be posed at the extremity of the vertebral column as on a pivot, not bowed down forward, his face not looking towards the ground. This position of the head of man, who can easily turn it to different sides, enables him to see better a larger number of objects at one time, than the much inclined position of the head of other mammals allows them to see.

" Secondly, the remarkable mobility of the fingers of the hand of man, which he employs either all together or several together, or each separately, according to his pleasure, and besides, the sense of touch highly developed at the extremity of these same fingers, enables him to judge the nature of the bodies which surround him, to recognize them, to make use of them—means which no other animals possess to such a degree.

" Thirdly, by the state of his organization man is able to hold himself up and walk erect. He has, for this attitude which is natural to him, large muscles at the lower extremities which are adapted to this end, and it would thus be as difficult to walk habitually on his four extremities as it would be for the other mammals, and even for the *Quadrumana*, to walk so habitually erect on the soles of their feet.

" Moreover, man is not truly quadrumanous; for he has not, like the monkeys, an almost equal facility in using the fingers of his feet, and of seizing objects with them. In the feet of man the thumbs are not in opposition to the other fingers to use in grasping, as in monkeys, etc.

" I appreciate all these reasons, and I see that man, although near the *Quadrumana*, is so distinct that he alone represents a separate order, belonging to a single genus and species, offering, however, many different varieties. This order may be, if it is desired, that of the *Bimana*.

" However, if we consider that all the characteristics which have been cited are only differences in degree of structure, may we not suppose that this special condition of organization of man *has been gradually acquired at the close of a long period of time, with the aid of circumstances which have proved favorable?* * What a subject for reflection for those who have the courage to enter into it!

" If the *Quadrumana* have not the occipital opening situated directly at the base of the cranium as in man, it is assuredly much less raised posteriorly than

---

* Author's italics.

in the dog, cat, and all the other mammals. Thus they all may quite often stand erect, although this attitude for them is very irksome.

" I have not observed the situation of the occipital opening of the jacko or orang-outang (*Simia satyrus* L.); but as I know that this animal almost habitually walks erect, though it has no strength in its legs, I suppose that the occipital foramen is not situated so far from the base of the skull as in the other *Quadrumana*.

" The head of the negro, less flattened in front than that of the European man, necessarily has the occipital foramen central.

" The more should the jacko contract the habit of walking about, the less mobility would he have in his toes, so that the thumbs of the feet, which are already much shorter than the other digits, would gradually cease to be placed in opposition to the other toes, and to be useful in grasping. The muscles of its lower extremities would acquire proportionally greater thickness and strength. Then the increased or more frequent exercise of the fingers of its hands would develop nervous masses at their extremities, thus rendering the sense of touch more delicate. This is what our train of reasoning indicates from the consideration of a multitude of facts and observations which support it." *

The subject is closed by a quotation from Grandpré on the habits of the chimpanzee. It is not of sufficient importance to be here reproduced.

Seven years after the publication of these views,

---

* " How much this unclean beast resembles man !"—*Ennius.*

" Indeed, besides other resemblances the monkey has mammæ, a clitoris, nymphs, uterus, uvula, eye-lobes, nails, as in the human species ; it also lacks a suspensory ligament of the neck. Is it not astonishing that man, endowed with wisdom, differs so little from such a disgusting animal !"—*Linnæus.*

Lamarck again returns to the subject in his *Philoso-phie zoologique*, which we translate.

" *Some Observations Relative to Man.*

" If man were distinguished from the animals by his structure alone, it would be easy to show that the structural characters which place him, with his varieties, in a family by himself, are all the product of former changes in his actions, and in the habits which he has adopted and which have become special to the individuals of his species.

" Indeed, if any race whatever of *Quadrumana*, especially the most perfect, should lose, by the neces-sity of circumstances or from any other cause, the habit of climbing trees, and of seizing the branches with the feet, as with the hands, to cling to them; and if the individuals of this race, during a series of generations, should be obliged to use their feet only in walking, and should cease to use their hands as feet, there is no doubt, from the observations made in the preceding chapter, that these *Quadrumana* would be finally transformed into *Bimana*, and that the thumbs of their feet would cease to be shorter than the fingers, their feet only being of use for walking.

" Moreover, if the individuals of which I speak were impelled by the necessity of rising up and of looking far and wide, of endeavoring to stand erect, and of adopting this habit constantly from genera-tion to generation, there is no doubt that their feet would gradually and imperceptibly assume a con-formation adapted for an erect posture, that their legs would develop calves, and that these creatures would not afterwards walk as they do now, painfully on both hands and feet.

" Also, if these same individuals should cease using their jaws for biting in self-defence, tearing or seizing, or using them like nippers in cutting leaves for food, and should they only be used in chewing food, there is no doubt that their facial angle would become higher, that their muzzle would become shorter and shorter, and that in the end this being entirely effaced, their incisor teeth would become vertical.

" Now supposing that a race of *Quadrumana*, as for example the most perfect, had acquired, by habits constant in every individual, the structure I have just described, and the power of standing erect and of walking upright, and that as the result of this it had come to dominate the other races of animals, we should then conceive:

" 1. That this race farther advanced in its faculties, having arrived at the stage when it lords it over the others, will be spread over the surface of the globe in every suitable place;

" 2. That it will hunt the other higher races of animals and will struggle with them for preëminence (*lui disputer les biens de la terre*) and that it will force them to take refuge in regions which it does not occupy;

" 3. That being injured by the great multiplication of closely allied races, and having banished them into forests or other desert places, it will arrest the progress of improvement in their faculties, while its own self, the ruler of the region over which it spreads, will increase in population without hindrance on the part of others, and, living in numerous tribes, will in succession create new needs which should stimulate industry and gradually render still more perfect its means and powers;

" 4. That, finally, this preëminent race having acquired an absolute supremacy over all the others, there arose between it and the highest animals a difference and indeed a considerable interval.

" Thus the most perfect race of *Quadrumana* will

have been enabled to become dominant, to change its habits as the result of the absolute dominion which it will have assumed over the others, and with its new needs, by progressively acquiring modifications in its structure and its new and numerous powers, to keep within due limits the most highly developed of the other races in the state to which they had advanced, and to create between it and these last very remarkable distinctions.

" The Angola orang (*Simia troglodytes* Lin.) is the highest animal; it is much more perfect than the orang of the Indies (*Simia satyrus* Lin.), which is called the orang-outang, and, nevertheless, as regards their structure they are both very inferior to man in bodily faculties and intelligence. These animals often stand erect; but this attitude is not habitual, their organization not having been sufficiently modified, so that standing still (*station*) is painful for them.

" It is known, from the accounts of travellers, especially in regard to the orang of the Indies, that when immediate danger obliges it to fly, it immediately falls on all fours. This betrays, they tell us, the true origin of this animal, since it is obliged to abandon the alien unaccustomed partially erect attitude which is thrust upon it.

" Without doubt this attitude is foreign to it, since in its change of locality it makes less use of it, which shows that its organization is less adapted to it; but though it has become easier for man to stand up straight, is the erect posture wholly natural to him ?

" Although man, who, by his habits, maintained in the individuals of his species during a great series of generations, can stand erect only while changing from one place to another, this attitude is not less in his case a condition of fatigue, during which he is able to maintain himself in an upright position only

during a limited time and with the aid of the contraction of several of his muscles.

"If the vertebral column of the human body
should form the axis of this body, and sustain the
head in equilibrium, as also the other parts, the man
standing would be in a state of rest. But who does
not know that this is not so; that the head is not
articulated at its centre of gravity; that the chest
and stomach, as also the viscera which these cavities
contain, weigh heavily almost entirely on the an-
terior part of the vertebral column; that the latter
rests on an oblique base, etc.? Also, as M. Richerand
observes, there is needed in standing a force active
and watching without ceasing to prevent the body
from falling over, the weight and disposition of parts
tending to make the body fall forward.

"After having developed the considerations regarding the standing posture of man, the same
savant then expresses himself: ' The relative weight
of the head, of the thoracic and abdominal viscera,
tends therefore to throw it in front of the line,
according to which all the parts of the body bear
down on the ground sustaining it; a line which
should be exactly perpendicular to this ground in
order that the standing position may be perfect. The
following fact supports this assertion: I have observed that infants with a large head, the stomach
protruding and the viscera loaded with fat, accustom
themselves with difficulty to stand up straight, and
it is not until the end of their second year that they
dare to surrender themselves to their proper forces;
they stand subject to frequent falls and have a natural tendency to revert to the quadrupedal state.'
(*Physiologie*, vol. ii., p. 268.)

"This disposition of the parts which cause the
erect position of man, being a state of activity, and
consequently fatiguing, instead of being a state of
rest, would then betray in him an origin analogous

to that of the mammals, if his organization alone should be taken into consideration.

"Now in order to follow, in all its particulars, the hypothesis presented in the beginning of these observations, it is fitting to add the following considerations:

"The individuals of the dominant race previously mentioned, having taken possession of all the inhabitable places which were suitable for them, and having to a very considerable extent multiplied their necessities in proportion as the societies which they formed became more numerous, were able equally to increase their ideas, and consequently to feel the need of communicating them to their fellows. We conceive that there would arise the necessity of increasing and of varying in the same proportion the *signs* adopted for the communication of these ideas. It is then evident that the members of this race would have to make continual efforts, and to employ every possible means in these efforts, to create, multiply, and render sufficiently varied the *signs* which their ideas and their numerous wants would render necessary.

"It is not so with any other animals; because, although the most perfect among them, such as the *Quadrumana*, live mostly in troops, since the eminent supremacy of the race mentioned they have remained stationary as regards the improvement of their faculties, having been driven out from everywhere and banished to wild, desert, usually restricted regions, whither, miserable and restless, they are incessantly constrained to fly and hide themselves. In this situation these animals no longer contract new needs, they acquire no new ideas; they have but a small number of them, and it is always the same ones which occupy their attention, and among these ideas there are very few which they have need of communicating to the other individuals of their

24

species. There are, then, only very few different *signs* which they employ among their fellows, so that some movements of the body or of certain of its parts, certain hisses and cries raised by the simple inflexions of the voice, suffice them.

"On the contrary, the individuals of the dominant race already mentioned, having had need of multiplying the *signs* for the rapid communication of their ideas, now become more and more numerous, and, no longer contented either with pantomimic signs or possible inflexions of their voice to represent this multitude of signs now become necessary, would succeed by different efforts in forming *articulated sounds :* at first they would use only a small number, conjointly with the inflexions of their voice; as the result they would multiply, vary, and perfect them, according to their increasing necessities, and according as they would be more accustomed to produce them. Indeed, the habitual exercise of their throat, their tongue, and their lips to make articulate sounds, will have eminently developed in them this faculty.

"Hence for this particular race the origin of the wonderful power of *speech ;* and as the distance between the regions where the individuals composing it would be spread would favor the corruption of the signs fitted to express each idea, from this arose the origin of languages, which must be everywhere diversified.

"Then in this respect necessities alone would have accomplished everything; they would give origin to efforts; and the organs fitted for the articulation of sounds would be developed by their habitual use.

"Such would be the reflections which might be made if man, considered here as the preëminent race in question, were distinguished from the animals only by his physical characters, and if his origin were not different from theirs."

This is certainly, for the time it was written, an original, comprehensive, and bold attempt at explaining in a tentative way, or at least suggesting, the probable origin of man from some arboreal creature allied to the apes. It is as regards the actual evolutional steps supposed to have been taken by the simian ancestors of man, a more detailed and comprehensive hypothesis than that offered by Darwin in his *Descent of Man*,* which Lamarck has anticipated. Darwin does not refer to this theory of Lamarck, and seems to have entirely overlooked it, as have others since his time. The theory of the change from an arboreal life and climbing posture to an erect one, and the transformation of the hinder pair of hands into the feet of the erect human animal, remind us of the very probable hypothesis of Mr. Herbert Spencer, as to the modification of the quadrumanous posterior pair of hands to form the plantigrade feet of man.

---

* Vol. i., chapter iv., pp. 135–151 ; ii., p. 372.

CHAPTER XIX

LAMARCK'S THOUGHTS ON MORALS, AND ON THE RELATION BETWEEN SCIENCE AND RELIGION

ONE who has read the writings of the great French naturalist, who may be regarded as the founder of evolution, will readily realize that Lamarck's mind was essentially philosophic, comprehensive, and synthetic. He looked upon every problem in a large way. His breadth of view, his moral and intellectual strength, his equably developed nature, generous in its sympathies and aspiring in its tendencies, naturally led him to take a conservative position as to the relations between science and religion. He should, as may be inferred from his frequent references to the Author of nature, be regarded as a deist.

When a very young man, he was for a time a friend of the erratic and gifted Rousseau, and was afterwards not unknown to Condorcet, the secretary of the French Academy of Sciences, so liberal in his views and so bitter an enemy of the Church; and though constantly in contact with the radical views and burning questions of that day, Lamarck throughout his life preserved his philosophic calm, and maintained his lofty tone and firm temper. We find no trace in his writings of sentiments other than the most elevated and inspiring, and we know that in character he was pure and sweet, self-sacrificing, self-denying, and free from self-assertion.

The quotations from his *Philosophie zoologique*, published in 1809, given below, will show what were the results of his meditations on the relations between science and religion. Had his way of looking at this subject prevailed, how much misunderstanding and ill-feeling between theologians and savants would have been avoided! Had his spirit and breadth of view animated both parties, there would not have been the constant and needless opposition on the part of the Church to the grand results of scientific discovery and philosophy, or too hasty dogmatism and scepticism on the part of some scientists.

In Lamarck, at the opening of the past century, we behold the spectacle of a man devoting over fifty years of his life to scientific research in biology, and insisting on the doctrine of spontaneous generation; of the immense length of geological time, so opposed to the views held by the Church; the evolution of plants and animals from a single germ, and even the origin of man from the apes, yet as earnestly claiming that nature has its Author who in the beginning established the order of things, giving the initial impulse to the laws of the universe.

As Duval says, after quoting the passage given below: " Deux faits son à noter dans ce passage: d'une part, les termes dignes et conciliants dans lesquels Lamarck établit la part de la science et de la religion; cela vaut, mieux, même en tenant compte des différences d'epoques, que les abjurations de Buffon." *

The passage quoted by M. Duval is the following one:

" Surely nothing exists except by the will of the Sublime Author of all things. But can we not assign him laws in the execution of his will, and determine the method which he has followed in this respect ? Has not his infinite power enabled him to create an *order of things* which has successively given existence to all that we see, as well as to that which exists and that of which we have no knowledge ? As regards the decrees of this infinite wisdom, I have confined myself to the limits of a simple observer of nature." †

In other places we find the following expressions:

" There is then, for the animals as for the plants, an order which belongs to nature, and which results, as also the objects which this order makes exist, from the power which it has received from the SUPREME AUTHOR of all things. She is herself only the general and unchangeable order that this Sublime Author has created throughout, and only the totality of the general and special laws to which this order is subject. By these means, whose use it continues without change, it has given and will perpetually give existence to its productions; it varies and renews them unceasingly, and thus everywhere preserves the whole order which is the result of it." ‡

" To regard nature as eternal, and consequently

---

* Mathias Duval : " Le transformiste français Lamarck," *Bulletin de la Société d'Anthropologie de Paris*, xii., 1889, p. 345.
† *Philosophie zoologique*, p. 56.
‡ *Loc. cit.*, i., p. 113.

as having existed from all time, is to me an abstract idea, baseless, limitless, improbable, and not satisfactory to my reason. Being unable to know anything positive in this respect, and having no means of reasoning on this subject, I much prefer to think that *all nature* is only a result: hence, I suppose, and I am glad to admit it, a first cause, in a word, a supreme power which has given existence to nature, and which has made it in all respects what it is." *

" Nature, that immense totality of different beings and bodies, in every part of which exists an eternal circle of movements and changes regulated by law; totality alone unchangeable, so long as it pleases its SUBLIME AUTHOR to cause its existence, should be regarded as a whole constituted by its parts, for a purpose which its Author alone knows, and not exclusively for any one of them.

" Each part is necessarily obliged to change, and to cease to be one in order to constitute another, with interests opposed to those of all; and if it has the power of reasoning it finds this whole imperfect. In reality, however, this whole is perfect and completely fulfils the end for which it was designed." †

Lamarck's work on general philosophy ‡ was written near the end of his life, in 1820. He begins his " Discours préliminaire " by referring to the sudden loss of his eyesight, his work on the invertebrate animals being thereby interrupted. The book was, he says, " rapidly " dictated to his daughter, and the ease with which he dictated was due, he says, to his long-continued habit of meditating on the facts he had observed.

---

* *Loc. cit.*, i., p. 361. † *Loc. cit.*, ii., p. 465.
‡ *Système analytique des Connaissances de l'Homme*, etc.

In the "Principes primordiaux" he considers man as the only being who has the power of observing nature, and the only one who has perceived the necessity of recognizing a superior and only cause, creator of the order of the wonders of the world of life. By this he is led to raise his thoughts to the *Supreme Author* of all that exists.

" In the creation of his works, and especially those we can observe, this omnipotent Being has undoubtedly been the ruling power in pursuing the method which has pleased him, namely, his will has been:

" Either to create instantaneously and separately every particular living being observed by us, to personally care for and watch over them in all their changes, their movements, or their actions, to unremittingly care for each one separately, and by the exercise of his supreme will to regulate all their life;

" Or to reduce his creations to a small number, and among these, to institute an order of things general and continuous, pervaded by ceaseless activity (*mouvement*), especially subject to laws by means of which all the organisms of whatever nature, all the changes they undergo, all the peculiarities they present, and all the phenomena that many of them exhibit, may be produced.

" In regard to these two modes of execution, if observation taught us nothing we could not form any opinion which would be well grounded. But it is not so; we distinctly see that there exists an order of things truly created (*véritablement créé*), as unchangeable as its author allows, acting on matter alone, and which possesses the power of producing all visible beings, of executing all the changes, all the modifications, even the extinctions, so also the renewals or recreations that we observe among them. It is to this order of things that we have given the name of *nature*. The Supreme Author of all that exists is, then, the immediate creator of matter as also of nature, but he is only indirectly the creator of what nature can produce.

" The end that God has proposed to himself in creating matter, which forms the basis of all bodies, and nature, which divides (*divise*) this matter, forms the bodies, makes them vary, modifies them, changes them, and renews them in different ways, can be easily known to us; for the Supreme Being cannot meet with any obstacle to his will in the execution of his works; the general results of these works are necessarily the object he had in view. Thus this end could be no other than the existence of nature, of which matter alone forms the sphere, and should not be that causing the creation of any special being.

" Do we find in the two objects created, *i.e.*, *matter* and *nature*, the source of the good and evil which have almost always been thought to exist in the events of this world ? To this question I shall answer that good and evil are only relative to particular objects, that they never affect by their temporary existence the general result expected (*prévu*), and that for the end which the Creator designed, there is in reality neither good nor evil, because everything in nature perfectly fulfils its object.

" Has God limited his creations to the existence of only matter and nature ? This question is vain, and should remain without an answer on our part; because, being reduced to knowing anything only through observation, and to bodies alone, also to what concerns them, these being for us the only observable objects, it would be rash to speak affirmatively or negatively on this subject.

" What is a spiritual being ? It is what, with the aid of the imagination, one would naturally suppose (*l'on vaudra supposer*). Indeed, it is only by means of opposing that which is material that we can form the idea of spirit; but as this hypothetical being is not in the category of objects which it is possible for us to observe, we do not know how to take cognizance of it. The idea that we have of it is absolutely without base.

" We only know physical objects and only objects relative to these beings (*êtres*): such is the condition of our nature. If our thoughts, our reasonings, our principles have been considered as metaphysical objects, these objects, then, are not beings (*êtres*). They are only relations or consequences of relations (*rapports*), or only results of observed laws.

" We know that relations are distinguished as general and special. Among these last are regarded those of nature, form, dimension, solidity, size, quantity, resemblance, and difference; and if we add to these objects the being observed and the consideration of known laws, as also that of conventional objects, we shall have all the materials on which our thoughts are based.

" Thus being able to observe only the phenomena of nature, as well as the laws which regulate these phenomena, also the products of these last, in a word, only bodies (*corps*) and what concerns them, all that which immediately proceeds from supreme power is incomprehensible to us, as it itself [*i.e.*, supreme power] is to our minds. To create, or to make anything out of nothing, this is an idea we cannot conceive of, for the reason that in all that we can know, we do not find any model which represents it. GOD alone, then, can create, while nature can only produce. We must suppose that, in his creations, the Divinity is not restricted to the use of any time, while, on the other hand, nature can effect nothing without the aid of long periods of time."

Without translating more of this remarkable book, which is very rare, much less known than the *Philoso-*

phie zoologique, the spirit of the remainder may be imagined from the foregoing extracts.

The author refers to the numerous evils resulting from ignorance, false knowledge, lack of judgment, abuse of power, demonstrating the necessity of our confining ourselves within the circle of the objects presented by nature, and never to go beyond them if we do not wish to fall into error, because the profound study of nature and of the organization of man alone, and the exact observation of facts alone, will reveal to us " the truths most important for us to know," in order to avoid the vexations, the perfidies, the injustices, and the oppressions of all sorts, and " incalculable disorders " which arise in the social body. In this way only shall we discover and acquire the means of obtaining the enjoyment of the advantages which we have a right to expect from our state of civilization. The author endeavors to state what science can and should render to society. He dwells on the sources from which man has drawn the knowledge which he possesses, and from which he can obtain many others—sources the totality of which constitutes for him the field of realities.

Lamarck also in this work has built up a system for moral philosophy.

Self-love, he says, perfectly regulated, gives rise:

1. To moral force which characterizes the laborious man, so that the length and difficulties of a useful work do not repel him.

2. To the courage of him who, knowing the danger, exposes himself when he sees that this would be useful.

3. To love of wisdom.

Wisdom, according to Lamarck, consists in the observance of a certain number of rules or virtues. These we cite in a slightly abridged form.

Love of truth in all things; the need of improving one's mind; moderation in desires; decorum in all actions; a wise reserve in unessential wants; indulgence, toleration, humanity, good will towards all men; love of the public good and of all that is necessary to our fellows; contempt for weakness; a kind of severity towards one's self which preserves us from that multitude of artificial wants enslaving those who give up to them; resignation and, if possible, moral impassibility in suffering reverses, injustices, oppression, and losses; respect for order, for public institutions, civil authorities, laws, morality, and religion.

The practice of these maxims and virtues, says Lamarck, characterizes true philosophy.

And it may be added that no one practised these virtues more than Lamarck. Like Cuvier's, his life was blameless, and though he lived a most retired life, and was not called upon to fill any public station other than his chair of zoölogy at the Jardin des Plantes, we may feel sure that he had the qualities of courage, independence, and patriotism which would have rendered such a career most useful to his country.

As Bourguin eloquently asserts: "Lamarck was the brave man who never deserted a dangerous post, the laborious man who never hesitated to meet any difficulty, the investigating spirit, firm in his convictions, tolerant of the opinions of others, the simple man, moderate in all things, the enemy of weakness, devoted to the public good, imperturbable under the attaints of fortune, of suffering, and of unjust and passionate attacks '

CHAPTER XX

THE RELATIONS BETWEEN LAMARCKISM AND DARWINISM ; NEOLAMARCKISM

SINCE the appearance of Darwin's *Origin of Species,* and after the great naturalist had converted the world to a belief in the general doctrine of evolution, there has arisen in the minds of many working naturalists a conviction that natural selection, or Darwinism as such, is only one of other evolutionary factors ; while there are some who entirely reject the selective principle. Darwin, moreover, assumed a tendency to fortuitous variation, and did not attempt to explain its cause. Fully persuaded that he had discovered the most efficient and practically sole cause of the origin of species, he carried the doctrine to its extreme limits, and after over twenty years of observation and experiment along this single line, pushing entirely aside the Erasmus-Darwin and Lamarckian factors of change of environment, though occasionally acknowledging the value of use and disuse, he triumphantly broke over all opposition, and lived to see his doctrine generally accepted. He had besides the support of some of the strongest men in science : Wallace in a twin paper advocated the same views ; Spencer, Lyell, Huxley, Hooker, Haeckel, Bates, Semper, Wyman, Gray, Leidy, and other rep-

resentative men ·more or less endorsed Darwin's
views, or at least some form of evolution, and owing
largely to their efforts in scientific circles and in the
popular press, the doctrine of descent rapidly permeated every avenue of thought and became generally accepted.

Meanwhile, the general doctrine of evolution thus
proved, and the "survival of the fittest" an accomplished fact, the next step was to ascertain "how,"
as Cope asked, "the fittest originated?" It was felt
by some that natural selection alone was not adequate to explain the first steps in the origin of
genera, families, orders, classes, and branches or
phyla. It was perceived by some that natural selection by itself was not a *vera causa*, an efficient agent,
but was passive, and rather expressed the results of
the operations of a series of factors. The transforming should naturally precede the action of the selective agencies.

We were, then, in our quest for the factors of organic evolution, obliged to fall back on the action of
the physico-chemical forces such as light, or its absence, heat, cold, change of climate; and the physiological agencies of food, or in other words on changes
in the physical environment, as well as in the biological environment. Lamarck was the first one who,
owing to his many years' training in systematic botany
and zoölogy, and his philosophic breadth, had stated
more fully and authoritatively than any one else the
results of changes in the action of the primary factors
of evolution. Hence a return on the part of many
in Europe, and especially in America, to Lamarckism

or its modern form, Neolamarckism. Lamarck had already, so far as he could without a knowledge of modern morphology, embryology, cytology, and histology, suggested those fundamental principles of transformism on which rests the selective principle.

Had his works been more accessible, or, where available, more carefully read, and his views more fairly represented ; had he been favored in his lifetime by a single supporter, rather than been unjustly criticised by Cuvier, science would have made more rapid progress, for it is an axiomatic truth that the general acceptance of a working evolutionary theory has given a vast impetus to biology.

We will now give a brief historical summary of the history of opinion held by Lamarckians regarding the causes of the " origin of the fittest," the rise of variations, and the appearance of a population of plant and animal forms sufficiently extensive and differentiated to allow for the play of the competitive forces, and of the more passive selective agencies which began to operate in pre-cambrian times, or as soon as the earth became fitted for the existence of living beings.

The first writer after Lamarck to work along the lines he laid down was Mr. Herbert Spencer. In 1866–71, in his epochal and remarkably suggestive *Principles of Biology*, the doctrine of use and disuse is implicated in his statements as to the effects of motion on structure in general ; * and in his theory as to the origin of the notochord, and of the segmenta-

---

* Vol. ii., p. 167, 1871.

tion of the vertebral column and the segmental arrangement of the muscles by muscular strains,* he
laid the foundations for future work along this line.
He also drew attention in the same work to the com-
plementary development of parts, and likewise instanced the decreased size of the jaws in the civilized
races of mankind, as a change not accounted for by
the natural selection of favorable variations.† In
fact, this work is largely based on the Lamarckian
principles, as affording the basis for the action of
natural selection, and thirty years later we find him
affirming : " The direct action of the medium was the
primordial factor of organic evolution." ‡ In his well-
known essay on " The Inadequacy of Natural Selection " (1893) the great philosopher, with his accustomed vigor and force, criticises the arguments of
those who rely too exclusively on Darwinism alone,
and especially Neodarwinism, as a sufficient factor to
account for the origin of special structures as well as
species.

The first German author ·to appreciate the value
of the Lamarckian factors was that fertile and comprehensive philosopher and investigator Ernst Haeckel,
who also harmonized Lamarckism and Darwinism in
these words:

" We should, on account of the grand proofs just
enumerated, have to adopt Lamarck's Theory of
Descent for the explanation of biological phenomena, even if we did not possess Darwin's Theory of

---

* Vol. ii., p. 195.
† Vol. i., § 166, p. 456.
‡ *The Factors of Organic Evolution*, 1895, p. 460.

25

Selection. The one is so completely and *directly proved* by the other, and established by mechanical causes, that there remains nothing to be desired. The laws of *Inheritance* and *Adaptation* are universally acknowledged *physiological* facts, the former traceable to propagation, the latter to the *nutrition* of organisms. On the other hand, the *struggle for existence* is a *biological* fact, which with mathematical necessity follows from the general disproportion between the average number of organic individuals and the numerical excess of their germs." *

A number of American naturalists at about the same date, as the result of studies in different directions, unbiassed by a too firm belief in the efficacy of natural selection, and relying on the inductive method alone, worked away at the evidence in favor of the primary factors of evolution along Lamarckian lines, though quite independently, for at first neither Hyatt nor Cope had read Lamarck's writings.

In 1866 Professor A. Hyatt published the first of a series of classic memoirs on the genetic relations of the fossil cephalopods. His labors, so rich in results, have now been carried on for forty years, and are supplemented by careful, prolonged work on the sponges, on the tertiary shells of Steinheim, and on the land shells of the Hawaiian Islands.

His first paper was on the parallelism between the different stages of life in the individual and those of the ammonites, carrying out D'Orbigny's discovery of embryonic, youthful, adult, and old-age stages in ammonites,† and showing that these forms are

---

* *Schöpfungsgeschichte*, 1868.   *The History of Creation*, New York, ii., p. 355.

† Alcide d'Orbigny, *Paléontologie française*, Paris, 1840–59.

due to an acceleration of growth in the mature forms, and a retardation in the senile forms.

In a memoir on the " Biological Relations of the Jurassic Ammonites," * he assigns the causes of the progressive changes in these forms, the origination of new genera, and the production of young, mature, and senile forms to " the favorable nature of the physical surroundings, primarily producing characteristic changes which become perpetuated and increased by inheritance within the group."

The study of the modifications of the tertiary forms of Planorbis at Steinheim, begun by Hilgendorf, led among others (nine in all) to the following conclusions:

" First, that the unsymmetrical spiral forms of the shells of these and of all the Mollusca probably resulted from the action of the laws of heredity, modified by gravitation.

" Second, that there are many characteristics in these shells and in other groups, which are due solely to the uniform action of the physical influence of the immediate surroundings, varying with every change of locality, but constant and uniform within each locality.

" Third, that the Darwinian law of Natural Selection does not explain these relations, but applies only to the first stages in the establishment of the differences between forms or species in the same locality. That its office is to fix these in the organization and bring them within the reach of the laws of heredity."

These views we find reiterated in his later palæon-

---

* Abstract in Proceedings of the Boston Society of Natural History, xvii., December 16, 1874.

tological papers.   Hyatt's views on acceleration were
adopted by Neumayr.*   Waagen,† from his studies
on the Jurassic cephalopods, concludes that the
factors in the evolution of these forms were changes
in external conditions, geographical isolation, competition, and that the fundamental law was not that
of Darwin, but " the law of development."   Hyatt
has also shown that at first evolution was rapid.
" The evolution is a purely mechanical problem in
which the action of the habitat is the working agent
of all the major changes; first acting upon the adult
stages, as a rule, and then through heredity upon
the earlier stages in successive generations."   He
also shows that as the primitive forms migrated and
occupied new, before barren, areas, where they met
with new conditions, the organisms " changed their
habits and structures rapidly to accord with these
new conditions." ‡

While the palæontological facts afford complete
and abundant proofs of the modifying action of
changes in the environment, Hyatt, in 1877, from his
studies on sponges,§ shows that the origin of their
endless forms " can only be explained by the action
of physical surroundings directly working upon the
organization and producing by such direct action
the modifications or common variations above described."

---

* *Zeitschr. der deutsch. geol. Gesellschaft*, 1875.
† *Palæontologica Indica.* Jurassic Fauna of Kutch. I. Cephalopoda,
pp. 242-243.   (See Hyatt's *Genesis of the Arietidæ*, pp. 27, 42.)
‡ " Genera of Fossil Cephalopods," Proc. Bost. Soc. Nat. Hist.,
xxii., April 4, 1883, p. 265.
§ " Revision of the North American Poriferæ."   Memoirs Bost.
Soc. Nat. Hist., ii., part iv., 1877.

Mr. A. Agassiz remarks that the effect of the nature of the bottom of the sea on sponges and rhizopods " is an all-important factor in modifying the organism." *

While Hyatt's studies were chiefly on the ammonites, molluscs, and existing sponges, Cope was meanwhile at work on the batrachians. His *Origin of Genera* appeared shortly after Hyatt's first paper, but in the same year (1866). This was followed by a series of remarkably suggestive essays based on his extensive palæontological work, which are in part reprinted in his *Origin of the Fittest* (1887); while in his epoch-making book, *The Primary Factors of Organic Evolution* (1896), we have in a condensed shape a clear exposition of some of the Lamarckian factors in their modern Neolamarckian form.

In the Introduction, p. 9, he remarks:

" In these papers by Professor Hyatt and myself is found the first attempt to show by concrete examples of natural taxonomy that the variations that result in evolution are not multifarious or promiscuous, but definite and direct, contrary to the method which seeks no origin for variations other than natural selection. In other words, these publications constitute the first essays in systematic evolution that appeared. By the discovery of the paleontologic succession of modifications of the articulations of the vertebrate, and especially mammalian, skeleton, I first furnished an actual demonstration of the reality of the Lamarckian factor of use, or motion, as friction, impact, and strain, as an efficient cause of evolution." †

---

* *Three Cruises of the " Blake,"* 1888, ii., p. 158.
† The earliest paper in which he adopted the Lamarckian doctrines

The discussion in Cope's work of kinetogenesis, or of the effects of use and disuse, affords an extensive series of facts in support of these factors of Lamarck's. As these two books are accessible to every one, we need only refer the reader to them as storehouses of facts bearing on Neolamarckism.

The present writer, from a study of the development and anatomy of Limulus and of Arthropod ancestry, was early (1870)* led to adopt Lamarckian views in preference to the theory of Natural Selection, which never seemed to him adequate or sufficiently comprehensive to explain the origin of variations.

In the following year,† from a study of the insects and other animals of Mammoth Cave, we claimed that "the characters separating the genera and species of animals are those inherited from adults, modified by their physical surroundings and adaptations to changing conditions of life, inducing certain alterations in parts which have been transmitted with more or less rapidity, and become finally fixed and habitual."

In an essay entitled "The Ancestry of Insects" ‡

---

of use and effort was his "Methods of Creation of Organic Types" (1871). In this paper Cope remarks that he "has never read Lamarck in French, nor seen a statement of his theory in English, except the very slight notices in the *Origin of Species* and *Chambers' Encyclopædia*, the latter subsequent to the first reading of this paper." It is interesting to see how thoroughly Lamarckian Cope was in his views on the descent theory.

* Proceedings of the American Association for the Advancement of Science, Troy meeting, 1870. Printed in August, 1871.

† *American Naturalist*, v., December, 1871, p. 750. See also pp. 751, 759, 760.

‡ Printed in advance, being chapter xiii. of *Our Common Insects*, Salem, 1873, pp. 172, 174, 179, 180, 181, 185.

(1873) we adopted the Lamarckian factors of change
of habits and environment, of use and disuse, to account for the origin of the appendages, while we
attributed the origin of the metamorphoses of insects to change of habits or of the temperature of
the seasons and of climates, particularly the change
in the earth's climates from the earlier ages of the
globe, "when the temperature of the earth was
nearly the same the world over, to the times of the
present distribution of heat and cold in zones."

From further studies on cave animals, published
in 1877,* we wrote as follows:

" In the production of these cave species, the ex-
ceptional phenomena of darkness, want of sufficient
food, and unvarying temperature, have been plainly
enough *veræ causæ*. To say that the principle of
natural selection accounts for the change of structure is no explanation of the phenomena; the phrase
has to the mind of the writer no meaning in connection with the production of these cave forms, and
has as little meaning in accounting for the origination of species and genera in general. Darwin's
phrase 'natural selection,' or Herbert Spencer's
term 'survival of the fittest,' expresses simply the
final result, while the process of the origination of
the new forms which have survived, or been selected
by nature, is to be explained by the action of the
physical environments of the animals coupled with
inheritance-force. It has always appeared to the
writer that the phrases quoted above have been mis-
used to state the cause, when they simply express
the result of the action of a chain of causes which
we may, with Herbert Spencer, call the 'environ-

---

* "A New Cave Fauna in Utah." *Bulletin of the United States
Geological Survey*, iii., April 9, 1877, p. 167.

ment' of the organism undergoing modification; and thus a form of Lamarckianism, greatly modified by recent scientific discoveries, seems to meet most of the difficulties which arise in accounting for the origination of species and higher groups of organisms. Certainly ' natural selection' or the ' survival of the fittest' is not a *vera causa*, though the ' struggle for existence' may show us the causes which have led to the *preservation* of species, while changes in the environment of the organism may satisfactorily account for the original tendency to variation assumed by Mr. Darwin as the starting-point where natural selection begins to act.''

In our work on *The Cave Animals of North America*,* after stating that Darwin in his *Origin of Species* attributed the loss of eyes " wholly to disuse," remarking (p. 142) that after the more or less perfect obliteration of the eyes, " natural selection will often have effected other changes, such as an increase in the length of the antennæ or palpi, as a compensation for blindness,'' we then summed up as follows the causes of the production of cave faunæ in general:

" 1. Change in environment from light, even partial, to twilight or total darkness, and involving diminution of food, and compensation for the loss of certain organs by the hypertrophy of others.

" 2. Disuse of certain organs.

" 3. Adaptation, enabling the more plastic forms to survive and perpetuate their stock.

" 4. Isolation, preventing intercrossing with out-

---

* Memoirs of the National Academy of Sciences, iv., 1888, pp. 156; 27 plates. See also *American Naturalist*, Sept., 1888, xxii., p. 808, and Sept., 1894, xxviii:, p. 333.

of-door forms, thus insuring the permanency of the new varieties, species, or genera.

" 5. Heredity, operating to secure for the future the permanence of the newly originated forms as long as the physical conditions remain the same.

"Natural selection perhaps expresses the total result of the working of these five factors rather than being an efficient cause in itself, or at least constitutes the last term in a series of causes. Hence Lamarckism in a modern form, or as we have termed it, Neolamarckism, seems to us to be nearer the truth than Darwinism proper or natural selection." *

In an attempt to apply Lamarck's principle of the origin of the spines and horns of caterpillars and other insects as well as other animals to the result of external stimuli,† we had not then read what he says on the subject. (See p. 316.) Having, however, been led to examine into the matter, from the views held by recent observers, especially Henslow, and it appearing that Lamarck was substantially correct in supposing that the blood (his " fluids ") would flow to parts on the exposed portions of the body and thus cause the origin of horns, on the principle of the saying, " *ubi irritatio, ibi affluxus,*" we came to the following conclusions:

---

* Carl H. Eigenman, in his elaborate memoir, *The Eyes of the Blind Vertebrates of North America* (*Archiv für Entwickelungs-mechanik der Organismen*, 1899, viii.), concludes that the Lamarckian view, that through disuse and the transmission by heredity of the characters thus inherited the eyes of blind fishes are diminished, " is the only view so far examined that does not on the face of it present serious objections " (pp. 605–609).

† " Hints on the Evolution of the Bristles, Spines, and Tubercles of Certain Caterpillars, etc." Proceedings Boston Society of Natural History, xxiv., 1890, pp. 493–560 ; 2 plates.

" The Lamarckian factors (1) change (both direct and indirect) in the *milieu*, (2) need, and (3) habit, and the now generally adopted principle that a change of function induces change in organs,* and in some or many cases actually induces the hypertrophy and specialization of what otherwise would be indifferent parts or organs;—these factors are all-important in the evolution of the colors, ornaments, and outgrowths from the cuticle of caterpillars."

Our present views as to the relations between the Lamarckian factors and the Darwinian one of natural selection are shown by the following summary at the end of this essay.

" 1. The more prominent tubercles, and spines or bristles arising from them, are hypertrophied piliferous warts, the warts, with the seta or hair which they bear, being common to all caterpillars.

" 2. The hypertrophy or enlargement was probably [we should rather say *possibly*] primarily due to a change of station from herbs to trees, involving better air, a more equable temperature, perhaps a different and better food.

" 3. The enlarged and specialized tubercles developed more rapidly on certain segments than on others, especially the more prominent segments, because the nutritive fluids would tend more freely to supply parts most exposed to external stimuli.

" 4. The stimuli were in great part due to the visits of insects and birds, resulting in a mimicry of the spines and projections on the trees; the colors

---

* E. J. Marey : " Le Transformisme et la Physiologie Expérimentale, Cours du Collège de France," *Revue Scientifique*, 2me série, iv., p. 818. (Function makes the organ, especially in the osseous and muscular systems.) See also A. Dohrn : *Der Ursprung der Wiebelthiere und das Princip des Functionswechsels*, Leipzig, 1875. See also Lamarck's opinion, p. 295.

(lines and spots) were due to light or shade, with the general result of protective mimicry, or adaptation to tree-life.

" 5. As the result of some unknown factor some of the hypodermic cells at the base of the spines became in certain forms specialized so as to secrete a poisonous fluid.

" 6. After such primitive forms, members of different families, had become established on trees, a process of arboreal segregation or isolation would set in, and intercrossing with low-feeders would cease.

" 7. Heredity, or the unknown factors of which heredity is the result, would go on uninterruptedly, the result being a succession of generations perfectly adapted to arboreal life.

" 8. Finally the conservative agency of natural selection operates constantly, tending towards the preservation of the new varieties, species, and genera, and would not cease to act, in a given direction, so long as the environment remained the same.

" 9. Thus in order to account for the origin of a species, genus, family, order, or even a class, the first steps, causing the origination of variations, were in the beginning due to the primary (direct and indirect) factors of evolution (Neolamarckism), and the final stages were due to the secondary factors, segregation and natural selection (Darwinism)."

From a late essay * we take the following extracts explaining our views:

" In seeking to explain the causes of a metamorphosis in animals, one is compelled to go back to the

---

* " On the Inheritance of Acquired Characters in Animals with a Complete Metamorphosis." Proceedings Amer. Acad. Arts and Sciences, Boston, xxix. (N. S., xxi.), 1894, pp. 331–370; also monograph of " Bombycine Moths," Memoirs Nat. Acad. Sciences, vii., 1895, p. 33.

primary factors of organic evolution, such as the change of environment, whether the factors be cosmical (gravity), physical changes in temperature, effects of increased or diminished light and shade, under- or over-nutrition, and the changes resulting from the presence or absence of enemies, or from isolation. The action of these factors, whether direct or indirect, is obvious, when we try to explain the origin or causes of the more marked metamorphoses of animals. Then come in the other Lamarckian factors of use and disuse, new needs resulting in new modes of life, habits, or functions, which bring about the origination, development, and perfection of new organs, as in new species and genera, etc., or which in metamorphic forms may result in a greater increase in the number of, and an exaggeration of the features characterizing the stages of larval life.

"VI. *The Adequacy of Neolamarckism.*

" It is not to be denied that in many instances all through the ceaseless operation of these fundamental factors there is going on a process of sifting or of selection of forms best adapted to their surroundings, and best fitted to survive, but this factor, though important, is quite subordinate to the initial causes of variation, and of metamorphic changes.

" Neolamarckism,* as we understand this doctrine,

---

* In 1885, in the Introduction to the *Standard Natural History*, we proposed the term Neolamarckianism, or Lamarckism in its modern form, to designate the series of factors of organic evolution, and we take the liberty to quote the passage in which the word first occurs. We may add that the briefer form, Neolamarckism, is the more preferable.

" In the United States a number of naturalists have advocated what may be called Neo-Lamarckian views of evolution, especially the conception that in some cases rapid evolution may occur. The present writer, contrary to pure Darwinians, believes that many species, but more especially types of genera and families, have been produced by changes in the environment acting often with more or less rapidity

has for its foundation a combination of the factors suggested by the Buffon and Geoffroy St. Hilaire school, which insisted on the direct action of the *milieu*, and of Lamarck, who relied both on the direct (plants and lowest animals) and on the indirect action of the environment, adding the important factors of need and of change of habits resulting either in the atrophy or in the development of organs by disuse or use, with the addition of the hereditary transmission of characters acquired in the lifetime of the individual.

" Lamarck's views, owing to the early date of his work, which was published in 1809, before the foundation of the sciences of embryology, cytology, palæontology, zoögeography, and in short all that distinguishes modern biology, were necessarily somewhat crude, though the fundamental factors he suggested are those still invoked by all thinkers of Lamarckian tendencies.

---

on the organism, resulting at times in a new genus, or even a family type. Natural selection, acting through thousands, and sometimes millions, of generations of animals and plants, often operates too slowly ; there are gaps which have been, so to speak, intentionally left by Nature. Moreover, natural selection was, as used by some writers, more an idea than a *vera causa*. Natural selection also begins with the assumption of a tendency to variation, and presupposes a world already tenanted by vast numbers of animals among which a struggle for existence was going on, and the few were victorious over the many. But the entire inadequacy of Darwinism to account for the primitive origin of life forms, for the original diversity in the different branches of the tree of life forms, the interdependence of the creation of ancient faunas and floras on geological revolutions, and consequent sudden changes in the environment of organisms, has convinced us that Darwinism is but one of a number of factors of a true evolution theory ; that it comes in play only as the last term of a series of evolutionary agencies or causes ; and that it rather accounts, as first suggested by the Duke of Argyll, for the *preservation* of forms than for their origination. We may, in fact, compare Darwinism to the apex of a pyramid, the larger mass of the pyramid representing the complex of theories necessary to account for the world of life as it has been and now is. In other words, we believe in a modified and greatly extended Lamarckianism, or what may be called Neo-Lamarckianism."

" Neolamarckism gathers up and makes use of the factors both of the St. Hilaire and Lamarckian schools, as containing the more fundamental causes of variation, and adds those of geographical isolation or segregation (Wagner and Gulick), the effects of gravity, the effects of currents of air and of water, of fixed or sedentary as opposed to active modes of life, the results of strains and impacts (Ryder, Cope, and Osborn), the principle of change of function as inducing the formation of new structures (Dohrn), the effects of parasitism, commensalism, and of symbiosis—in short, the biological environment; together with geological extinction, natural and sexual selection, and hybridity.

" It is to be observed that the Neolamarckian in relying mainly on these factors does not overlook the value of natural selection as a guiding principle, and which began to act as soon as the world became stocked with the initial forms of life, but he simply seeks to assign this principle to its proper position in the hierarchy of factors.

" Natural selection, as the writer from the first has insisted, is not a *vera causa*, an initial or impelling cause in the origination of new species and genera. It does not start the ball in motion; it only, so to speak, guides its movements down this or that incline. It is the expression, like that of " the survival of the fittest " of Herbert Spencer, of the results of the combined operation of the more fundamental factors. In certain cases we cannot see any room for its action; in some others we cannot at present explain the origin of species in any other way. Its action increased in proportion as the world became more and more crowded with diverse forms, and when the struggle for existence had become more unceasing and intense. It certainly cannot account for the origination of the different branches, classes, or orders of organized beings. It in the main simply corresponds to artificial selection; in the latter case, man selects forms already produced by domestication, the latter affording sports and varieties due to change in the surroundings, that is, soil, climate, food, and other physical features, as well as education.

" In the case also of heredity, which began to operate as soon as the earliest life forms appeared, we have at the outset to invoke the principle of the heredity of characters acquired during the lifetime of lowest organisms.

" Finally, it is noticeable that when one is over-mastered by the dogma of natural selection he is apt, perhaps unconsciously, to give up all effort to work out the factors of evolution, or to seek to work out this or that cause of variation. Trusting too implicitly to the supposed *vera causa*, one may close his eyes to the effects of change of environment or to the necessity of constant attempts to discover the real cause of this or that variation, the reduction or increase in size of this or that organ; or become insensible to the value of experiments. Were the dogma of natural selection to become universally accepted, further progress would cease, and biology would tend to relapse into a stage of atrophy and degeneration. On the other hand, a revival of Lamarckism in its modern form, and a critical and doubting attitude towards natural selection as an efficient cause, will keep alive discussion and investigation, and especially, if resort be had to experimentation, will carry up to a higher plane the status of philosophical biology."

Although now the leader of the Neodarwinians, and fully assured of the " all-sufficiency " of natural selection, the veteran biologist Weismann, whose earlier works were such epoch-making contributions to insect embryology, was, when active as an investigator, a strong advocate of the Lamarckian factors. In his masterly work, *Studies in the Theory of Descent* * (1875), although accepting Darwin's principle of natural selection, he also relied on " the transforming influence of direct action as upheld by Lamarck," although he adds, " its extent cannot as yet be estimated with any certainty." He concluded from his studies in seasonal dimorphism, " that differences of specific value can originate through the direct action of external conditions of life only." While conceding that sexual selection plays a very important part in the markings and coloring of butterflies, he adds " that a change produced directly by climate may be still further increased by sexual selection." He also inquired into the origin of variability, and held that it can be elucidated by seasonal dimorphism. He thus formulated the chief results of his investigations: " A species is only caused to change through the influence of changing external conditions of life, this change being in a fixed direction which entirely depends on the physical nature of the varying organism, and is different in different species or even in the two sexes of the same species."

The influence of changes of climate on variation has been studied to especial advantage in North America, owing to its great extent, and to the fact that its territory ranges from the polar to the tropical regions, and from the Atlantic to the Pacific

---

* *Studies in the Theory of Descent.* By Dr. August Weismann. Translated and edited, with notes, by Raphael Meldola. London, 1882. 2 vols.

Ocean. As respects climatic variation in birds, Professor Baird first took up the inquiry, which was greatly extended, with especial relation to the formation of local varieties, by Dr. J. A. Allen,* who was the first to ascertain by careful measurements, and by a study of the difference in plumage and pelage of individuals inhabiting distant portions of a common habitat, the variations due to climatic and local causes.

" That varieties," he says, " may and do arise by the action of climatic influences, and pass on to become species; and that species become, in like manner, differentiated into genera, is abundantly indicated by the facts of geographical distribution, and the obvious relation of local forms to the conditions of environment. The present more or less unstable condition of the circumstances surrounding organic beings, together with the known mutations of climate our planet has undergone in past geological ages, point clearly to the agency of physical conditions as one of the chief factors in the evolution of new forms of life. So long as the environing conditions remain stable, just so long will permanency of character be maintained; but let changes occur, however gradual or minute, and differentiations begin." He inclines to regard the modifications as due rather to the direct action of the conditions of environment than to " the round-about process of natural selection." He also admits that

* " The Influence of Physical Conditions in the Genesis of Species," *Radical Review*, i., May, 1877. See also J. A. Allen in Bull. Mus. Comp. Zoöl., ii., 1871 ; also R. Ridgway, *American Journal of Science*, December, 1872, January, 1873.

change of habits and food, use and disuse, are factors.

The same kind of inquiry, though on far less complete data, was extended by the present writer[*] in 1873 to the moths, careful measurements of twenty-five species of geometrid moths common to the Atlantic and Pacific coasts of North America showing that there is an increase in size and variation in shape of the wings, and in some cases in color, in the Pacific Coast over Eastern or Atlantic Coast individuals of the same species, the differences being attributed to the action of climatic causes. The same law holds good in the few Notodontian moths common to both sides of our continent. Similar studies, the results depending on careful measurements of many individuals, have recently been made by C. H. Eigenmann (1895–96), W. J. Moenkhaus (1896), and H. C. Bumpus (1896–98).

The discoveries of Owen, Gaudry, Huxley, Kowalevsky, Cope, Marsh, Filhol, Osborn, Scott, Wortmann, and many others, abundantly prove that the lines of vertebrate descent must have been the result of the action of the primary factors of organic evolution, including the principles of migration, isolation, and competition; the selective principle being secondary and preservative rather than originative.

Important contributions to dynamic evolution or kinetogenesis are the essays of Cope, Ryder, Dall, Osborn, Jackson, Scott, and Wortmann.

---

[*] Annual Report of the United States Geological and Geographical Survey Territories, 1873. 1 p. 543–560. See also the author's monograph of Geometrid Moths or Phalænidæ of the United States, 1876, pp. 584–589, and monograph of Bombycine Moths (Notodontidæ), p. 50.

Ryder began in 1877 to publish a series of remarkably suggestive essays on the " mechanical genesis,"
through strains, of the vertebrate limbs and teeth,
including the causes of the reduction of digits.   In
discussing the origin of the great development of
the incisor teeth of rodents, he suggested that " the
more severe strains to which they were subjected by
enforced or intelligently assumed changes of habit,
were the initiatory agents in causing them to assume
their present forms, such forms as were best adapted
to resist the greatest strains without breaking." *

He afterwards † claimed that the articulations of
the cartilaginous fin-rays of the trout (*Salmo fonti-
nalis*) are due to the mechanical strains experienced
by the rays in use as motors of the body of the fish
in the water.

In the line of inquiry opened up by Cope and by
Ryder are the essays of Osborn ‡ on the mechanical
causes for the displacement of the elements of the
feet in the mammals, and the phylogeny of the
teeth.   Also Professor W. B. Scott thus expresses
the results of his studies : §

    " To sum up the results of our examination of cer-
tain series of fossil mammals, one sees clearly that
transformation, whether in the way of the addition
of new parts or the reduction of those already present, acts just *as if* the direct action of the environ-

---

* Proceedings Academy of Natural Science, Philadelphia (1877),
p. 318.
   † Proceedings of the American Philosophical Society (1889), p. 546.
   ‡ Transactions American Philosophical Society, xvi. (1890), and
later papers.
   § *American Journal of Morphology* (1891), pp. 395, 398.

ment and the habits of the animal were the efficient cause of the change, and any explanation which excludes the direct action of such agencies is confronted by the difficulty of an immense number of the most striking coincidences. . . . So far as I can see, the theory of determinate variations and of use-inheritance is not antagonistic but supplementary to natural selection, the latter theory attempting no explanation of the *causes* of variation. Nor is it pretended for a moment that use and disuse are the sole or even the chief factors in variation.''

As early as 1868 the Lamarckian factor of isolation, due to migration into new regions, was greatly extended, and shown by Moritz Wagner* to be a most important agent in the limitation and fixation of varieties and species.

'' Darwin's work,'' he says, '' neither satisfactorily explains the external cause which gives the first impulse to increased individual variability, and consequently to natural selection, nor that condition which, in connection with a certain advantage in the struggle for life, renders the new characteristics indispensable. The latter is, according to my conviction, solely fulfilled by the voluntary or passive migration of organisms and colonization, which depends in a great measure upon the configuration of the country; so that only under favorable conditions would the home of a new species be founded.''

---

* '' Über die Darwinische Theorie in Besug auf die geographische Verbreitung der Organismen.'' Sitzenb. der Akad. München, 1868. Translated by J. L. Laird under the title, *The Darwinian Theory and the Law of the Migration of Organisms.* London, 1873. Also *Ueber den Einfluss der geographischen Isolirung und Colonierbildung auf die morphologischen Veränderungen der Organismen.* München, 1870.

This was succeeded by Rev. J. T. Gulick's profound essays "On Diversity of Evolution under One Set of External Conditions" * (1872), and on "Divergent Evolution through Cumulative Segregation" † (1887).

These and later papers are based on his studies on the land shells of the Hawaiian Islands. The cause of their extreme diversity of local species is, he claims, not due to climatic conditions, food, 'enemies, or to natural selection, but to the action of what he calls the "law of segregation."

Fifteen years later Mr. Romanes published his theory of physiological selection, which covered much the same ground.

A very strong little book by an ornithologist of wide experience, Charles Dixon,‡ and refreshing to read, since it is packed with facts, is Lamarckian throughout. The chief factor in the formation of local species is, he thinks, isolation; the others are climatic influences (especially the glacial period), use and disuse, and sexual selection as well as chemical agency. Dixon insists on the "vast importance of isolation in the modification of many forms of life, without the assistance of natural selection." Again he says: "Natural selection, as has often been remarked, can only preserve a beneficial variation—it cannot originate it, it is not a cause of variation; on

---

* *Linnæan Society's Journal:* Zoölogy, xi., 1872.
† *Linnæan Society's Journal:* Zoölogy, xx., 1887, pp. 189–274, 496–505 ; also *Nature*, July 18, 1872.
‡ *Evolution without Natural Selection ; or, The Segregation of Species without the aid of the Darwinian Hypothesis*, London (1885), pp. 1–80.

the other hand, the use or disuse of organs is a direct cause of variation, and can furnish natural selection with abundance of material to work upon " (p. 49). The book, like the papers of Allen, Ridgway, Gulick, and others, shows the value of isolation or segregation in special areas as a factor in the origination of varieties and species, the result being the prevention of interbreeding, which would otherwise swamp the incipient varieties.

Here might be cited Delbœuf's law : *

" When a modification is produced in a very small number of individuals, this modification, even were it advantageous, would be destroyed by heredity, as the favored individuals would be obliged to unite with the unmodified individuals. *Il n'en est rien, cependant.* However great may be the number of forms similar to it, and however small may be the number of dissimilar individuals which would give rise to an isolated individual, we can always, while admitting that the different generations are propagated under the same conditions, meet with a number of generations at the end of which the sum total of the modified individuals will surpass that of the unmodified individuals." Giard adds that this law is capable of mathematical demonstration. " Thus the continuity or even the periodicity of action of a primary factor, such, for example, as a variation of the *milieu*, shows us the necessary and sufficient condition under which a variety or species originates without the aid of any secondary factor."

Semper,† an eminent zoölogist and morphologist,

---

* *Revue Scientifique*, xix. (1877), p. 669.　Quoted by Giard in *Rev. Sci.*, 1889, p. 646.

† *Animal Life as Affected by the Natural Conditions of Existence.* By Karl Semper.　The International Scientific Series.　New York, 1881.

who also was the first (in 1863) to criticise Darwin's
theory of the mode of formation of coral atolls,
though not referring to Lamarck, published a strong,
catholic, and original book, which is in general essentially Lamarckian, while not undervaluing Darwin's
principle of natural selection. " It appears to me,"
he·says, in the preface, " that of all the properties
of the animal organism, Variability is that which
may first and most easily be traced by exact investigation to its efficient causes."

· " By a rearrangement of the materials of his argument, however, we obtain, as I conceive, convincing
proof that external conditions can exert not only
a very powerful selective force, but a transforming
one as well, although it must be the more limited of
the two.

" An organ no longer needed for its original purpose may adapt itself to the altered circumstances,
and alter correspondingly if it contains within itself,
as I have explained above, the elements of such a
change. Then the influence exerted by the changed
conditions will be *transforming*, not *selective*.

" This last view may seem somewhat bold to those
readers who know that Darwin, in his theory of
selection, has almost entirely set aside the direct
transforming influence of external circumstances.
Yet he seems latterly to be disposed to admit that
he had undervalued the transforming as well as the
selective influence of external conditions; and it
seems to me that his objection to the idea of such
an influence rested essentially on the method of his
argument, which seemed indispensable for setting
his theory of selection and his hypothesis as to the
transformation of species in a clear light and on
a firm footing " (p. 37).

Dr. H. de Varigny has carried on much farther the kind of experiments begun by Semper. In his *Experimental Evolution* he employs the Lamarckian factors of environment and use and disuse, regarding the selective factors as secondary.

The Lamarckian factors are also depended upon by the late Professor Eimer in his works on the variation of the wall-lizard and on the markings of birds and mammals (1881–88), his final views being comprised in his general work.* The essence of his point of view may be seen by the following quotation:

" According to my conception, the physical and chemical changes which organisms experience during life through the action of the environment, through light or want of light, air, warmth, cold, water, moisture, food, etc., and which they transmit by heredity, are the primary elements in the production of the manifold variety of the organic world, and in the origin of species. From the materials thus supplied the struggle for existence makes its selection. These changes, however, express themselves simply as growth " (p. 22).

In a later paper † Eimer proposes the term "orthogenesis," or direct development, in rigorous conformity to law, in a few definite directions. Although this is simply and wholly Lamarckism, Eimer claims that it is not, " for," he strangely enough says, " Lamarck ascribed no efficiency whatever to

* *Organic Evolution as the Result of the Inheritance of Acquired Characters, according to the Laws of Organic Growth.* Translated by J. T. Cunningham, 1890.
† *On Orthogenesis and the Impotence of Natural Selection in Species Formation.* Chicago, 1898.

the effects of outward influences on the animal body, and very little to their effects upon vegetable organisms." Whereas if he had read his Lamarck carefully, he would have seen that the French evolutionist distinctly states that the environment acts directly on plants and the lower animals, but indirectly on those animals with a brain, meaning the higher vertebrates. The same anti-selection views are held by Eimer's pupil, Piepers,* who explains organic evolution by " laws of growth, . . . uncontrolled by any process of selection."

Dr. Cunningham likewise, in the preface to his translation of Eimer's work, gives his reasons for adopting Neolamarckian views, concluding that " the theory of selection can never get over the difficulty of the origin of entirely new characters; " that " selection, whether natural or artificial, could not be the essential cause of the evolution of organisms." In an article on " The New Darwinism " (*Westminster Review*, July, 1891) he claims that Weismann's theory of heredity does not explain the origin of horns, venomous teeth, feathers, wings of insects, or mammary glands, phosphorescent organs, etc., which have arisen on animals whose ancestors never had anything similar.

Discussing the origin of whales and other aquatic mammals, W. Kükenthal suggests that the modifications are partially attributable to mechanical principles. (*Annals and Mag. Nat. Hist.*, February, 1891.)

From his studies on the variation of butterflies,

---

* *Die Farbenevolution bei den Pieriden.* Leiden, 1898.

Karl Jordan * proposes the term " mechanical selection " to account for them, but he points out that this factor can only work on variations produced by other factors.   Certain cases, as the similar variation in the same locality of two species of different families, but with the same wing pattern, tell in favor of the direct action of the local surroundings on the markings of the wings.

In the same direction are the essays of Schroeder † on the markings of caterpillars, which he ascribes to the colors of the surroundings; of Fischer ‡ on the transmutations of butterflies as the result of changes of temperature, and also Dormeister's § earlier paper. Steinach ‖ attributes the color of the lower vertebrates to the direct influence of the light on the pigment cells, as does Biedermann.¶

In his address on evolution and the factors of evolution, Professor A. Giard ** has given due credit to Lamarck as " the creator of transformism," and to the position to be assigned to natural selection as a secondary factor.   He quotes at length Lamarck's

---

* " On Mechanical Selection and Other Problems." *Novitates Zoologicæ*, iii.   Tring, 1896.

† *Entwicklung der Raupenzeichnung und Abhängigkeit der letzeren von der Farbe der Umgebung*, 1894.

‡ *Transmutation der Schmetterlinge infolge Temperatur-veränderungen*, 1895.

§ *Ueber den Einfluss der Temperatur bei der Erzeugung der Schmetterlings-varietäten*, 1880.

‖ *Ueber Farbenwechsel bei niederen Wirbelthieren, bedingt durch directe Wirkung des Lichts auf die Pigmentzellen.   Centralblatt für Physiologie*, 1891, v., p. 326.

¶ *Ueber den Farbenwechsel der Frösche*.   Pflüger's *Archiv für Physiologie*, 1892, li., p. 455.

** *Leçon d'Ouverture du Cours de l'Évolution des Êtres organisés*. Paris, 1888, and " Les Facteurs de l'Évolution," *Revue Scientifique*, November 23 1889.

views published in 1806. After enumerating the primary factors of organic evolution, he places natural selection among his secondary factors, such as heredity, segregation, amixia, etc. On the other hand, he states that Lamarck was not happy in the choice of the examples which he gave to explain the action of habits and use of parts. "Je ne rappellerai par l'histoire tant de fois critique du cou de la giraffe et des cornes de l'escargot."

Another important factor in the evolution of the metazoa or many-celled animals, from the sponges and polyps upward from the one-celled forms or protozoa, is the principle of animal aggregation or colonization advanced by Professor Perrier. As civilization and progressive intelligence in mankind arose from the aggregation of men into tribes or peoples which lived a sedentary life, so the agricultural, building, and other arts forthwith sprang up; and as the social insects owe their higher degree of intelligence to their colonial mode of life, so as soon as unicellular organisms began to become fixed, and form aggregates, the sponge and polyp types of organization resulted, this leading to the gastræa, or ancestral form from which all the higher phyla may have originated.

M. Perrier appears to fully accept Lamarck's views, including his speculations as to wants, and use and disuse. He, however, refuses to accept Lamarck's extreme view as to the origin through effort of entirely new organs. As he says: "Unfortunately, if Lamarck succeeded in explaining in a plausible way the modification of organs already existing, their adaptation to different uses, or even their disappear-

ance from disuse, in regard to the appearance of
new organs he made hypotheses so venturesome
that they led to the momentary forgetfulness of his
other forceful conceptions." *

The popular idea of Lamarckism, and which from
the first has been prejudicial to his views, is that an
animal may acquire an organ by simply wishing for
or desiring it, or, as his French critics put it, " Un
animal finit toujours par posséder un organe quand il
le veut."   " Such," says Perrier,† " is not the idea
of Lamarck, who simply attributes the transformations of species to the stimulating action of external
conditions, construing it under the expression of
wants (*besoins*), and explaining by that word what
we now call *adaptations*.   Thus the long neck of the
giraffe results from the fact that the animal inhabits
a country where the foliage is situated at the tops of
high trees ; the long legs of the wading birds have
originated from the fact that these birds are obliged
to seek their food in the water without wetting
themselves," etc.   (See p. 350.)

" Many cases," says Perrier, " may be added to-
day to those which Lamarck has cited to support
his first law [pp. 303, 346] ; the only point which is open
to discussion is the extent of the changes which an
organ may undergo, through the use it is put to by
the animal.   It is a simple question of measurement.
The possibility of the creation of an organ in conse-

---

* *Revue Encyclopédique*, 1897, p. 325.   Yet we have an example of
the appearance of a new organ in the case of the duckbill, in which
the horny plates take the place of the teeth which Poulton has discovered in the embryo.   Other cases are the adductor muscles of
shelled crustacea.   (See p. 418.)

† *La Philosophie Zoologique avant Darwin.*   Paris, 1884, p. 76.

quence of external stimuli is itself a matter which deserves to be studied, and which we have no right to reject without investigation, without observations, or to treat as a ridiculous dream; Lamarck would doubtless have made it more readily accepted, if he had not thought it well to pass over the intermediate steps by means of wants. It is incontestable that by lack of exercise organs atrophy and disappear."

Finally, says Perrier: " Without doubt the real mechanism of the improvement (*perfectionnement*) of organisms has escaped him [Lamarck], but neither has Darwin explained it. The law of natural selection is not the indication of a process of transformation of animals; it is the expression of the total results. It states these results without showing us how they have been brought about. We indeed see that it tends to the preservation of the most perfect organisms; but Darwin does not show us how the organisms themselves originated. This is a void which we have only during these later years tried to fill " (p. 90).

Dr. J. A. Jeffries, author of an essay " On the Epidermal System of Birds," in a later paper * thus frankly expresses his views as to the relations of natural selection to the Lamarckian factors. Referring to Darwin's case of the leg bones of domestic ducks compared with those of wild ducks, and the atrophy of disused organs, he adds:

" In this case, as with most of Lamarck's laws, Darwin has taken them to himself wherever natural selection, sexual selection, and the like have fallen to the ground.

" Darwin's natural selection does not depend, as

* " Lamarckism and Darwinism." Proceedings Boston Society Natural History, xxv., 1890, pp. 42–49.

is popularly supposed, on direct proof, but is adduced as an hypothesis which gains its strength from being compatible with so many facts of correlation between an organism and its surroundings. Yet the same writer who considers natural selection proved will call for positive experimental proof of Lamarck's theory, and refuse to accept its general compatibility with the facts as support. Almost any case where natural selection is held to act by virtue of advantage gained by use of a part is equally compatible with Lamarck's theory of use and development. The wings of birds of great power of flight, the relations of insects to flowers, the claws of beasts of prey, are all cases in point.''

Professor J. A. Thomson's useful *Synthetic Summary of the Influence of the Environment upon the Organism* (1887) takes for its text Spencer's aphorism, that the direct action of the medium was the primordial factor of organic evolution. Professor Geddes relies on the changes in the soil and climate to account for the origin of spines in plants.

The botanist Sachs, in his *Physiology of Plants* (1887), remarks: '' A far greater portion of the phenomena of life are [is] called forth by external influences than one formerly ventured to assume.''

Certain botanists are now strong in the belief that the species of plants have originated through the direct influence of the environment. Of these the most outspoken is the Rev. Professor G. Henslow. His view is that self-adaptation, by response to the definite action of changed conditions of life, is the true origin of species. In 1894* he insisted, '' *in the*

---

* '' The Origin of Species without the Aid of Natural Selection,'' *Natural Science*, Oct., 1894. Also, '' The Origin of Plant Structures.''

strictest sense of the term, that natural selection is not wanted as an 'aid' or a 'means' in originating species." In a later paper* he reasserts that all variations are definite, that there are no indefinite variations, and that natural selection "can take no part in the origination of varieties." He quotes with approval the conclusion of Mr. Herbert Spencer in 1852, published

" seven years before Darwin and Dr. Wallace superadded natural selection as an aid in the origin of species. He saw no necessity for anything beyond the natural power of change with adaptation; and I venture now to add my own testimony, based upon upwards of a quarter of a century's observations and experiments, which have convinced me that Mr. Spencer was right and Darwin was wrong. His words are as follows: ' The supporters of the development hypothesis can show . . . that any existing species, animal or vegetable, when placed under conditions different from its previous ones, immediately begins to undergo certain changes of structure fitting it for the new conditions; . . . that in the successive generations these changes continue until ultimately the new conditions become the natural ones. . . . They can show that throughout all organic nature there is at work a modifying influence of the kind they assign as the causes of specific differences; an influence which, though slow in its action, does in time, if the circumstances demand it, produce marked changes.' " †

Mr. Henslow adduces observations and experiments by Buckman, Bailey, Lesage, Lothelier, Cos-

---

* " Does Natural Selection play any Part in the Origin of Species among Plants?" *Natural Science*, Sept., 1897.
† "Essay on the Development Hypothesis," 1852, London *Times*.

tantin, Bonnier, and others, all demonstrating that the environment acts directly on the plant.

Henslow also suggests that endogens have originated from exogenous plants through self-adaptation to an aquatic habit,* which is in line with our idea that certain classes of animals have diverged from the more primitive ones by change of habit, although this has led to the development of new class-characteristics by use and disuse, phenomena which naturally do not operate in plants, owing to their fixed conditions.

Other botanists—French, German, and English—have also been led to believe in the direct influence of the *milieu*, or environment. Such are Viet,† and Scott Elliot,‡ who attributes the growth of bulbs to the " direct influence of the climate."

In a recent work Costantin § shares the belief emphatically held by some German botanists in the direct influence of the environment not only as modifying the form, but also as impressing, without the aid of natural selection, that form on the species or part of its inherited stock; and one chapter is devoted to an attempt to establish the thesis that acquired characters are inherited.

---

* " A Theoretical Origin of Endogens from Exogens through Self-Adaptation to an Aquatic Habit," *Linnean Society Journal*: Botany, 1892, *l. c.*, xxix., pp. 485–528. A case analogous to kinetogenesis in animals is his statement based on mathematical calculations by Mr. Hiern, "that the best form of the margin of floating leaves for resisting the strains due to running water is circular, or at least the several portions of the margin would be circular arcs " (p. 517).

† " De l'Influence du Milieu sur la Structure anatomique des Végétaux," *Ann. Sci. Nat. Bot.*, ser. 6, xii., 1881, p. 167.

‡ " Notes on the Regional Distribution of the Cape Flora," *Transactions* Botanical Society, Edinburgh, 1891, p. 241.

§ *Les Végétaux et les Milieux cosmiques*, Paris, 1898, pp. 292.

In his essay "On Dynamic Influences in Evolution" W. H. Dall * holds the view that—

" The environment stands in a relation to the individual such as the hammer and anvil bear to the blacksmith's hot iron. The organism suffers during its entire existence a continuous series of mechanical impacts, none the less real because invisible, or disguised by the fact that some of them are precipitated by voluntary effort of the individual itself. . . . It is probable that since the initiation of life upon the planet no two organisms have ever been subjected to exactly the same dynamic influences during their development. . . . The reactions of the organism against the physical forces and mechanical properties of its environment are abundantly sufficient, if we are granted a single organism, with a tendency to grow, to begin with; time for the operation of the forces; and the principle of the survival of the fittest."

In his paper on the hinge of Pelecypod molluscs and its development, he has pointed out a number of the particular ways in which the dynamics of the environment may act on the characters of the hinge and shell of bivalve molluscs. He has also shown that the initiation and development of the columellar plaits in Voluta, Mitra, and other gastropod molluscs " are the necessary mechanical result of certain comparatively simple physical conditions; and that the variations and peculiarities connected with these plaits perfectly harmonize with the results which follow within organic material subjected to analogous stresses."

* Proceedings Biological Society of Washington, 1890.

27

In the same line of study is Dr. R. T. Jackson's [*]
work on the mechanical origin of characters in the
lamellibranch molluscs. "The bivalve nature of the
shell doubtless arose," he says, "from the splitting on
the median line of a primitive univalvular ancestor;"
and he adds: "A parallel case is seen in the development of a bivalve shell in ancient crustaceans;" in
both types of shells "the form is induced by the
mechanical conditions of the case." The adductor
muscles of bivalve molluscs and crustaceans are, he
shows plainly, the necessary consequence of the
bivalvular condition.

In his theory as to the origin of the siphon of the
clam (*Mya arenaria*), he explains it in a manner
identical with Lamarck's explanations of the origin
of the wading and swimming birds, etc., even to the
use of the words "effort" and "habit."

"In *Mya arenaria* we find a highly elongated
siphon. In the young the siphon hardly extends
beyond the borders of the valves, and then the animal lives at or close to the surface. In progressive
growth, as the animal burrows deeper, the siphon
elongates, until it attains a length many times the
total length of the valves.

"The ontogeny of the individual and the paleontology of the family both show that Mya came from
a form with a very abbreviated siphon, and it seems
evident that the long siphon of this genus was
brought about by the effort to reach the surface
induced by the habit of deep burial."

---

[*] "Phylogeny of the Pelecypoda," Memoirs Boston Society Natural
History, iv., 1890, pp. 277–400. Also, *American Naturalist*, 1891,
xxv., pp. 11–21.

" The tendency to equalize the form of growth in a horizontal plane, or the geomalic tendency of Professor Hyatt,* is seen markedly in pelecypods. In forms which crawl on the free borders of the valves, the right and left growth in relation to the perpendicular is obvious, and agrees with the right and left sides of the animal. In Pecten the animal at rest lies on the right valve, and swims or flies with the right valve lowermost. Here equalization to the right and left of the perpendicular line passing through the centre of gravity is very marked (especially in the Vola division of the group); but the induced right and left aspect corresponds to the dorsal and ventral sides of the animal, not the right and left sides, as in the former case. Lima, a near ally of Pecten, swims with the edges of the valves perpendicular. In this case the geomalic growth corresponds to the right and left sides of the animal.

" The oyster has a deep or spoon-shaped attached valve, and a flat or flatter free valve. This form, or a modification of it, we find to be characteristic of all pelecypods which are attached to a foreign object of support by the cementation of one valve. All are highly modified, and are strikingly different from the normal form seen in locomotive types of the group. The oyster may be taken as the type of the form adopted by attached pelecypods. The two valves are unequal, the attached valve being concave, the free valve flat; but they are not only unequal, they are often very dissimilar—as different as if they belonged to a distinct type in what would be considered typical forms. This is remarkable as a case of acquired and inherited characteristics finding very different expression in the two valves of a group belonging to a class typically equivalvular. The

* " Transformations of Planorbis at Steinheim, with Remarks on the Effects of Gravity upon the Forms of Shells and Animals." Proceedings A. A. A. S., xxix., 1880.

attached valve is the most highly modified, and the free is least modified, retaining more fully ancestral characters. Therefore, it is to the free young before fixation takes place and to the free, least-modified valve that we must turn in tracing genetic relations of attached groups. Another characteristic of attached pelecypods is camerated structure, which is most frequent and extensive in the thick attached valve. The form as above described is characteristic of the Ostreidæ, Hinnites, Spondylus, and Plicatula, Dimya, Pernostrea, Aetheria, and Mulleria; and Chama and its near allies. These various genera, though ostreiform in the adult, are equivalvular and of totally different form in the free young. The several types cited are from widely separated families of pelecypods, yet all, under the same given conditions, adopt a closely similar form, which is strong proof that common forces acting on all alike have induced the resulting form. What the forces are that have induced this form it is not easy to see from the study of this form alone; but the ostrean form is the base of a series, from the summit of which we get a clearer view." (*Amer. Nat.*, pp. 18–20.)

Here we see, plainly brought out by Jackson's researches, that the Lamarckian factors of change of environment and consequently of habit, effort, use and disuse, or mechanical strains resulting in the modifications of some, and even the appearance of new organs, as the adductor muscles, have originated new characters which are peculiar to the class, and thus a new class has been originated. The mollusca, indeed, show to an unusual extent the influence of a change in environment and of use and disuse in the formation of classes.

Lang's treatment, in his *Text-book of Comparative Anatomy* (1888), of the subjects of the musculature of worms and crustacea, and of the mechanism of the motion of the segmented body in the Arthropoda, is of much value in relation to the mechanical genesis of the body segments and limbs of the members of this type. Dr. B. Sharp has also discussed the same subject (*American Naturalist*, 1893, p. 89), also Graber in his works, while the present writer in his *Text-book of Entomology* (1898) has attempted to treat of the mechanical origin of the segments of insects, and of the limbs and their jointed structure, along the lines laid down by Herbert Spencer, Lang, Sharp, and Graber.

W. Roux* has inquired how natural selection could have determined the special orientation of the sheets of spongy tissue of bone. He contends that the selection of accidental variation could not originate species, because such variations are isolated, and because, to constitute a real advantage, they should rest on several characters taken together. His example is the transformation of aquatic into terrestrial animals.

G. Pfeffer† opposes the efficacy of natural selection, as do C. Emery ‡ and O. Hertwig. The essence of Hertwig's *The Biological Problem of To-day* (1894) is that " in obedience to different external influ-

---

* *Der Kampf der Theile im Organismus.* Leipzig, 1881. Also *Gesammelte Abhandlungen über Entwickelungsmechanik der Organismen.* Leipzig, 1895.

† *Die Unwandlung der Arten ein Vorgang functioneller Selbsgestaltung.* Leipzig, 1894.

‡ *Gedanken zur Descendenz- und Vererbungstheorie : Biol. Centralblatt*, xiii., 1893, 397–420.

ences the same rudiments may give rise to different adult structures " (p. 128). Delage, in his *Théories sur l'Hérédité*, summarizes under seven heads the objections of these distinguished biologists. Species arise, he says, from general variations, due to change in the conditions of life, such as food, climate, use and disuse, very rarely individual variations, such as sports or aberrations, which are more or less the result of disease.

Mention should also be made of the essays and works of H. Driesch,* De Varigny,† Danilewsky,‡ Verworn,§ Davenport,‖ Gadow,¶ and others.

In his address on " Neodarwinism and Neolamarckism," Mr. Lester F. Ward, the palæobotanist, says:

" I shall be obliged to confine myself almost exclusively to the one great mind, who far more than all others combined paved the way for the new science of biology to be founded by Darwin, namely, Lamarck." After showing that Lamarck established the functional, or what we would call the dynamic factors, he goes on to say that " Lamarck, although he clearly grasped the law of competition, or the struggle for existence, the law of adaptation, or the correspondence of the organism to the changing environment, the transmutation of species, and the

---

* *Entwickelungmecanische Studien*, 1892–93.

† *Experimental Evolution*, 1892 ; also, "Recherches sur le Nanisme experimental," *Journ. Anat. et Phys.*, 1894.

‡ " Ueber die organsplastischen Kräfte der Organismen," *Arbeit. nat. Ges.*, Petersburg, xvi., 1885 ; Protok, 79–82.

§ *General Physiology*, 1899.

‖ *Experimental Morphology*, 1897–99, 2 vols.

¶ " Modifications of Certain Organs which seem to be Illustrations of the Inheritance of Acquired Characters in Mammals and Birds," *Zool. Jahrb. Syst. Abth.*, 1890, iv., pp. 629–646 ; also, *The Lost Link*, by E. Haeckel, with notes, etc., by H. Gadow, 1899.

genealogical descent of all organic beings, the more complex from the more simple; he nevertheless failed to conceive the selective principle as formulated by Darwin and Wallace, which so admirably complemented these great laws.'' *

As is well known, Huxley was, if we understand his expressions aright, not fully convinced of the entire adequacy of natural selection.

'' There is no fault to be found with Mr. Darwin's method, then; but it is another question whether he has fulfilled all the conditions imposed by that method. Is it satisfactorily proved, in fact, that species may be originated by selection ? that there is such a thing as natural selection ? that none of the phenomena exhibited by species are inconsistent with the origin of species in this way ?

. . . .

'' After much consideration, with assuredly no bias against Mr. Darwin's views, it is our clear conviction that, as the evidence stands, it is not absolutely proven that a group of animals, having all the characters exhibited by species in nature, has ever been originated by selection, whether artificial or natural. Groups having the morphological character of species, distinct and permanent races, in fact, have been so produced over and over again; but there is no positive evidence, at present, that any group of animals has, by variation and selective breeding, given rise to another group which was even in the least degree infertile with the first. Mr. Darwin is perfectly aware of this weak point, and brings forward a multitude of ingenious and important arguments to diminish the force of the objection.'' †

* Proceedings Biological Society of Washington, vi., 1892, pp. 13, 19.
† *Lay Sermons, Addresses, and Reviews*, 1870, p. 323.

We have cited the foregoing conclusions and opinions of upwards of forty working biologists, many of whom were brought up, so to speak, in the Darwinian faith, to show that the pendulum of evolutionary thought is swinging away from the narrow and restricted conception of natural selection, pure and simple, as the sole or most important factor, and returning in the direction of Lamarckism.

We may venture to say of Lamarck what Huxley once said of Descartes, that he expressed " the thoughts which will be everybody's two or three centuries after " him. Only the change of belief, due to the rapid accumulation of observed facts, has come in a period shorter than " two or three centuries; " for, at the end of the very century in which Lamarck, whatever his crudities, vagueness, and lack of observations and experiments, published his views, wherein are laid the foundations on which natural selection rests, the consensus of opinion as to the direct and indirect influence of the environment, and the inadequacy of natural selection as an initial factor, was becoming stronger and deeper-rooted each year.

We must never forget or underestimate, however, the inestimable value of the services rendered by Darwin, who by his patience, industry, and rare genius for observation and experiment, and his powers of lucid exposition, convinced the world of the truth of evolution, with the result that it has transformed the philosophy of our day. We are all of us evolutionists, though we may differ as to the nature of the efficient causes.

A BIBLIOGRAPHY OF THE WRITINGS OF J. B. DE LAMARCK *

1778—1828

1778

Flore française ou description succinte de toutes les plantes qui croissent naturellement en France, disposées selon une nouvelle méthode d'analyse et à laquelle on a joint la citation de leurs vertus les moins équivoques en médecine et de leur utilité dans les arts. Paris (Impr. Nationale), 1778. 8vo, 3 vol.

  Vol. I. Ext. du Rapport fait par MM. Duhamet et Guettard de cet ouvrage. pp. 1–4.

  Discours préliminaire. pp. i–cxix.

  Principes élémentaires de Botanique. pp. 1–223.

  Méthode analytique.—Plantes cryptogames. pp. 1–132, viii, pl.

  Vol. II. Méthode analytique.—Plantes adultes, ou dont les fleurs sont dans un état de développement parfait. pp. iv, 684.

  Vol. III. Méthode analytique. pp. 654, x.

  Idem. 2e édit. Paris, 1793.

(1805-15)

Flore française ou description succinte de toutes les plantes qui croissent naturellement en France, disposées selon une nouvelle méthode d'analyse, et précédées par un exposé des principes élémentaires de la Botanique.

  (En collaboration avec A. P. de Candolle). Édition III. Paris (Agasse), 1805. 4 vol., 8vo.

  Vol. I. Lettre de M. de Candolle à M. Lamarck. pp. xv.

  Discours préliminaire. (Réimpression de la 1re édit.) pp. 1–60.

  Principes élémentaires de Botanique. pp. 61–224.

---

* Prepared by M. G. Malloisel, with a few titles added by the author.

Méthode analytique : $\begin{cases} \text{analyse des genres. pp. 1-76.} \\ \text{analyse des espèces. pp. 77-388, 10 pl.} \end{cases}$

Vol. II. Explication de la Carte botanique de France. pp. i-xii. Plantes acotylédonées. pp. 1-600. Carte coloriée.

Vol. III. Monocotylédonées phanérogames. pp. 731.

Vol. IV. " " pp. 944.

Même édition, augmentée du tome 5 et tome 6, contenant 1300 espèces non décrites dans les cinq premiers volumes. Paris (Desray), 1815. 8vo, pp. 622.

Lettre de M. A. P. de Candolle à M. Lamarck. pp. 10.

1783

Dictionnaire botanique.—(En Encyclopédie méthodique. Paris, in 4to.) I, 1783 ; II, 1786 ; pour le IIIe volume, 1789, Lamarck a été aidé par Desrousseaux. Le IVe, 1795, est de Desrousseaux, Poiret et Savigny. Les derniers : V, 1804; VI, 1804; VII, 1806; et VIII, 1808, sont de Poiret.

Lamarck et Poiret. Encyclopédie méthod. : Botanique. 8 vols. et suppl. 1 à 3, avec 900 pl.

1784

Mémoire sur un nouveau genre de plante nommé Brucea, et sur le faux Brésillet d'Amérique. Mém. Acad. des Sci. 21 janvier 1784. pp. 342-347.

1785

Mémoire sur les classes les plus convenables à établir parmi les végétaux et sur l'analogie de leur nombre avec celles déterminées dans le règne animal, ayant égard de part et d'autre à la perfection graduée des organes. (De la classification des végétaux.) Mém. Acad. des Sci. 1785. pp. 437-453.

1788

Mémoire sur le genre du Muscadier, Myristica. Mém. Acad. des Sci. 1788. pp. 148-168, pl. v.-ix.

1790

Mémoire sur les cabinets d'histoire naturelle, et particulièrement sur celui du Jardin des Plantes; contenant l'exposition du régime et de l'ordre qui conviennent à cet établissement, pour qu'il soit vraiment utile. (No imprint.) 4to, pp. 15.

Considérations en faveur du Chevalier de la Marck, ancien officier au Régiment de Beaujolais, de l'Académie Royale des Sciences; Botaniste du Roi, attaché au Cabinet d'Histoire Naturelle. [Paris] 1790. 8vo, pp. 7.

1791

Instruction aux voyageurs autour du monde, sur les observations les plus essentielles à faire en botanique. Soc. Philom. (Bull.) Paris, 1791, pp. 8.

Illustrations des genres, ou exposition des caractères de tous les genres de plantes établis par les botanistes (Encyclopédie méthodique): I, 1791; II, 1793; III, 1800, avec 900 planches. (Le supplément, qui constitue le tome IV, 1823, est de Poiret.)

Extrait de la flore française. Paris, 1792. 1 vol. in-8vo.

Tableau encyclopédique et méthodique des trois règnes de la nature. Botanique continuée par J. L. M. Poiret. Paris (Panckoucke), 1791–1823. Text, 3 v.; Pls., 4 v. (Encyclopédie méthodique.) 4to.

Tableau encyclopédique et méthodique des trois règnes de la nature. Mollusques testacés (et polypes divers). Paris (Panckoucke) [etc.], 1791–1816. Text (3), 180 pp. Pls. 2 v. (Encyclopédie méthodique.) 4to.

Idem. Continuator Bruguière, Jean Guillaume. Histoire naturelle des vers. Par Bruguière [et J. B. P. A. de Lamarck ; continuée par G. P. Deshayes]. Paris (Panckoucke) [etc.], 1792–1832, 3 v. (Encyclopédie méthodique.) 4to.

1792

Journal d'Histoire naturelle, rédigé par MM. Lamarck, Bruguière, Olivier, Haüy et Pelletier. Tomes I, II. Pl. 1-24, 25-40. Paris (Impr. du Cercle social), 1792. In-8vo, 2 vol.

Le même, sous le titre : Choix de mémoires sur divers objets d'histoire naturelle, par Lamarck ; formant les collections du Journal d'Hist. nat. 3 vol. in-8vo, tirés de format in-4to, dont le 3me contient 42 pl. Paris (Imprim. du Cercle social), 1792.

Nota.—Tous les exemplaires de cet ouvrage que l'on rencontre sont incomplets. Un exemplaire de format in-8vo, provenant de la Bibliothèque Cuvier (et qui se trouve à la Bibliothèque du Muséum), contient les pages 320 à 360 ; 8 pages copiées à la main terminent le volume, dont on connaît complet un seul exemplaire.

Sur l'histoire naturelle en général.

Sur la nature des articles de ce journal qui concernent la Botanique.

Philosophie botanique. L'auteur propose dans cet article un nouveau genre de plante : le Genre Rothia (Rothia Carolinensis, p. 17, pl. 1). Journ. d'Hist. nat. I, 1792. pp. 1-19. (Ce recueil porte aussi le titre suivant: Choix de mémoires sur divers objets d'Histoire naturelle, par MM. Lamarck, Bruguière, Olivier, Haüy et Pelletier.)

Sur le Calodendron (Calodendron Capense), pp. 56, pl. 3. Journ. d'Hist. nat. I, 1792. pp. 56-62.

Philosophie botanique. Journ. d'Hist. nat. I, 1792. pp. 81-92. (Dans cet article l'auteur donne la description de : Mimosa obliqua. pp. 89, pl. 5.)

Sur les travaux de Linné. Journ. d'Hist. nat. I, 1792. pp. 136-144. (L'auteur conclut que tout ce que fit Linnæus pour la botanique, il le fit aussi pour la zoologie ; et ne donna pas moins de preuves de son génie en traitant le règne minéral, quoique dans cette partie de l'histoire naturelle il fut moins heureux en principes et en convenances dans les rapprochements et les déterminations, que dans les deux autres règnes.)

Sur une nouvelle espèce de Vantane. Ventanea parviflora. p. 145, pl. 7. Journ. d'Hist. nat. I, 1792. pp. 144-148.

Exposition d'un nouveau genre de plante nommé Drapètes. Drapetes muscosus et seq. p. 189, pl. 10, fig. 1. Journ. d'Hist. nat. I, 1792. pp. 1-190.

Sur le Phyllachne. Phyllachne uliginosa. p. 192, pl. 10, fig. 2. Journ. d'Hist. nat. I, 1792. pp. 190-192.

Sur l'Hyoseris Virginica. p. 222, pl. 12. Journ. d'Hist. nat. I, 1792. pp. 222-224.

Sur le genre des Acacies ; et particulièrement sur l'Acacie hétérophille. Mimosa heterophylla. p. 291, pl. 15. Journ. d'Hist. nat. I, 1792. pp. 288-292.

Sur les Systèmes et les Méthodes de Botanique et sur l'Analyse. Journ. d'Hist. nat. I, 1792. pp. 300-307.

Sur une nouvelle espèce de Grassette. Pinguicula campanulata. p. 336, pl. 18, fig. 1. Journ. d'Hist. nat. I, 1792. pp. 334-338.

Sur l'étude des rapports naturels. Journ. d'Hist. nat. I, 1792. pp. 361-371.

Sur les relations dans leur port ou leur aspect, que les plantes de certaines contrées ont entre elles, et sur une nouvelle espèce d'Hydrophylle. Hydrophyllum Magellanicum. p. 373, pl. 19. Journ. d'Hist. nat. I, 1792. pp. 371-376.

Notice sur quelques plantes rares ou nouvelles, observées dans l'Amérique Septentrionale par M. A. Michaux ; adressée à la Société d'Histoire naturelle de Paris par l'auteur ; et rédigée avec des observations. Canna flava—Pinguicula lutea—Ilex Americana—Ilex æstivalis—Ipomæa rubra—Mussænda frondosa—Kalmia hirsuta—Andromeda mariana—A. formosissima. Journ. d'Hist. nat. I, 1792. pp. 409–419.

Sur une nouvelle espèce de Loranthe. Loranthus cucullaris. p. 444, pl. 23. Journ. d'Hist. nat. I, 1792. pp. 444–448.

Sur le nouveau genre Polycarpea. Polycarpæa Teneriffæ. p. 5, pl. 25. Journ. d'Hist. nat. II, 1792. pp. 3–8.

Sur l'augmentation continuelle de nos connaissances à l'égard des espèces et sur une nouvelle espèce de Sauge. Salvia scabiosæfolia. p. 44, pl. 27. Journ. d'Hist. nat. II, 1792. pp. 41–47.

Sur une nouvelle espèce de Pectis. Pectis pinnata. p. 150, pl. 31. Journ. d'Hist. nat. II, 1792. pp. 148–154.

Sur le nouveau genre Sanvitalia. Sanvitalia procumbens. p. 178, pl. 35. Journ. d'Hist. nat. II, 1792. pp. 176–179.

Sur l'augmentation remarquable des espèces dans beaucoup de genres qui n'en offraient depuis longtemps qu'une, et particulièrement sur une nouvelle espèce d'Hélénium. Helenium caniculatum. p. 213, pl. 35. Journ. d'Hist. nat. II, 1792. pp. 210–215.

Observations sur les coquilles, et sur quelques-uns des genres qu'on a établis dans l'ordre des Vers testacés. Purpurea, Fusus, Murex, Terebra, etc. Journ. d'Hist. nat. II, 1792. pp. 269–280.

Sur l'Administration forestière, et sur les qualités individuelles des bois indigènes, ou qui sont acclimatés en France ; auxquels on a joint la description des bois exotiques, que nous fournit le commerce. Par *P. C. Varenne-Tenille*, Bourg (Philippon), 1792. 2 vol. 8vo. Journ. d'Hist. nat. II, 1792. pp. 299–301.

Sur quatre espèces d'Hélices. Journ. d'Hist. nat. II, 1792. pp. 347–353.

Prodrome d'une nouvelle classification des coquilles, comprenant une rédaction appropriée des caractères génériques et l'établissement d'un grand nombre de genres nouveaux.—In Mém. Soc. Hist. nat., Paris, I, 1792. p. 63.

Sur les ouvrages généraux en Histoire naturelle ; et particulièrement sur l'édition du Systema Naturæ de Linneus, que M. Gmelin vient de publier. Act. Soc. Hist. nat., Paris, I. 1re Part., 1792. pp. 81–85.

1794

Recherches sur les Causes des principaux Faits physiques, et particulièrement sur celles de la Combustion, de l'Elévation de l'eau dans l'état de vapeurs ; de la Chaleur produite par le frottement des corps solides entre eux ; de la Chaleur qui se rend sensible dans les décompositions subites, dans les effervescences et dans le corps de beaucoup d'animaux pendant la durée de leur vie ; de la Causticité, de la Saveur et de l'Odeur de certains composés ; de la Couleur des corps ; de l'Origine des composés et de tous les minéraux ; enfin, de l'Entretien de la vie des êtres organiques, de leur accroissement, de leur état de vigueur, de leur dépérissement et de leur mort. Avec une planche. Tomes 1, 2. Paris, seconde année de la république [1794]. 8vo.

Mémoire sur les molécules essentiels des composés. Soc. philom. Rapp., 1792–98. pp. 56–57.

Voyage de Pallas dans plusieurs provinces de l'empire de Russie et dans l'Asie septentrionale, traduit de l'allemand par Gauthier de la Peyronnerie. Nouvelle édition revue et enrichie de notes par Lamarck, Langlès et Billecoq. Paris, an II (1794). 8 vol. in-8vo, avec un atlas de 108 pl. folio.

1796

Voyage au Japon, par le cap de Bonne-Espérance, les îles de la Sonde, etc., par Thunberg, traduit, rédigé (sur la version anglaise), etc., par Langlès, et *revu, quant à l'histoire naturelle*, par Lamarck. Paris, 1796. 2 vol. in-4to (8vo, 4 vol.), av. fig.

Réfutation de la théorie pneumatique et de la nouvelle théorie des chimistes modernes, etc. Paris, 1796. 1 vol. 8vo.

1797

Mémoires de physique et d'histoire naturelle, établis sur des bases de raisonnement indépendantes de toute théorie ; avec l'explication de nouvelles considérations sur la cause générale des dissolutions, sur la matière du feu ; sur la couleur des corps ; sur la formation des composés; sur l'origine des minéraux; et sur l'organisation des corps vivants. Lus à la première classe de l'Institut national, dans ses séances ordinaires. Paris, an V (1797). 1 vol. 8vo. pp. 410.

De l'influence de la lune sur l'atmosphère terrestre, etc. Bull. Soc. philom. I., 1797 ; pp. 116–118. Gilbert Annal. VI, 1800 ; pp. 204–223 ; et Nicholson's Journal, III, 1800 ; pp. 438–489.

Mémoires de Physique et d'Histoire naturelle. Paris, 1797. 8vo. Biogr. un., Suppl. LXX. p. 22.

1798

De l'influence de la lune sur l'atmosphère terrestre. Journ. de Phys. XLVI, 1798 ; pp. 428–435. Gilbert Annal. VI, 1800; pp. 204–223.

Tilloch, Philos. Mag. I, 1798 ; pp. 305-306. Paris, Soc. philom. (Bull.) II, 1797 ; pp. 116-118. Nicholson's Journ. III, 1800. pp. 488-489.

Sensibility of Plants. (Translated from the Mémoires de Physique.) Tilloch, Philos. Mag. I, 1798. pp. 305-306.

Mollusques testacés du tableau encyclopédique et méthodique des trois règnes de la nature. Paris, an VI (1798). 1 vol. in-4to de 299 pl., formant suite à l'Histoire des Vers de Bruguière (1792), continuée par Deshayes (1830), de l'Encyclopédie méthodique.

1799

Mémoire sur la matière du feu, considéré comme instrument chimique dans les analyses. 1°, De l'action du feu employé comme instrument chimique par la voie sèche ; p. 134. 2°, De l'action du feu employé comme instrument chimique par la voie humide ; p. 355. Journ. de Phys. XLVIII, 1799. pp. 345-361.

Mémoire sur la matière du son. (Lu à l'Institut national, le 16 brumaire an VIII, et le 26 du même mois.) Journ. de Phys. XLIX, 1799. pp. 397-412.

Sur les genres de la Sèche, du Calmar et du Poulpe, vulgairement nommés polypes de mer. (Lu à l'Institut national le 21 floréal an VI.) Soc. Hist. nat., Paris (Mém.), 1799. pp. 1-25, pl. 1, 2. Bibl. Paris, Soc. philom. (Bull.) I, Part. 2, 1799. pp. 129-131 (Extrait).

Prodrome d'une nouvelle Classification des coquilles, comprenant une rédaction appropriée des caractères génériques, et l'établissement d'un grand nombre de genres nouveaux. (Lu à l'Institut national le 21 frimaire an VII.) Soc. Hist. nat., Paris (Mém.), 1789. pp. 63-91. Tableau systématique des Genres—126 g.

Sur les fossiles et l'influence du mouvement des eaux, considérés comme indices du déplacement continuel du bassin des mers, et de son transport sur différents points de la surface du globe. (Lu à l'Institut national le 21 pluviôse an VII [1799]. Hydrogéologie, p. 172.

Annuaire météorologique pour l'an VIII de la République française, etc. (Annonce.) Paris, Soc. philom. (Bull.) III, 1799. p. 56.

1800

Annuaire météorologique pour l'an VIII de la République. Paris, 1800. 1 vol. 16mo ; 116 pp. Bibl., Gilbert Annal. VI, 1800. pp. 216-217.

Mémoire sur le mode de rédiger et de noter les observations météorologiques, afin d'en obtenir des résultats utiles, et sur les considérations que l'on doit avoir en vue pour cet objet. Journ. de Phys. LI, 1800. pp. 419–426.

Annuaire météorologique, contenant l'exposé des probabilités acquises par une longue suite d'observations sur l'état du ciel et sur les variations de l'atmosphère, etc. Paris, 1800–1810, 11 volumes, dont les 2 premiers in-18mo, les autres in-8vo.

1801

Système des Animaux sans Vertèbres ou Tableau général des classes, des ordres et des genres de ces animaux. Présentant leurs caractères essentiels et leur distribution d'après leurs rapports naturels, et de leur organisation ; et suivant l'arrangement établi dans les galeries du Muséum d'Histoire naturelle parmi les dépouilles conservées. Précédé du discours d'Ouverture du Cours de Zoologie donné dans le Muséum d'Histoire naturelle l'an VIII de la République, le 21 floréal. Paris (Déterville), an IX (1801), VIII. pp. 452. Bibl., Paris, Soc. philom. (Bull.) III, 1802–4. pp. 7–8.

Recherches sur la périodicité présumée des principales variations de l'atmosphère, et sur les moyens de s'assurer de son existence et de sa détermination. (Lues à l'Institut national de France, le 26 ventôse an IX.) Journ. de Phys. LII, 1801. pp. 296–316.

Réfutation des résultats obtenus par le C. Cotte, dans ses recherches sur l'influence des constitutions lunaires, et imprimés dans le Journal de Physique, mois de fructidor an IX. p. 221. Journ. de Phys. LIII, 1801. pp. 277–281.

Sur la distinction des tempêtes d'avec les orages, les ouragans, etc. Et sur le caractère du vent désastreux du 18 brumaire an IX (9 novembre 1800). (Lu à l'Institut national le 11 frimaire an IX.) Journ. de Phys. LII, floréal, 1801. pp. 377–382.

1802

Sur les variations de l'état du ciel dans les latitudes moyennes entre l'équateur et le pôle, et sur les principales causes qui y donnent lieu. Journ. de Phys. LVI, 1802. pp. 114–138.

Recherches sur l'Organisation des Corps vivants et particulièrement sur son origine, sur la cause de ses développements et des progrès de sa composition, et sur celles qui, tendant continuellement à la détruire, dans chaque individu, amènent nécessairement sa mort. (Précédé du

Discours d'Ouverture du Cours de Zoologie au Mus. nat. d'Hist. nat., an X de la République.) Paris (Maillard) [1802]. 1 vol. 8vo. pp. 216.

Affinites chimiques, p. 73.—Anéantissement de la colonne vertébrale, p. 21.—Du cœur, p. 26.—De l'organe de la vue, p. 32.—Annélides, p. 24.—Arachnides, p. 27.—La Biologie, p. 186.—Création de la faculté de se reproduire, p. 114.—Crustacés, p. 25.—Dégradation de l'organisation d'une extrémité à l'autre de la chaîne des animaux, p. 7.—Échelle animale, p. 39.—Les éléments, p. 12.—Les espèces, pp. 141–149.—Exercice d'un organe, pp. 53, 56, 65, 125.—Les facultés, pp. 50, 56, 84, 125.—Fécondation, p. 95.—Fluide nerveux, pp. 114, 157, 166, 169.—Formation directe des premiers traits de l'organisation, pp. 68, 92, 94, 98.—Générations spontanées, pp. 46, 100, 115.—Habitudes des animaux, pp. 50, 125, 129.—Homme, p. 124.—Imitation, p. 130.—Influence du fluide nerveux sur les muscles, p. 169.—Insectes, p. 28.—Irritabilité, pp. 109, 179, 186.—Mammaux, p. 15.—Molécules intégrants des composés, p. 150.—Mollusques, p. 23.—Mouvement organique, pp. 7–9.—Multiplication des individus, pp. 117–120.—Nature animale, p. 8.—Nutrition, p. 8.—Oiseaux, p. 16.—Orgasme vital, pp. 79–83.—Organes des corps vivants, p. 111.—Organes de la pensée, p. 127.—Organisation, pp. 9, 98, 104, 134.—Pensée, p. 166.—Poissons, p. 20.—Polypes, p. 35.—Quadrumanes, pp. 131, 135, 136.—Radiaires, p. 32.—Raison, p. 125.—Reptiles, p. 18.—Sentiment, p. 177.—Troglodyte, p. 126.—Tableau du règne animal, p. 37.—Vie, p. 71.

Mémoire sur la Tubicinelle. (Lu à l'Assemblée des Professeurs du Muséum d'Histoire naturelle.) Ann. Mus. Hist. nat., Paris, I, 1802. pp. 4, pl. 464. Bull. Soc. philom. III, Paris, 1801–1804. pp. 170–171. (Extrait.)

Mémoires sur les Cabinets d'Histoire naturelle et particulièrement sur celui du Jardin des Plantes ; contenant l'exposition du régime et de l'ordre qui conviennent à cet établissement, pour qu'il soit vraiment utile. Ext. des Ann. du Mus. (1802). Paris. in-4to. 15 p.

Des diverses sortes de Cabinets où l'on rassemble des objets d'Histoire naturelle. p. 2.

Vrais principes que l'on doit suivre dans l'institution d'un Cabinet d'Histoire naturelle. p. 3.

Sur le Cabinet d'Histoire naturelle du Jardin des Plantes. p. 5.

Hydrogéologie, ou recherches de l'influence générale des eaux sur la surface du globe terrestre ; sur les causes de l'existence du bassin des mers ; de son déplacement et de son transport successif sur les différents points de la surface de ce globe ; enfin, sur les changements que les corps vivants exercent sur la nature et l'état de cette surface. Paris, an X [1802]. 8vo. pp. 268.

1802-6

Mémoires sur les fossiles des environs de Paris, comprenant la détermination des espèces qui appartiennent aux animaux marins sans vertèbres, et dont la plupart sont figurés dans la Collection des Velins du Muséum.

1er Mémoire. Mollusques testacés dont on trouve les dépouilles fossiles dans les environs de Paris.

Paris, Mus. Hist. nat. (Ann.) I, 1802. pp. 299–312 ; 383–391 ; 474–479.

Paris, Mus. Hist. nat. (Ann.) II, 1803. pp. 57–64 ; 163–169 ; 217–227 ; 315–321 ; 385–391.

Paris, Mus. Hist. nat. (Ann.) III, 1804. pp. 163–170 ; 266–274.

Paris, Mus. Hist. nat. (Ann.) IV, 1804. pp. 46–55 ; 105–115 ; 212–222 ; 289–298 ; 429–436.

Paris, Mus. Hist. nat. (Ann.) V, 1804. pp. 28–36 ; 91–98 ; 179–180 ; 237–245 ; 349–356.

Paris, Mus. Hist. nat. (Ann.) VI, 1805. pp. 117–126 ; 214–221 ; 222–228 ; 337–345.

Paris, Mus. Hist. nat. (Ann.) VII, 1806. pp. 53–62 ; 136–140 ; 231–242 ; 419–430.

Paris, Mus. Hist. nat. (Ann.) VIII, 1806. pp. 156–166 ; 347–355 ; 461–469.

Tirage à part. Paris. In-4to. 1806. pp. 284.

1er mémoire. Genres Chiton, Patella, Fissurella. pp. 308–312.

2e " " Emarginula, Calyptræa, Conus, Cypræa, Terebellum et Oliva. pp. 383–391.

3e mémoire. Genres Ancilla, Voluta. pp. 474–479.

Paris, Mus. Hist. nat. (Ann.) I, 1802.

4e mémoire. Genres Mitra, Marginella, Cancellaria, Purpura. pp. 57–64.

5e mémoire. Genres Buccinum, Terebra, Harpa, Cassis. pp. 163–169.

6e mémoire.   Genres Strombus, Rostellaria, Murex. pp. 217–227.

7e mémoire.   Genre Fusus. pp. 315–321.

8e   "   Genres Fusus, Pyrula. pp. 385–391.
     Paris, Mus. Hist. nat. (Ann.) II, 1803.

9e mémoire.   Genre Pleurotoma. pp. 163–170.

10e mémoire.   Genres Pleurotoma, Cerithium. pp. 266–274.

11e et 12e mémoires.   Genre Cerithium. pp. 343–352 ; 436–441.
     Paris, Mus. Hist. nat. (Ann.) III, 1804.

13e mémoire.   Genres Trochus, Solarium. pp. 46–55.

14e   "   "   Turbo, Delphinula, Cyclostoma. pp. 105–115.

15e mémoire.   Genres Scalaria, Turritella, Bulla. pp. 212–222.

16e   "   "   Bulimus, Phasianella, Lymnæa. pp. 289–298.

17e mémoire.   Genres Melania, Auricula. pp. 429–436.
     Paris, Mus. Hist. nat. (Ann.) IV, 1804.

18e mémoire.   Genres Volvaria, Ampullaria, Planorbis. pp. 28–36.

19e mémoire.   Genres Helicina, Nerita, Natica. pp. 91–98.

20e   "   "   Nautilus, Discorbis, Rotalia, Lenticulina. pp. 179–188.

21e mémoire.   Genres Nummulites, Lituola, Spirolina. pp. 237–245.

22e mémoire.   Genres Miliola, Renulina, Gyrogona. pp. 349–357.
     Paris, Mus. Hist. nat. (Ann.) V, 1804.

23e mémoire.   Genres Pinna, Mytilus, Modiola, Nucula. pp. 117–126.

24e mémoire.   Genres Pectunculus, Arca, pp. 214–221.

25e   "   "   Cucullæa, Cardita, Cardium. pp. 337–346.

26e mémoire.   Genres Crassatella, Mactra, Erycina. pp. 407–415.
     Paris, Mus. Hist. nat. (Ann.) VI, 1805.

27e mémoire.   Genres Erycina, Venericardia, Venus. pp. 53–62.

28e   "   "   Venus, Cytherea, Donax. pp. 130–140.

29e   "   "   Tellina, Lucina. pp. 231–239.

30e   "   "   Cyclas, Solen, Fistulana. pp. 419–430.
     Paris, Mus. Hist. nat. (Ann.) VII, 1806.

31e mémoire. Genre Ostrea. pp. 156–158.

32e " Genres Chama, Spondylus, Pecten. pp. 347–356.

33e mémoire. Genres Lima, Corbula. pp. 461–470.

Paris, Mus. Hist. nat. (Ann.) VIII, 1806.

Sur la crénatule, nouveau genre de coquillage. Pl. 2. Cr. avicularis.—Cr. mytiloides.—Cr. phasianoptera. Ann. Mus. Hist. nat., Paris, III, 1804. pp. 25–31, pl. 2.

Sur deux nouveaux genres d'insectes de la Nouvelle Hollande : Chiroscelis bifenestra ; p. 262. Panops Baudini ; p. 265. Ann. Mus. Hist. nat., Paris, III, 1804. pp. 260–265.

Sur une nouvelle espèce de Trigonie, et sur une nouvelle espèce d'Huître, découvertes dans le voyage du Capitaine Baudin. Trigonia suborbiculata ; p. 355, pl. 4, fig. 1. Ostrea ovato-cuneiformis ; p. 358, pl. 4, fig. 2. Ann. Mus Hist. nat., Paris, IV, 1804. pp. 351–359.

Mémoire sur deux nouvelles espèces de Volutes des mers de la Nouvelle Hollande. Voluta undulata ; p. 157, pl. xii, fig. 1. Voluta nivosa ; p. 158, pl. xii, fig. 2, 3. Ann. Mus. Hist. nat., Paris, V, 1804. pp. 154-160.

Sur la Galathée, nouveau genre de coquillage bivalve. Galathea radiata. p. 433, pl. 28. Ann. Mus. Hist. nat., Paris, V, 1804. pp. 430–434.

1805

Considérations sur quelques faits applicables à la théorie du globe, observés par M. Péron dans son voyage aux terres australes, et sur quelques questions géologiques qui naissent de la connaissance de ces faits. (Observations zoologiques propres à constater l'ancien séjour de la mer sur le sommet des montagnes des îles de Diemen, de la Nouvelle Hollande et de l'île Timor.) Ann. Mus. Hist. nat., Paris, VI, 1805. pp. 26–52.

Zusatz das Nordlicht am 22sten Octob., 1804, betreffend. (Translated from the Moniteur.) Gilbert Annal. XIX, 1805. pp. 143, 249–250.

Sur la Dicerate, nouveau genre de coquillage bivalve. Diceras arietina. p. 300, pl. 55, fig. 2. Ann. Mus. Hist. nat., Paris, VI, 1805. pp. 298–302.

Sur l'Amphibulime. A. cucullata. p. 305, pl. 55, fig. 1. Ann. Mus. Hist. nat., Paris, VI, 1805. pp. 303–306.

Recherches asiatiques ou Mémoires de la Société établie au Bengale pour faire des recherches sur l'histoire et les antiquités, les arts, les sciences, etc., traduits de l'anglais par La Baume, revues et augmentés de notes, pour la partie orientale, par Langlès ; pour la partie des sciences, par Lamarck, etc. Paris, 1805. 2 vol. 4to, av. pl.

1805-1809

Recueil de planches des coquilles fossiles des environs de Paris, avec leurs explications. On y a joint 2 planches de Lymnées fossiles et autres coquilles qui les accompagnent, des environs de Paris ; par M. Brard. Ensemble 30 pl. gr. en taille douce. Paris (Dufour & d'Ocagne), 1823. In-4to.

Explic. des 4 premières planches, 1-4. Paris, Mus. Hist. nat. (Ann.) VI, 1805. pp. 122-228, pl. 43-46.

Explic. des 8 pl. suivantes, 5-7. Paris, Mus. Hist. nat. (Ann.) VII, 1806. pp. 442-444, pl. 13-15.

Explic. des 3 pl. suivantes, 8-10. Paris, Mus. Hist. nat. (Ann.) VIII, 1806. pp. 77-78, pl. 35-37.

Explic. des 4 pl. suivantes, 11-14. Paris, Mus. Hist. nat. (Ann.) VIII, 1806. pp. 383-388, pl. 59-62.

Explic. des 4 pl. suivantes, 15-18. Paris, Mus. Hist. nat. (Ann.) IX, 1807. pp. 236-240, pl. 17-20.

Explic. des 2 pl. suivantes, 19, 20. Paris, Mus. Hist. nat. (Ann.) IX, 1807. pp. 399-401, pl. 31-32.

Explic. des 4 pl. suivantes, 21-24. Paris, Mus. Hist. nat. (Ann.) XII, 1808. pp. 456-459, pl. 40-43.

Explic. des 4 pl. suivantes, 25-28. Paris, Mus. Hist. nat. (Ann.) XIV, 1809. pp. 374-375, pl. 20-23.

1806

Synopsis plantarum in Flora Gallica descriptarum. (En collab. avec A. P. Decandolle.) Paris (H. Agasse), 1806. 1 vol. 8vo. XXIV. 432 pp. Ordinum generumque anomalorum Clavis analytica. pp. i-xxiv.

Discours d'Ouverture du Cours des Animaux sans Vertèbres, prononcé dans le Muséum d'Histoire naturelle en mai 1806. Paris, 1806. br., in-8vo.

1807

Sur la division des Mollusques acéphalés conchylifères, et sur un nouveau genre de coquille appartenant à cette division (Etheria). Ann. Mus. X, 1807. pp. 389-408, 4 pl.

Etwas über die Meteorologie. Gilbert Annal. XVII, 1807. pp. 355-359.

Sur la division des Mollusques acéphalés conchylifères et sur un nouveau genre de coquille appartenant à cette division. (Genre Etheria.) Ann. Mus. Hist. nat., Paris, X, 1807. pp. 389-398.

Sur l'Éthérie, nouveau genre de coquille bivalve de la famille des Camacées. Etheria elliptica; p. 401, pl. 29 et 31, fig. 1. Etheria trigonule; p. 403, pl. 30 et 31, fig. 2. Etheria semi-lunata; p. 404, pl. 32, fig. 1, 2. Etheria transversa; p. 406, pl. 32, fig. 3, 4. Ann. Mus. Hist. nat., Paris, X, 1807. pp. 398-408. (Ce mémoire se rattache au précédent.)

1809

Philosophie zoologique, ou exposition des considérations relatives à l'histoire naturelle des animaux; à la diversité de leur organisation et des facultés qu'ils en obtiennent; aux causes physiques qui maintiennent en eux la vie et donnent lieu aux mouvements qu'ils exécutent; enfin, à celles qui produisent, les unes les sentiments, et les autres l'intelligence de ceux qui en sont doués. Paris (Dentu), 1809. 2 vol. in-8vo, XXV, 428. 475 pages.

Idem, nouvelle Édition. Paris, J. B. Baillière. 1830. (A reprint of the first edition.)

2me Édition. Revue et précédée d'une introduction biographique par Charles Martins. Paris, Savy. 1873. 2 vol. 8vo. LXXXIV, 412; 431 pages.

> Vol. I. Première Partie.—Considération sur l'histoire naturelle des animaux, leurs caractères, leurs rapports, leur organisation, leur distribution, leur classification et leurs espèces.
>
> Chap. I. Des parties de l'art dans les productions de la nature. p. 17.
>
> Chap. II. Importance de la considération des rapports. p. 39.
>
> Chap. III. De l'Espèce parmi les corps vivants et de l'idée que nous devons attacher à ce mot. p. 53.
>
> Chap. IV. Généralités sur les animaux. p. 82.
>
> Chap. V. Sur l'état actuel de la distribution et de la classification des animaux. p. 102.
>
> Chap. VI. Dégradation et simplification de l'organisation d'une extrémité à l'autre de la chaîne animale, en procédant du plus composé vers le plus simple. p. 130.
>
> Chap. VII. De l'influence des circonstances sur les actions et

les habitudes des animaux, et de celle des actions et des habitudes de ces corps vivants, comme causes qui modifient leur organisation et leurs parties. p. 218.

Chap. VIII. De l'ordre naturel des animaux, et de la disposition qu'il faut donner à leur distribution générale pour la rendre conforme à l'ordre même de la nature. p. 269.

Deuxième Partie.—Considérations sur les causes physiques de la vie, les conditions qu'elle exige pour exister, la force excitatrice de ses mouvements, les facultés qu'elle donne aux corps qui la possèdent et les résultats de son existence dans ces corps.

Chap. I. Comparaison des corps inorganiques avec les corps vivants, suivie d'une parallèle entre les animaux et les végétaux. p. 377.

Chap. II. De la vie, de ce qui la constitue, et des conditions essentielles à son existence dans un corps. p. 400.

Vol. II. 2me Partie.

Chap. III. De la cause excitatrice des mouvements organiques. p. 1.

Chap. IV. De l'orgasme et de l'irritabilité. p. 20.

Chap. V. Du tissu cellulaire, considéré comme la gangue dans laquelle toute organisation a été formée. p. 46.

Chap. VI. Des générations directes ou spontanées. p. 61.

Chap. VII. Des résultats immédiats de la vie dans un corps. p. 91.

Chap. VIII. Des facultés communes à tous les corps vivants. p. 113.

Chap. IX. Des facultés particulières à certains corps vivants. p. 127.

Troisième Partie.—Considérations sur les causes physiques du sentiment ; celles qui constituent la force productrice des actions ; enfin, celles qui donnent lieu aux actes d'intelligence qui s'observent dans différents animaux. p. 169.

Chap. I. Du système nerveux, de sa formation et des différentes sortes de fonctions qu'il peut exciter. p. 180.

Chap. II. Du fluide nerveux. p. 235.

Chap. III. De la sensibilité et du mécanisme des sensations. p. 252.

Chap. IV. Du sentiment intérieur, des émotions qu'il est susceptible d'éprouver, et de la puissance qu'il en acquiert pour la production des actions. p. 276.

Chap. V. De la force productrice des actions des animaux, et de quelques faits particuliers qui résultent de l'emploi de cette force ; p. 302. De la consommation et de l'épuisement du fluide nerveux dans la production des actions animales ; p. 314. De l'origine du penchant aux mêmes actions ; p. 318. De l'instinct des animaux ; p. 320. De l'industrie de certains animaux ; p. 327.

Chap. VI. De la volonté. p. 330.

Chap. VII. De l'entendement, de son origine, et de celle des idées. p. 346.

Chap. VIII. Des principaux actes de l'entendement, ou de ceux du premier ordre dont tous les autres dérivent ; p. 388. De l'imagination ; p. 411. De la raison et de sa comparaison avec l'instinct ; p. 441.

(Ces notes ont été relevées sur l'édition de 1809.)

1810-1811

Sur la détermination des espèces parmi les animaux sans vertèbres, et particulièrement parmi les mollusques testacés. (Tirage à part, Paris, 1817. 4to. 5 pls.)

Ann. Mus. Hist. nat., Paris, XV, 1810. pp. 20-26.

Descript. des Espèces.—Cône (Conus). pp. 26-40 ; pp. 269-292 ; pp. 422-442.

Descript. des Espèces.—Porcelaine (Cypræa). pp. 443-454.

Ann. Mus. Hist. nat., Paris, XVI, 1810.

Descript. des Espèces.—Porcelaine (Cypræa), suite. pp. 89-108.

Descript. des Espèces.—Ovule (Ovula). pp. 109-114.

"   "   "   Tarrière (Terebellum). pp. 300-302.

"   "   "   Ancillaire (Ancillaria). pp. 302-306.

"   "   "   Olive (Oliva). pp. 306-328.

Ann. Mus. Hist. nat. XVII, 1811.

Descript. des Espèces.—Volute (Voluta). pp. 54-80.

"   "   "   Mitre (Mitra). pp. 195-222.

Description des Espèces du Genre Conus. Ann. Muséum, XV, 1810. pp. 29-40, 263-292, 422-442.

Description du genre Porcelaine (Cypræa) et des Espèces qui le composent. Ann. Mus. XV, 1810. pp. 443-454.

Suite de la détermination des Espèces de Mollusques testacés. Continuation du genre Porcelaine. Ann. Mus. XVI, 1811. pp. 89-114.

1812

Extrait du cours de zoologie du Muséum d'Histoire naturelle sur les Animaux sans Vertèbres, présentant la distribution et classification de ces animaux, les caractères des principales divisions et une simple liste des genres, à l'usage de ceux qui suivent ce cours. Paris, octobre 1812. 8vo. pp. 127.

1813

Sur les polypiers empâtés.

Ann. Mus. Hist. nat., Paris, XX, 1813.

Pinceau (Penicillus). pp. 294, 297-299.

Flabellaire (Flabellaria). pp. 298-303.

Synoique (Synoicum). pp. 303-304.

Éponge (Spongia). pp. 305-312 ; 370-386 ; 432-458.

Ann. Mus. Hist. nat., Paris, I, 1815.

Téthie (Tethya). pp. 69-71.

Alcyon (Alcyonium). pp. 72-80 ; 162-168 ; 331-333.

Géodie (Geodia). pp. 333-334.

Botrylle (Botryllus). pp. 335-338.

Polycycle (Polycyclus). pp. 338-340.

1813-15

Sur les polypiers corticifères.

Mém. Mus. Hist. nat., Paris, I, 1813. p. 401.

Corail (Coraillium). pp. 407-410.

Mélite (Melitæa). pp. 410-413.

Isis. pp. 413-416.

Cymosaire (Cymosaria). pp. 467-468.

Antipate (Antipathes). pp. 469-476.

Mém. Mus. Hist. nat., Paris, II, 1815.

Gorgone (Gorgonia). pp. 76-84 ; 157-164.

Coralline (Corallina). pp. 227-240.

Rapport fait à l'Institut (en collaboration avec Cuvier) sur les observations sur les Lombrics, ou les Vers de terre, etc., par Montègre. Paris, 1815. Br., in-8vo, 1 pl.

1815-22

Histoire naturelle des Animaux sans Vertèbres, présentant les caractères généraux et particuliers de ces animaux, leur distribution, leurs classes, leurs familles, leurs genres, et la citation des principales Espèces qui s'y rapportent ; précédée d'une introduction offrant la détermination des caractères essentiels de l'Animal, sa distinction du Végétal et des autres corps naturels ; enfin, l'exposition des principes fondamentaux de la zoologie. Paris, mars 1815 à août 1822. 7 vol. 8vo. 2e édit., Paris, 1835-45. 11 vol. in-8vo.

1818

Suite de la détermination des Espèces de Mollusques testacés. Genres Volute et Mitre. Ann. Mus. XVII, 1818. pp. 54-80 et 195-222.

Description des genres Tarrière (Terebellum), Ancillaria et Oliva. Ann. Mus. XVII, 1818. pp. 300-328.

1820

Système analytique des connaissances de l'homme restreintes à celles qui proviennent directement ou indirectement de l'observation. Paris (Belin), 1820. In-8vo. pp. 362.

Première Partie.—Des Objets que l'homme peut considérer hors de lui, et que l'observation peut lui faire connaître. p. 13.

Chap. I. De la Matière. p. 5.

Chap. II. De la Nature ; p. 20. Définition de la nature, et exposé des parties dont se compose l'ordre des choses qui la constitue ; p. 50. Objets métaphysiques dont l'ensemble constitue la nature ; p. 51. De la nécessité d'étudier la nature, c'est-à-dire l'ordre des choses qui la constitue, les lois qui régissent ses actes, et surtout, parmi ces lois, celles qui sont relatives à notre être physique ; p. 60. Exposition des sources où l'homme a puisé les connaissances qu'il possède et dans lesquelles il pourra en recueillir quantité d'autres ; sources dont l'ensemble constitue pour lui le champ des réalités ; p. 85.

Des Objets évidemment produits ; p. 97.

Chap. I. Des Corps inorganiques. p. 100.

Chap. II. Des Corps vivants ; p. 114. Des Végétaux ; p. 125. Des Animaux ; p. 134.

Deuxième Partie.—De l'Homme et de certains systèmes organiques observés en lui, lesquels concourrent à l'exécution de ses actions ; p. 149. Généralités sur le sentiment ; p. 161. Analyse des phénomènes qui appartiennent au sentiment ; p. 175.

Sect. I.—De la sensation. p. 177.
Chap. I. Des sensations particulières. p. 180.
Chap. II. De la sensation générale.

Sect. II.—Du sentiment intérieur et de ses principaux produits. p. 191.
Chap. I. Des penchants naturels. p. 206.
Chap. II. De l'instinct. p. 228.

Sect. III.—De l'intelligence, des objets qu'elle emploie, et des phénomènes auxquels elle donne lieu. p. 255.
Chap. I. Des idées. p. 290.
Chap. II. Du jugement et de la raison. p. 325.
Chap. III. Imagination. p. 348.

1823

Recueil de planches de coquilles fossiles des environs de Paris, avec leurs explications. On y a joint deux planches de Lymnées fossiles et autres coquilles qui les accompagnent, des environs de Paris ; par M. Brard. Paris, 1823. 1 vol. in-4to de 30 pl.

1828

Histoire naturelle des Végétaux par Lamarck et Mirbel. Paris, Déterville (Roret). In-18mo. 15 vol., avec 120 pl.

Cet ouvrage fait partie de Buffon : Cours complet d'Histoire naturelle (Edit. de Castel). 80 vol. in-18mo. Paris, 1799–1802. Déterville (Roret).

Storia naturale de' vegetabili per famiglie con la citazione de la Classe et dell' ordine di Linnes, e l' indicazione dell' use che si può far delle piante nelle arti, nel commercio, nell' agricultura, etc. Con disegni tratti dal naturale e un genere completo, secondo il sistema linneano, con de' rinvii alla famiglie naturali, di A. L. Jussieu. Da G. B. Lamarck e da B. Mirbel. Recata in lingua italiana dal A. Farini con note ed aggiunte. 3 Tom. de 5–7. Fasc. 1835–41. (Engelmann's Bibliothec. Hist. nat., 1846.)

Eulogies and Biographical Articles on Lamarck

Geoffroy St. Hilaire, Étienne.—Discours sur Lamarck. (Recueil publié par l'Institut. 4to. Paris, 1829.)

Cuvier, George.—Éloge de M. de Lamarck, par M. le Baron Cuvier. Lu à l'Académie des Sciences, le 26 novembre 1832. [No imprint.] Paris. (Trans. in Edinburgh New Philosophical Journ. No. 39.)

Bourguin, L. B.—Les grands naturalistes français au commencement du XIXe siècle (Annales de la Société linnéenne du Département de Maine-et-Loire. 6me Année. Angers, 1863. 8vo. pp. 185-221). Introduction, pp. 185-193.

Lacaze-Duthiers, H. de.—De Lamarck. (Cours de zoologie au Muséum d'Histoire naturelle.) Revue scientifique, 1866. Nos. 16-18-19.

Memoir of Lamarck, by J. Duncan. See Jardine (Sir W.), Bart., The Naturalist's Library. Vol. 36, pp. 17-63. Edinburgh, 1843.

Quatrefages, A. de.—Charles Darwin et ses précurseurs français. Étude sur le transformisme. Paris, 1870. 8vo. pp. 378.

Martins, Charles.—Un naturaliste philosophe. Lamarck, sa vie et ses œuvres. Extrait de la Revue des Deux Mondes. Livraison du 1er mars 1873. Paris.

Haeckel, Ernst.—Die Naturanschauung von Darwin, Goethe und Lamarck. Vortrag in der ersten öffentlichen Sitzung der fünf und fünfzigsten Versammlung Deutscher Naturforscher und Aerzte zu Eisenach am 18 September 1882. Jena, 1882. 8vo. pp. 64.

Perrier, Edmond.—La philosophie zoologique avant Darwin. Paris, 1884. pp. 292.

Perrier, Edmond.—Lamarck et le transformisme actuel. (Extrait du volume commémoratif du Centenaire de la fondation du Muséum d'Histoire naturelle.) Paris, 1893. Folio. pp. 61.

Bourguignat, J. R.—Lamarck, J. B. P. A. de Monnet de. (Biographical sketch, with a partial bibliography of his works, said to have been prepared by M. Bourguignat.) Revue biographique de la Société malacologique de France. Paris, 1886. pp. 61-85. With a portrait after Vaux-Bidon.

Mortillet, Gabriel de.—Lamarck. Par G. de Mortillet. (L'Homme, IV, No. 1. 10 jan. 1887. pp. 1-8. With portrait and handwriting, including autograph of Lamarck.

Mortillet, Gabriel de, and others.—Lamarck. Par un groupe de transformistes, ses disciples. (Reprinted from L'Homme, IV. Paris, 1887. 8vo. pp. 31.) With portrait and figures.

Mortillet, Gabriel de.—Réunion Lamarck. (La Société, l'École et le Laboratoire d'Anthropologie de Paris, à l'Exposition universelle de Paris.) Paris, 1889. pp. 72–84.

Mortillet, Adrien de.—Recherches sur Lamarck (including acte de naissance, acte de décès, and letter from M. Mondière regarding his place of burial). L'Homme, IV, No. 10. Mai 25 1887. pp. 289–295. With portrait and view of the house he lived in. On p. 620, a note referring to a movement to erect a monument to Lamarck.

Giard, Alfred.—Leçon d'ouverture du cours de l'évolution des êtres organisés. (Bull. sc. de la France et de la Belgique.) Paris, 1888. pp. 28. Portrait.

Claus, Carl.—Lamarck als Begründer des Descendenzlehre. Wien, 1888. 8vo. pp. 35.

Duval, Mathias.—Le transformiste français Lamarck. (Bull. Soc. d'Anthopologie de Paris. Tome XII, IIIe Série.) pp. 336–374.

Lamarck.—Les maîtres de la science : Lamarck. Paris, 1892. G. Masson, Éditeur. 12mo. pp. 98.

Hamy, E. T.—Les derniers jours du Jardin du Roi et la fondation du Muséum d'Histoire naturelle. pp. 40. (Extrait du volume commémoratif du Centenaire de la fondation du Muséum d'Histoire naturelle.) Paris, 10 juin 1893. Folio. pp. 162. Paris, 1893.

Osborn, H. F.—From the Greeks to Darwin. An outline of the development of the evolution idea. New York, 1894. 8vo. pp. 259.

Houssay, Frédéric.—Lamarck, son œuvre et son esprit. Revue encyclopédique. Année 1897. pp. 969–973. Paris, Librairie Larousse.

Hermanville, F. J. F.—Notice biographique sur Lamarck. Sa vie et ses œuvres. Beauvais, 1898. 8vo. pp. 45. Portrait, after Thorel-Perrin.

Packard, A. S.—Lamarck, and Neo-Lamarckism. (The Open Court, Feb., 1897.) Chicago, 1897. pp. 70–81.

Packard, A. S.—Lamarck's Views on the Evolution of Man, on Morals, and on the Relation of Science to Religion. The Monist, Chicago, Oct., 1900. Chapters XVIII and XIX of the present work.

INDEX

ADAPTATION, 322, 367, 392, 412.

Ærobates, 338.

Ai, 320.

Amphibia, 342.

Ant-eater, 307, 313.

Antlers, origin of, 316.

Ant-lion, 337.

Appetence, doctrine of, 219, 234, 236, 350, 412.

Aspalax, 307.

Atrophy, 274, 290, 303, 306, 307, 309, 311, 315, 343.

Audouin, J. V., 63.

BARUS, C., estimate of Lamarck's work in physics, 85.

Batrachia, 342.

Battle, law of, 219, 224.

Beaver, 312.

Besoins, 245, 270, 274, 281, 295, 302, 324, 334, 346, 350, 352, 412.

Bird, humming, 313.

Birds, domestic, atrophy in, 274; origin of, 342; origin of swimming, 234, 311; perching, 234, 312; shore, 234, 312.

Blainville, H. D. de, 62, 64, 135.

Blumenbach, 138.

Bolton, H. C., 86.

Bonnet, C., ideas on evolution, 156; germs, 163.

Bosc, L. A. G., 52.

Bourguin, L. B., 30, 31.

Bradypus tridactylus, 320.

Brain, 337, 360; human, 358.

Bruguière, J. G., 38, 113.

Buffalo, 315.

Buffon, G. L. L., 19, 92, 198; factors of evolution, 205, 356; views on descent, 201.

Bulla, 348.

CALLOSITIES, origin of, 203.

Camelo-pardalis, 316, 351.

Carnivora, 317; origin of, 343.

Catastrophism, 105, 117, 126, 146, 153; anti-, 105, 114, 153.

Cave life, 390, 392.

Cetacea, 343, 409; rudimentary teeth of, 307.

Chain of being, 167, 181, 191, 208, 235, 241, 242.

Changes in environment, 302; local, 301; slow, 301.

Characters, acquired, heredity of, 219, 224, 246, 276, 303, 319.

Chimpanzee, 367.

Chiton, 348.

Circumstances, influence of, 246, 247, 292, 294, 302, 305, 320, 323, 363, 400.

Clam, origin of siphon of, 353, 418.

Classifications, artificial, 282.

Claws of birds, 312; Carnivora, 317, 414.

Climate, 204, 218, 244, 283, 400, 402, 416.

Coal, origin of, 113, 122.

Colonies, animal, 411.

Colors, animal, 221.

Competition, 236, 287.

Conditions, changes of, 292, 294, 302, 305, 310, 400, 407, 414.

Consciousness, 325, 326, 353.

Cope, E. D., 383, 389.

Corals, 115.

Correlation, law of, 136, 142, 145; of tertiary beds, 133.

Costantin, 416.

Creation by evolution, 130.

Crossing, swamping effects of, 246, 320.

Crustacea, origin of, 341.

Cunningham, J. T., 409.
Cuvier, George, 66, 140; eulogy on Lamarck, 65; first paper, 185.

DALL, W. H., estimate of Lamarck's work, 196.
Darkness, influence of, 308.
Darwin, Charles, 423, 424; estimate of Lamarck's views, 73; factors tabulated, 356; origin of man, compared with Lamarck's, 371; views on descent, 217, 407.
Darwin, Erasmus, factors of evolution, 217, 223, 356; life of, 216.
Daubenton, 19, 26, 29, 136.
Deer, 316.
Degeneration, as used by Buffon, 204, 209; by Geoffroy, 213; by Lamarck, 182, 274, 290.
Delbœuf's law, 406.
Desiring, 236, 351, 412.
Digits, modifications of, 234, 311, 317, 321, 338, 344; reduction of, 315.
Direct action of environment, 324, 409, 410, 414, 416.
Disuse, 274, 290, 296, 303, 306, 307, 311, 318, 343, 392, 412.
Dixon, C., 405.
Dogs, tailless, 220; domestication in, 299; races of, 299, 304.
Domestic animals, 274, 304.
Domestication, effects of, 298, 323.
D'Orbigny, A., 386.
Duck, 298, 312, 318.
Duckbill, 412.

EARTH, great age of, 119; revolutions of, 109, 147, 150; theory of, 149.
Earth's interior, 105.
Effort, 218, 234, 257, 295, 339, 348, 351, 353, 354, 370, 411, 420.
Egypt, mummied species of, 271, 286.
Eigenman, C. H., 393.
Eimer, G. H. T., 408.
Elephant, 315.
Emotion, 353.
Encasement theory, 162, 218, 222.
Environment, 214, 410, 417, 421.
Epigenesis, 156.

Erosion, 101.
Evil, 377.
Evolution, dynamic, 417; Lamarck's views on, 322.
Exercise, 211, 256.
Existence, struggle for, 207, 237, 287.
Extinct species, 126, 129, 130.
Eyeless animals, 307, 309.
Eyes, 308; of flounder, 313.

FAUJAS DE ST. FOND, 23, 140.
Feelings, internal, 324, 325, 330, 347.
Fishes, flat, 313; form due to medium, 291; origin of, 341.
Fittest, origin of, 383.
Flamingo, 250.
Flounder, 313.
Flying mammals, origin of, 338.
Fossilization, 120.
Fossils, 109, 110, 112, 125, 138; deep-sea, 113; of Paris basin, 134.
Frog, 312.
Function, change of, 394.

GALEOPITHECUS, 339.
Gasteropods, 348, 417.
Generation, spontaneous, 158, 176, 201, 285.
Geoffroy St. Hilaire, E., 36, 67, 307; factors tabulated, 356; life, 212; views on descent, 215; views on species, 213.
Geographical distribution, 205, 246.
Geological time, 119, 130, 222.
Geology, Lamarck's work in, 100.
Germs of life, first, 259, 261, 268; preëxistence of, 162, 218, 222.
Giard, A., 406, 410.
Giraffe, 316, 351, 411, 412.
Goose, 298, 312, 313.
Granite, origin of, 120, 149.
Guettard, J. E., 95, 132, 136.
Gulick, J. T., 405.

HABITS, 235, 247, 295, 303, 305, 314, 316, 321, 323, 324, 340, 394.
Haeckel, E., 385; estimate of Lamarck's theory, 69.
Hamy, E. T., 19, 22, 25.
Hearing, 308.

Henslow, G., 414.
Heredity, 250, 276, 303, 306, 319, 336; of acquired characters, 219, 224, 246, 276, 303, 319.
Hertwig, R., 282.
Hoofs, origin of, 315.
Hooke, Robert, 132.
Horns, origin of, 316, 354, 393, 409.
Horse, 274, 304, 315.
Hutton, James, 99.
Huxley, T. H., 423, 424; estimate of Lamarck's scientific position, 74, 90.
Hyatt, A., 386, 419.
Hybridity, 223.
Hybrids, 284.
Hydrogéologie, 89.

IMITATION, 361.
Indirect action of environment, 324, 409.
Industry, animal, 336.
Infusoria, 328.
Insects, wingless, 309.
Intestines of man, 310.
Instinct, 223, 286, 330, 331, 332, 349; variations in, 335, 337, 349.
Isolation, 392, 394, 404; in man, 320, 369.

JACKO, 364.
Jardin des Plantes, 23.
Jeffries, J. A., 413.
Jordan, K., 410.
Juncus bufonius, 252.

KANGAROO, 318.

LACAZE-DUTHIERS, H. DE, reminiscences of Lamarck, 75.
Lakanal, J., 28.
Lamarck, Cornelie de, 55.
Lamarck, J. B. de, birth, 6; birthplace, 4; blindness, 51; botanical career, 15, 19, 173; burial place, 57; death, 51; estimates of his life-work, 69; factors of evolution, 233, 356; founder of palæontology, 124; house in Paris, 42; meteorology and physical science, 79; military career, 11; origin of man, 357; parentage, 7; share in reorganization of Museum, 24; shells, collections

of, 46; on spontaneous generation, 158; style, 179; travels, 20; views on religion, 372; work in geology, 89; zoölogical work, 32, 180.
Lamarckism, relations to Darwinism, 382.
Land, changes of level of, 107.
Latreille, P. A., 62.
Law of battle, 219, 224.
Laws of evolution, Lamarck's, 303, 346.
Legs, atrophy of, 290, 309, 343.
Lemur volans, 339.
Life, 346; conditions of, 292, 294, 302, 305, 310, 400, 414; definitions of, 168, 169, 280.
Light, 410.
Limbs, atrophy of, 290, 309; genesis of, 421; of seal, 338, 344; whale, 343.
Lizard, 313.
Local changes, 301.
Lyell, Charles, estimate of Lamarck's theory, 71.

MAMMALS, aquatic, 343; flying, 338.
Man, as a check on animal life, 288; origin of, 357; origin of language, 370; origin of his plantigrade feet, 365; posture, 362, 368; relation to apes, 362; segregation of, from apes, 369; shape of his skull, 365; sign-language, 368; speech, origin of, 370; swamping effects of crossing in, 320.
Medium, 214.
Milieu, 214, 416.
Mimicry, protective, 220, 221, 225.
Minerals, growth of, 164.
Mole, 307.
Molluscs, 420; eyeless, 309; gasteropod, 348; pelecypod, 417; lamellibranch, 418; Lamarck's work on, 189.
Monet, de, 8.
Monotremes, origin from birds, 342.
Morals, 372.
Mortillet, G. de, 30.
Mountains formed by erosion, 101, 103.
Muscles, adductor, 418.
Museum of Natural History, Paris, 34.
Mya arenaria, 353, 418.

Myrmecophaga, 307.

Myrmeleon, 337.

NAILS, 321.

Natural selection, inadequacy of, 393, 397, 401, 407, 410, 413, 415, 421, 423.

Nature, balance of, 207; definition of, 169, 345, 375.

Neck, elongation of, in birds, 274, 311, 317; giraffe, 316, 351; ostrich, 317.

Needs, 245, 270, 274, 281, 295, 302, 324, 334, 346, 350, 351, 352.

Neodarwinism, 422.

Neolamarckism, 2, 382, 396, 398, 422.

OPHIDIA, atrophy of legs of, 290, 309.

Organic sense, 325, 327, 336.

Organs, changes in, 310; origin of, precedes their use, 223; follows their use, 305, 346; atrophy of, 274, 290, 303, 306, 307, 309, 311, 315; new production of, 346, 412, 420.

Orang-outang, 364.

Osborn, H. S., 403.

Ostrich, 317.

Otter, 312.

Ox, 315.

Oyster, 419.

PALÆONTOLOGY, 136; invertebrate, 135, 149.

Pallas, 137.

Penchants, 281, 293, 328, 331.

Perrier, E., 26, 411.

Petaurista, 338.

Philosophy, moral, Lamarck's, 379.

Phoca vitulina, 338, 344.

Phylogeny, 130.

Pigeons, 298; fantail, 304.

Planorbis, 387.

Plants, changes due to cultivation, etc., 251, 267, 274, 283, 296, 297; cultivated, 298.

Population, over-, checks on, 287, 288.

Preformation, 162, 218, 222.

Propensities, 281, 293, 328, 335, 349, 351.

Proteus, 308.

Pteromys, 339.

RANUNCULUS AQUATILIS, 251, 300.

Religion and science, 372.

Reptiles, 342.

Revolutions of the earth, 109, 142.

Rousseau, J. J., 17, 18.

Roux, W., 421.

Ruminants, 315.

Ryder, J. A., 403.

SCIENCE AND RELIGION, 372.

Sciurus volans, 338.

Scott, W. B., 403.

Sea, former existence of, 109, 110, 148.

Seal, 338, 344.

Segments, origin of, 421.

Segregation, in man, 320, 369.

Selection, mechanical, 410.

Semper, C., 406.

Series, animal, branching, 235, 264, 282.

Serpents, origin of, 290, 309; eyes of, 314.

Sexual selection, 219, 224.

Shell, bivalve, origin of, 418; crustacean, 418.

Shells, deep-water, 112; fossil, 40, 110, 125, 131; Lamarckian genera, 183.

Simia satyrus, 367; troglodytes, 364.

Sloth, 320.

Snakes, atrophy of legs of, 290, 309; eyes of, 314; origin of, 290, 309; tongue of, 313.

Sole, 314.

Species, Buffon's views on, 201, 211; definition of, 252, 255, 262, 267, 275; extinct, 126; Geoffroy St. Hilaire, views on, 214; Lamarck's views on, 183; modification of, 131; origin of, 131, 283; stability of, 271, 277, 401; variation in, 278.

Speech, 370.

Spencer, Herbert, 371, 382, 384, 415.

Spermist, 218.

Sphalax, 307.

Spines, 251, 393, 414.

Sponges, 194.

Squirrel, flying, 338, 339.

Stimulus, external, 348, 354, 393.

Struggle for existence, 207, 237, 287.

Surroundings, 214, 421; local, 410.

Symmetry, radial, 291.
Swan, 313.

TAIL, of kangaroo, 318.
Teeth, 307 ; atrophy of, 307 ; in embryo
  birds, 307 ; in whales, 307.
Temperature, 410.
Tentacles of snail, 348, 354.
Tertiary shells, 110, 125, 133.
Thought, definition of, 172.
Time, geological, 119, 130, 222, 236.
Toes, modifications of, 234, 311, 315, 317,
  321, 338, 344.
Tree, genealogical, first, 130, 181, 192,
  193, 349.
Trout, 403.
Tubercles, origin of, 394.
Tunicata, position of, 195.
Turbot, 314.
Turtle, sea, 312.

UNIFORMITARIANISM, 130.
Use, 248, 256, 257, 302, 303, 311, 318, 384,
  412.
Use-inheritance, 219, 224, 246, 276, 303,
  319, 346.

Use originates organs, 276, 311, 346.

VARIABILITY, 407.
Variation, climatic, 204, 218, 401 ; causes
  of, 218, 266.
Varieties, 401.
Varigny, H. de, 408.
Vestigial organs, 307, 308.
Vital force, 167.
Vitalism, 168.
Volucella, 338.

WAGNER, M., 404.
Wallace, A. R., on origin of giraffe's
  neck, 351.
Wants, 245, 270, 274, 281, 295, 302, 324,
  334, 346, 350, 351, 352.
Ward, L. F., 422.
Water, diversified condition of, 290.
Werner, 97.
Whale, 307, 343, 409.
Will, 319, 330, 337.
Willing, 236, 351, 412.
Weismann, A., 399.
Wings, atrophy of, in insects, 309.
Woodpecker, 313.

THREE CENTURIES
OF
SCIENCE IN AMERICA

An Arno Press Collection

Adams, John Quincy. **Report of the Secretary of State upon Weights and Measures.** 1821.

Archibald, Raymond Clare. **A Semicentennial History of the American Mathematical Society: 1888-1938** *and* **Semicentennial Addresses of the American Mathematical Society.** 2 vols. 1938.

Bond, William Cranch. **History and Description of the Astronomical Observatory of Harvard College** *and* **Results of Astronomical Observations Made at the Observatory of Harvard College.** 1856.

Bowditch, Henry Pickering. **The Life and Writings of Henry Pickering Bowditch.** 2 vols. 1980.

Bridgman, Percy Williams. **The Logic of Modern Physics.** 1927.

Bridgman, Percy Williams. **Philosophical Writings of Percy Williams Bridgman.** 1980.

Bridgman, Percy Williams. **Reflections of a Physicist.** 1955.

Bush, Vannevar. **Science the Endless Frontier.** 1955.

Cajori, Florian. **The Chequered Career of Ferdinand Rudolph Hassler.** 1929.

Cohen, I. Bernard, editor. **The Career of William Beaumont and the Reception of His Discovery.** 1980.

Cohen, I. Bernard, editor. **Benjamin Peirce: "Father of Pure Mathematics" in America.** 1980.

Cohen, I. Bernard, editor. **Aspects of Astronomy in America in the Nineteenth Century.** 1980.

Cohen, I. Bernard, editor. **Cotton Mather and American Science and Medicine: With Studies and Documents Concerning the Introduction of Inoculation or Variolation.** 2 vols. 1980.

Cohen, I. Bernard, editor. **The Life and Scientific Work of Othniel Charles Marsh.** 1980.

Cohen, I. Bernard, editor. **The Life and the Scientific and Medical Career of Benjamin Waterhouse: With Some Account of the Introduction of Vaccination in America.** 2 vols. 1980.

Cohen, I. Bernard, editor. **Research and Technology.** 1980.

Cohen, I. Bernard, editor. **Thomas Jefferson and the Sciences.** 1980.

Cooper, Thomas. **Introductory Lecture** *and* **A Discourse on the Connexion Between Chemistry and Medicine.** 2 vols. in one. 1812/1818.

Dalton, John Call. **John Call Dalton on Experimental Method.** 1980.

Darton, Nelson Horatio. **Catalogue and Index of Contributions to North American Geology: 1732-1891.** 1896.

Donnan, F[rederick] G[eorge] and Arthur Haas, editors. **A Commentary on the Scientific Writings of J. Willard Gibbs** *and* Duhem, Pierre. **Josiah-Willard Gibbs: A Propos de la Publication de ses Mémoires Scientifiques.** 3 vols. in two. 1936/1908.

Dupree, A[nderson] Hunter. **Science in the Federal Government: A History of Policies and Activities to 1940.** 1957.

Ellicott, Andrew. **The Journal of Andrew Ellicott.** 1803.

Fulton, John F. **Harvey Cushing: A Biography.** 1946.

Getman, Frederick H. **The Life of Ira Remsen.** 1940.

Goode, George Brown. **The Smithsonian Institution 1846-1896: The History of its First Half Century.** 1897.

Hale, George Ellery. **National Academies and the Progress of Research.** 1915.

Harding, T. Swann. **Two Blades of Grass: A History of Scientific Development in the U.S. Department of Agriculture.** 1947.

Hindle, Brooke. **David Rittenhouse.** 1964.

Hindle, Brooke, editor. **The Scientific Writings of David Rittenhouse.** 1980.

Holden, Edward S[ingleton]. **Memorials of William Cranch Bond, Director of the Harvard College Observatory, 1840-1859, and of his Son, George Phillips Bond, Director of the Harvard College Observatory, 1859-1865.** 1897.

Howard, L[eland] O[sslan]. **Fighting the Insects: The Story of an Entomologist, Telling the Life and Experiences of the Writer.** 1933.

Jaffe, Bernard. **Men of Science in America.** 1958.

Karpinski, Louis C. **Bibliography of Mathematical Works Printed in America through 1850.** Reprinted with Supplement and Second Supplement. 1940/1945.

Loomis, Elias. **The Recent Progress of Astronomy: Especially in the United States.** 1851.

Merrill, Elmer D. **Index Rafinesquianus: The Plant Names Published by C.S. Rafinesque with Reductions, and a Consideration of his Methods, Objectives, and Attainments.** 1949.

Millikan, Robert A[ndrews]. **The Autobiography of Robert A. Millikan.** 1950.

Mitchel, O[rmsby] M[acKnight]. **The Planetary and Stellar Worlds: A Popular Exposition of the Great Discoveries and Theories of Modern Astronomy.** 1848.

Organisation for Economic Co-operation and Development. **Reviews of National Science Policy: United States.** 1968.

Packard, Alpheus S. **Lamarck: The Founder of Evolution; His Life and Work.** 1901.

Pupin, Michael. **From Immigrant to Inventor.** 1930.

Rhees, William J. **An Account of the Smithsonian Institution.** 1859.

Rhees, William J. **The Smithsonian Institution: Documents Relative to its History.** 2 vols. 1901.

Rhees, William J. **William J. Rhees on James Smithson.** 2 vols. in one. 1980.

Scott, William Berryman. **Some Memories of a Palaeontologist.** 1939.

Shryock, Richard H. **American Medical Research Past and Present.** 1947.

Shute, Michael, editor. **The Scientific Work of John Winthrop.** 1980.

Silliman, Benjamin. **A Journal of Travels in England, Holland, and Scotland, and of Two Passages over the Atlantic in the Years 1805 and 1806.** 2 vols. 1812.

Silliman, Benjamin. **A Visit to Europe in 1851.** 2 vols. 1856

Silliman, Benjamin, Jr. **First Principles of Chemistry.** 1864.

Smith, David Eugene and Jekuthiel Ginsburg. **A History of Mathematics in America before 1900.** 1934.

Smith, Edgar Fahs. **James Cutbush: An American Chemist.** 1919.

Smith, Edgar Fahs. **James Woodhouse: A Pioneer in Chemistry, 1770-1809.** 1918.

Smith, Edgar Fahs. **The Life of Robert Hare: An American Chemist (1781-1858).** 1917.

Smith, Edgar Fahs. **Priestley in America: 1794-1804.** 1920.

Sopka, Katherine. **Quantum Physics in America: 1920-1935** (Doctoral Dissertation, Harvard University, 1976). 1980.

Steelman, John R[ay]. **Science and Public Policy: A Report to the President.** 1947.

Stewart, Irvin. **Organizing Scientific Research for War: The Administrative History of the Office of Scientifc Research and Development.** 1948.

Stigler, Stephen M., editor. **American Contributions to Mathematical Statistics in the Nineteenth Century.** 2 vols. 1980.

Trowbridge, John. **What is Electricity?** 1899.

True. Alfred. **Alfred True on Agricultural Experimentation and Research.** 1980.

True, F[rederick] W., editor. **The Semi-Centennial Anniversary of the National Academy of Sciences: 1863-1913** *and* **A History of the First Half-Century of the National Academy of Sciences: 1863-1913.** 2 vols. 1913.

Tyndall, John. **Lectures on Light: Delivered in the United States in 1872-73.** 1873.

U.S. House of Representatives. **Annual Report of the Board of Regents of the Smithsonian Institution...A Memorial of George Brown Goode together with a selection of his Papers on Museums and on the History of Science in America.** 1901.

U.S. National Resources Committee. **Research: A National Resource.** 3 vols. in one. 1938-1941.

U.S. Senate. **Testimony Before the Joint Commission to Consider the Present Organizations of the Signal Service, Geological Survey, Coast and Geodetic Survey, and the Hydrographic Office of the Navy Department.** 2 vols. 1866.